# Vision

## *A Study of its Basis*

*By*

## S. HOWARD BARTLEY
*Washington University School of Medicine*

---

WITH AN HISTORICAL PERSPECTIVE

BY

## EDWIN G. BORING
*Harvard University*

---

## HAFNER PUBLISHING COMPANY
NEW YORK     LONDON
1963

*Originally published 1941*
*Reprint 1963, with corrections*

*Printed and Published by*

HAFNER PUBLISHING COMPANY, INC.
31 East 10th St.
New York 3, N.Y.

LIBRARY OF CONGRESS CATALOG No. 63-18164

*To*
G. H. B.
*and*
R. H. W.

# PREFACE

The reader will better understand both the selection and the treatment of material in this book if he is told that it is a result of two things: an attempt on the one hand to select from the psychology of vision the material for which present day neurophysiology has something to offer, and, on the other hand, to discuss certain related visio-sensory phenomena for which physiology must provide an answer. This answer seems to be awaiting the development, not so much of added details in physiology, but possibly a new kind of fact and a different viewpoint.

Few individuals, whether they be well-informed laymen or workers in special fields of biology, are aware of the contribution of current electro-physiology to the understanding of problems of sensation and motor activity in the intact person. To inform them of the major events in a single one of the fields of sensation (vision) is the first intent of the present work.

Few workers in neurophysiology are aware of the connection between their work and the study of sensation, as experience. To suggest that sensation has as much to say about guiding physiological studies as the latter has to contribute to sensation has been the second intent.

It will be perfectly obvious to the reader or to one who scans the table of contents that but a limited aspect of vision has been touched upon, but it is hoped that it will be just as evident that much of the material has never before appeared between the covers of any book.

The writer has drawn extensively upon experimental work carried on in the Laboratory of Neurophysiology of the Washington University Medical School. This laboratory has been generously supported for a number of years by grants from the Rockefeller Foundation and the Scottish Rite Mason's Fund and, as one aspect of research on the brain, has devoted considerable time to the neurophysiology of vision. The bulk of the other more recent work referred to, represents the labors of such groups (and individuals) as Hartline and co-workers, Graham and colleagues, Hecht and his school, Crozier and his colleagues (mainly Wolf and Zerrahn-Wolf), and Adrian and Matthews. The index will complete the roster of those whose labors have given us the most of our specific information.

I am indebted to the following journals for their kindness in permitting the reproduction of figures found in their pages: *American Journal of Psychology, American Journal of Ophthalmology, American Journal of Physiology, Journal of the Optical Society of America, Journal of Cellular and Comparative Physiology, Journal of Experimental Psychology, Journal of General Physiology, Proceedings of the National Academy of Sciences, Psychological Review,* and the *Transactions of the American Academy of Ophthalmology and Otolaryngology.*

I likewise hereby express my gratitude for the graciousness manifested in each of the permissions given by individuals for reproducing figures used in their articles. Acknowledgment of both the journal and author is given in the legends of the figures used.

Leola Bevis Bartley has given the fullest help in typing the manuscript and correcting proof and has thereby been in a great degree responsible for its appearance in printed form, and appreciation is also due to Mrs. Annell Jensen for assisting her in the early part of the work.

S. HOWARD BARTLEY

*Saint Louis*
*January 1941*

# HISTORICAL PERSPECTIVE

Dr. Bartley has written a handbook on the psychophysiology of vision. Why?

Because the purpose of science is economy of thinking, and when, in spite of its generalizations, science gets too cumbersome for easy comprehension, there have to be handbooks. The writing of a handbook is part of the process of man's coming to terms with nature. That process begins very simply in perception. Man, confronted with the "great blooming buzzing confusion" which is experience, picks out the uniformities of nature and makes them into objects for himself. Objects are the constant items in a world that is all change. The next step in this process is science, which creates imaginary objects that are not directly experienced—things like molecules and cosmic rays and electricity. Such hypothetical objects have to be abstracted from experience in the interest of economy of thought. Man has to keep the terms of thinking simple in order to think at all. Science does not, however, remain static. It grows and presently transcends the possibility of comprehension. Sometimes then a great new generalization arrives to take the place of several lesser ones, but mostly man has to wait for such a simplification. In the meantime what is he to do? Essentially, he writes handbooks. If the facts of any subject can not be subsumed under a few big theories, at least they can be brought together, systematized, related and made accessible. Handbooks do just that, and they are necessary tools of science.

Now let us see what role the handbooks have played in the psychophysiology of vision during the last four centuries. We may omit the ancients: Euclid's Ὀπτικά was not a compilation of known facts but for the most part an original contribution by its author. Indeed, nearly all the old books mixed compilation with

original contribution.  Of this sort were Porta's *Magiae naturalis*
in 1591 (he invented the *camera obscura*), Kepler's *Dioptrice* in
1611, Aguilonius' *Opticorum libri sex* in 1613 (he discovered the
visual horopter), and Descartes' *La dioptrique* in 1637.  Robert
Boyle's *Experiments and Considerations Touching Colour* in 1663,
while similar, had also the important function of summarizing
the situation about color as it stood three years before Newton
went to the Stourbridge Fair to buy the prism which was to lead
him to a new theory of color.  Newton's *Opticks,* finally published in 1704, was not a handbook, for it dealt mostly with
Newton's own scientific work, most of which depended on his
remarkable discovery (at that time an impossible paradox!) that
white, seemingly the simplest of perceptions, is really a mixture
of colors.  After Newton a new handbook was needed.  Berkeley's *New Theory of Vision* in 1709 was not a compendium, but
Robert Smith's *Compleat System of Opticks* in 1738 was a true
handbook, as was also Porterfield's *Treatise on the Eye, the Manner and Phenomena of Vision* in 1759.  If one wants to know the
truth about vision as of the first half of the eighteenth century,
one simply goes to Smith and Porterfield.  Later there was
Albrecht von Haller's *Elementa physiologiae corporis humani* in
1763, a text which, treating of all the senses, is replete with references to the literature, and Joseph Priestley's *History and Present State of Discoveries Relating to Vision, Light and Colours* in
1772, a model handbook.  Let the modern who thinks the field
of visual science new, read Haller and Priestley.

The nineteenth century was appropriately ushered in by the
work of Thomas Young, who wrote no handbook, and then the
spirit of the future was delayed in 1810 by Goethe in *Zur Farben-
lehre,* who tried to write a handbook, but let his egoism, his faith
in phenomenological observation and his hatred of Newton's discovery and of experimentalism run away with him.  Johannes
Müller came near a handbook in 1826 with his *Zur vergleichende
Physiologie des Gesichtssinnes,* and then there were several compilations of facts: Treviranus' tables of the optical constants of
various animal eyes in 1828, A. W. Volkmann's text of 1846 and

Volkmann's and Listing's contributions to Wagner's *Handwörter-buch der Physiologie* in 1853. The first half of the nineteenth century of itself constitutes a period in the physiology of vision.

The second half of the century began with the best of all books in this field: Helmholtz's *Handbuch der physiologischen Optik,* published in 1856-1866. That text fits no simple formula for handbooks. It is the best historical source to its antecedents and the most important original contribution that the subject has known. So much of it was Helmholtz's own observation; and yet so good a handbook was it that it was reprinted with appendices in 1909-1911, and translated with the appendices into English in 1924-1925. The book had a great deal to do with the 'founding' of physiological psychology and was followed quickly by other important texts which were partly handbooks and partly original contributions: Hering's *Beiträge zur Physiologie* in 1861-1864 (all on vision), Aubert's *Physiologie der Netzhaut* in 1865, Hering's *Zur Lehre vom Lichtsinne* in 1872-1874, Aubert's *Grund-züge der physiologischen Optik* in 1876. These twenty years from 1856 to 1876 predetermined the nature of the psychophysiology of vision for a long time, and it was the systematic organization of knowledge in the handbooks of these three men that did it.

All the while the literature on vision was becoming immense. König added to the second edition of Helmholtz's *Handbuch* in 1896 a bibliography of 7833 titles. He had 1205 references to color blindness alone! If the speculative theories of color vision had been correct, if there had been any better theory of visual space perception than nativism or empiricism, then there might have been some major simplification possible. As it was there had to be handbooks, and handbooks there were. Rivers prepared the one for Schäfer's *Text-Book of Physiology* in 1900; five men, including Nagel and von Kries, contributed the visual chapters to Nagel's *Handbuch der Physiologie der Menschen* in 1905; and then in 1915 Parsons published his *Introduction to the Study of Colour Vision,* with a second edition in 1924, a text which stressed the British work too much at the expense of the German.

It was along about 1920 that a shift of point of view became obvious, a shift back from the phenomenology of Hering to the physicalism of Helmholtz. For two score years it had been the fashion first to consider the conscious sensory phenomena and then to look for physiological 'explanations' of them. Now, partly under the influence of the Optical Society of America and its journal, this procedure was reversed. The experts had regard first to the modes of variation of the stimulus, and then looked to see what sensory changes resulted. Troland, who in 1929 made this reversed point of view explicit in his *Principles of Psychophysiology,* thus wrote of the effects of wave-length and of energy upon hue and upon brilliance.

In the 1930's the physiology of vision came to the fore. New electrical techniques are available because of the modern possibilities for amplifying neural currents of action. The old interest in complete psychological systematization and in speculative theories has gone. The change was becoming apparent in 1934 in the *Handbook of General Experimental Psychology* (now out of print), where Troland gave the facts from the psychophysical point of view and Hecht and Graham from the psychophysiological. Now Dr. Bartley comes along with a text that properly represents the new physiological phase, an exposition of the literature from what has become accepted as the best line of approach, and a treatment that is both needed and inevitable in 1941.

That is why Dr. Bartley wrote this book, I suppose, whether he knows it or not. Every period of development in a field of this sort requires its handbook, and without such handbooks science, which has come a long way from Kepler and Newton, would overwhelm the scientists. And the students! They too must have these compilations as textbooks, if they are ever to comprehend nature's uniformities.

EDWIN G. BORING

*Harvard University*
*February 1941*

# CONTENTS

# Vision

# I

# INTRODUCTION

**Development of interest in vision.** Ninety generations ago, Euclid calculated the resolving power of the eye. In recent years we have been occupied by the very same investigation. And what is more, his conclusions compare favorably with the best measures of visual acuity we have today. Following Euclid's announcement, sixty-three long generations passed before anything of note happened to increase the understanding of the eye. In the thirteenth century eye-glasses were developed.

Time went on. The eye as an optical instrument and as an agent of vision somehow escaped the omnivorous curiosity of the genius Leonardo da Vinci and it was not until a century after his time that Father Scheiner demonstrated that a real image of the field of vision is formed on the retina. That was in 1625, just before the day of Newton, the age of the Discovery of Natural Law. And his discovery may be said to have been the first contribution of the Renaissance to the understanding of vision.

Forty years later Mariotte discovered the blind spot as a gap in the visual field, the existence of which is unknown to most individuals today. Men in succeeding generations puzzled and argued over the significance of the Mariotte phenomenon, but it was never settled. In recent years interest in the blind spot has been revived. Notwithstanding, fundamental matters concerning it are still in dispute.

From Mariotte's day on there were still long periods which contributed little to the concrete study of vision. Berkeley's Idealism, advocated just prior to the birth of our nation, made vision essentially a mental process, and cast aside any consideration of its problems as dependent upon optics and a physiological organism, a heritage that lurks in our thinking even today in some of our organized institutions, in only slightly different form.

It took another hundred years after Berkeley for the next notable step toward the understanding of vision to be made. We find photography being born, and with it incidentally a new approach to the study of the eye. Talbot, the father of photography, gave us the flicker method and the law now known by his name, both of which have since figured so largely in the study of vision. Nevertheless, it so happened that his findings and the similar but independent ones of his contemporary, Plateau, had to rest until sensory physiologists came on the scene to use them.

It was in the 1840's that electrical methods were first applied to the study of physiology, and thus to vision. Du Bois-Reymond, applying the slow-moving galvanometer to a wide variety of animal tissues, discovered the electrical potential between cornea and the back of the eye. We know this as the *resting*-potential, the forerunner of the *action*-potential and the important neurophysiological work of today.

The same period saw the birth of modern psychophysics, the attempt at quantitatively relating stimulation and sensation, or judgment of sensation. E. H. Weber, the father of this approach, reported on the discrimination of differences in lifted weights, giving out his findings in a day when Latin was still the language medium for scholars. The regularity he discovered, now known as Weber's law, was later applied to vision.

Quite often the phenomena of human experience become well known before the occasion arises for investigating them. In this category fall many mechanical devices which give rise to some unique experience. In the zoetrope we have an example. About the middle of the last century it appeared as a toy in the form of a hollow cylinder whose inner surface carried a row of pictures of an animal in various postures. A row of slits placed around the cylinder allowed one to view the pictures in succession when the cylinder was revolved, giving the impression of the animal's movement. Later Edison used the same principle of static serial presentation in his kinetoscope, the immediate forerunner of the motion picture and the common "moving" electric sign of today.

The study of movement as a visual or biological problem began some time ago, but only reached extensive pursuit following the appearance of Wertheimer's paper in 1912. Elucidation of the physiological processes involved in making movement a perceptual achievement still remains a basic task. This is none the less true, despite the present day myriads of commercial devices successfully using the phenomenon.

The retinal *action*-potential was not discovered until just after the Civil War. It was likewise in the year 1865 that Aubert made the first scientific investigation of dark adaptation, and a decade later that Boll discovered visual purple.

In 1893 Rood applied the flicker method to photometry and made possible brightness matching of heterochromatic fields. Porter, at the turn of the century, worked out an empirical law in the logarithmic relation between intensity of illumination and fusion frequency.

During the last few decades, vision has been studied in every conceivable way. The clinician now gives it more detailed examination. The photochemist has given increasing attention to the cycle of changes that occur in the eye in response to light. Psychologists have awakened to a new significance of the visual experience of movement since its study with stationary objects. Cytologists and histologists have laid before us more and more of the minute details of retinal cito-architecture. Comparative anatomists have pushed forward the classification of vertebrate eyes with reference to rod and cone types and populations. Electro-physiologists have begun to tell how the visual apparatus works as a neural mechanism. A new integration of the data available on sensation with those of neurology has begun to take form. Those studying the central nervous system for its own sake have found the retina and the visual pathway a most suitable preparation with which to work.

**Determinants of visual stimulation.** Man takes for granted a real world of *things,* external to himself. It is composed of objects which he can see and touch, objects which occupy space. He, himself, moves about in that space, as one of the objects. According to this view, objects are looked upon as fixed entities, and their visual properties as primarily dependent upon their existence as space-occupying bodies.

It may well be emphasized, however, that many of the visual entities or things in our world are products of a different sort.

**A**                                    **B**

Fig. 1.—The appearance of a disc of light in a dark field (A) when its intensity is medium or fairly great, and (B) when its intensity is very weak. In the latter case it is subjectively no longer a disc with sharp contours but a very indefinite spot of light not much brighter than its surrounds.

Mere changes in intensity or duration of illumination determine the emergence and disappearance of many visual realities. This may be illustrated by the use of a simple example, a visual field, all of which is completely dark except a small bright disc. This is accomplished by use of a completely darkened room and a lamp-house whose light is transmitted through a circular aperture covered with opal glass. For our purposes, this disc of light is the *object* and we are not interested in any except its visual properties. It is for us only something that can be seen. Visually it is a homogeneous circle of bright light. The boundary between it and darkness is sharp. Now, if the illumination producing the disc is greatly reduced, new properties emerge. The disc loses its sharp border and becomes a very dim patch of light whose size fluctuates, whose boundaries cannot be definitely discovered, and whose location in the visual field is no longer stable, but wanders about. We may even lose track of the object and have difficulty in finding it again. The "thing" we are now dealing with has become an entirely different entity both qualitatively and quantitatively, though the only physical change that took place was the simple reduction of intensity. The *physical* light source is still the same spatially. Light is reaching our eyes from the same fixed direction as before.

Were the intensity to be greatly increased rather than decreased, the boundaries would again undergo change, and the surrounding visual field which had formerly been dark would now appear to be dimly illuminated. We would again be dealing with a new psychological entity. Its predecessors would have ceased to exist.

Were the illumination of the disc to be made intermittent, a host of still other properties would emerge, depending upon intensity and the amounts of time involved in the light and dark phases of the cycle. If the major portion of the cycle is filled with light, a disc whose surface is intermittently blotted out by a wave of darkness will be seen. If the cycle is occupied mostly by darkness, a dark area intermittently replaced by a flash of light will be perceived. If the rate of intermittency is manipulated, a host of additional effects will be observable, each in its turn.

As a whole, these phenomena serve to demonstrate the dependence of the seen object upon such factors as intensity, area, and time, which happen to be the very factors of stimulation readily capable of experimental control. That is to say, what is seen is dependent upon illumination patterns provided the retina regardless of the existence of space-occupying solid objects in the environment.

Our illustration began with the simplest possible spatial organization which would give rise to the perception of a thing. It consisted in a single bright patch in a dark field. Few life situations are so phenomenologically simple, and not all experimental set-ups can possibly retain such a near-homogeneity. We are usually confronted with complex patterns which are often thought of as aggregations of separate items, each of which may engage our attention in turn. Nevertheless it is becoming increasingly apparent to investigators that the parts of the visual world are interdependent.

This introduces us to the fact that it is logically possible to choose one of two methods by which to deal with the world of experience. Our recognition of these two viewpoints here is not to rehearse and prolong the discussion which has been carried on in the literature during the past two or three decades, but merely to apprize the reader of their existence and enable him to view the problems of vision from such a background.

The one is known as mechanistic theory, elementalism or atomism; the other as configurationism, organismicism, Gestalt theory, or field theory. The former is the common method of analysis, the tearing apart of complex phenomena to find their constituents. It is obvious that in such a procedure the stopping-point is arbitrary, for parts themselves have parts. It is the belief back of this sort of analysis that the understanding of a chosen complex situation accrues from knowing what the parts are and what they do when isolated. The latter view, that of configurationism, is built on the recognition that a thing may act one way at one time and another way on some later occasion, depending upon what the thing is a part of. This view chooses therefore to begin with some larger situation of which the phenomenon in question is a part, and to understand its behavior as a function of the larger situation. It can thus be seen that the two procedures are logically opposed.

Our concern is what can be done under the guidance of either one of them. Human knowledge has found that the use of one set of rules leads to one set of results, another to another. It has at the same time found that since many sets of rules are mutually exclusive, they have of themselves no basis for conflict, just as the game of bridge does not conflict with the game of cribbage. But if the rules of the two games were to be mixed together, innumerable difficulties would arise. Certain results are obtained by following the rules of bridge and distinctly other ones are obtained from the rules of cribbage. The choice between the two is for the players to decide, but let them beware of the nature of each game.

What has just been said applies to the study of vision in the following way. Let any visual pattern be used for experimentation. Even though it be as geometrically simple as the already described bright disc on the dark background, the relation of the factors of intensity and size to the production of some constant sensory result may be determined. To picture which, a graph may be made showing the necessary value of one of the factors for any given value of the other. The bulk of all concrete and usable analysis has been of this sort, and has been achieved under the stimulus of the mechanistic viewpoint.

But let the experimental situation be further complicated. Let the area around the disc be illuminated. It will then be found that the level of this illumination changes the values required in our graph. In this case the experimenter is dealing with two things, the disc and the area around it. The latter is external to the former and may be seen as a separate visual entity.

It must be added, however, that along with regarding them separate it has been customary in mechanistic theory to assume ability to interact. The organismic theory insists that they cannot be separate and affect each other. In order to do that they must belong to the same system; be parts of the same whole. Even though the latter view, in declaring that action must take place within single spheres and not from sphere to sphere, may be more appealing, this logical appeal does not in itself demonstrate what can be done by using the theory. What this may be is a fundamental question, and a beginning answer will be given from time to time as we come to the description of certain experiments.

**Measurement.** Measurement of the senses is based on two things. *First, it is usually in terms of the stimulus.* There is no independent scale of sensory units similar to a yardstick in ordinary geometrical mensuration, and the derived scale is such that equal physical units do not represent equal steps in sensation.

*Second, measurement proceeds by the method of comparison.*
No individual can be expected to judge accurately whether a
given brightness is twice, three times, etc., as intense as another
even though the two surfaces lie adjacent. Two fields must be
compared when being adjusted so as to appear equal.

To ascertain the brightness value of a given surface, another
surface whose value is known when set at any required intensity

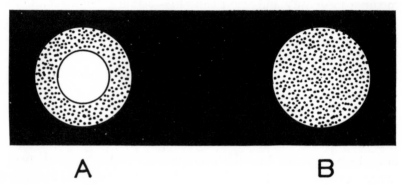

A                                            B

Fig. 2.—The field of a photometer as it appears to the observer (A) when
the standard and test portions are unequally bright, and (B) when these two
portions match in intensity. When the match is perfect the two portions are
not only of equal brightness but the boundary between them disappears.

must be used as a standard of comparison. It is adjusted until it
and the other surface are judged equal. To further the determination of equality, one of two other judgments can be made concerning two fields lying adjacent or within a reasonable distance
of each other; that one is just brighter than the other, or that it is
just less bright. The adjustment of one field till it and the other
are judged equal constitutes the essence of photometry, and for
many purposes where convenience and accuracy are required, the
procedure is enabled by instrumentation.

There are several types of these instruments (photometers),
but their details need not be discussed here. It is sufficient to
realize that the standard of comparison is generally varied by two
methods, (1) the use of filters which reduce its intensity by
known fractions, and (2) by moving the source which lights the

standard surface farther from or nearer to it. The effect of the latter procedure is calculated from the inverse square law. That is to say, the illumination of a surface is inversely proportioned to the square of the distance between it and the light source. Generally the photometer is optically arranged so that the test-field lies within the standard, rather than to one side of it. When the best match between the two brightnesses is made the bounding line fades to a minimum or disappears.

Judged equality is not exact. That is to say, the intensity of one of the surfaces may be adjusted up or down a finite amount without destroying the match. This narrow region above and below the ideal match is related to what will be known in later sections as a differential threshold. Repeated settings fall somewhere within such a range.

There is a second type of comparison possible. It, too, is a matching process. The eye may be confronted with three surfaces differing in brightness. The observer may be asked, in such cases, to adjust the intensity of the medium surface so that its intensity is midway between the other two. Here, instead of equal intensities, equal "sense intervals" are involved. In the usual terminology, it may be said that brightness contrast is being utilized as a basis of judgment.

**The nature of vision.** Vision is the means whereby we perceive space as a whole. Such a statement does not imply that all space is perceived at once, but rather that it is only by vision that spatial relations of objects outside the body and at a distance from it are satisfactorily dealt with in detail. Hearing is also a distance sense but its spatial characteristics are not totally distinguishable from visual qualities and it lacks precise detail.

Certain properties of vision exist when one is in pitch-darkness or is blindfolded, i.e., when the eye is not being differentially stimulated. Even then "visualness" persists in the spatial properties of the individual's experience. The matter of contemplating movement as well as performing it, imagining other objects as well as observing them, requires space perception in which the visual mechanism is involved. Again, to identify an object by touch without seeing it, is usually to identify it by visualizing it. In this case, the visual mechanism is indispensable, though obviously the supplied sensory information is tactual. Success in identification rests on satisfactory visualization. We do not know how the congenitally blind individual achieves his results, but we do know that he has a visual mechanism except for the use of his eyes and that when some part of it is injured or removed he behaves differently and less effectually than before.

Fig. 3.—Three squares of unequal brightness forming a series. The right and left squares are presented to the observer as fixed values, while the intensity of the middle square is adjusted by him so that its brightness seems midway between the brightnesses of the other two.

In the study of human experience many phenomena have come to light which indicate that one sense department possesses properties of another. Adjectives which are used to describe the supposed peculiar properties of one sense are indispensable in some others. In this respect, vision is dominant. Words signifying the visualness of the other senses appear, again and again.

There are still other ways by which the visualness of other sense modalities are made manifest. This is easily recognized in cases of brain lesions where both loss and revamping in behavior occurs. For example, in certain cases a surface which is smooth and is felt as smooth becomes rough to the observer when its color is changed. Equivalent, but perhaps less startling, examples pertain to most everyone. Blue light makes a room look cold, whereas yellow gives it a glow of warmth. The old way of accounting for this was that blue had been "associated" with cold and yellow with warm. In contrast to this, organismic theory would have these properties emerge as functions of the organism under the same laws as any other property.

**Illusions.** In the course of time individuals discover temporal and spatial discrepancies between visual experiences and the characteristics of the stimulation patterns which evoke them. Many such surprises are in store for the individual when he once begins to examine the origins of his visual experiences. This naturally leads to asking about their sources, for they violate his simplest expectations with regard to the relation between experience and the phenomena which arouse it. According to that expectation there should be a direct correlation, a one-to-one relationship between the two. Deviations from it are disturbing. When they appear the world runs the risk of being found filled with illusions.

The admission of illusion is the first step in denying the lawfulness in the nature of things. Discrepancies must be looked upon in some other way. Fruitful study is based upon the assumption of lawfulness in the emergence of all phenomena and when those laws are discovered discrepancies disappear. But no laws are discovered that are not provided for by the structure of the investigator's thinking.

**The visual system.** Regardless of the visual experience in any case, it is the outcome of the peculiar nature of the visual system itself and the manner of conducting the receptor output to other parts of the system, all of which takes place in a spatial framework. Color, brightness, visual size and all such things emerge from the behavior of the system and are not labels or working tools drawn from outside it. Their peculiarities are to be understood in terms of the system.

TO SUMMARIZE: In what has been said so far, it has not only been suggested that vision itself is not dependent for many of its characteristics upon differential stimulation of the retina, but it has also been pointed out that the other senses have a visual aspect or that the sensory message has to be usable in a visual way to perform its full function.

As yet few of these elusive but indubitable properties of vision
have yielded to investigation in such a way as to be identified
with specific neural correlates. Many of these properties accrue
from interrelationships between the various cell masses within the

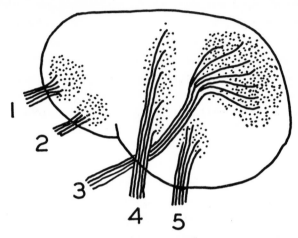

Fig. 4.—Schema to picture the brain and the incoming pathways from the
sense-organs. In each case, the "messages" are made up of the same kind of
constituents, nerve impulses; the resulting differences in sensation are dependent
upon the fact that each pathway does not lead to the same point in the brain.
The implication is that the qualitative differences between the senses are primarily dependent upon the place of arrival of the messages and therefore the
way in which they can affect the resident activity, rather than upon some qualitative difference in the messages themselves. Pathway (1) smell, (2) taste, (3)
vision, (4) cutaneous and muscle senses, and (5) hearing. For example, whatever succeeds in setting up any kind of a group of impulses in pathway (3) will
produce some sort of a visual experience, owing to the fact that the impulses
arrive at the visual cortex.

brain, rather than to the features dealt with in conventional neurophysiology. A beginning, however, was made a few years ago
by Bartley in his study of the gross differential activity of the
dog's cortex under various specific stimulus behavior situations.
Perkins, in the same laboratory, later applied the technique to
additional situations. These studies, although only crude beginnings, lie between the usual neurophysiological investigations and
extirpation experiments and point toward further possibilities in

understanding aspects of sensation which as yet seem to be approachable no other way.

**Restrictions imposed by the present purpose.** In the present treatment of vision all items which do not rather immediately contribute to a correlation between experience and neurophysiology will be laid aside. This restriction will account for the omission of a chapter or chapters on color vision. Although much accurate information has been accumulated with reference to color, very little as yet can be said with regard to what must happen in the nervous system to produce color. For the same reason, the dioptrics of the eye and the mechanics of eye movements are excluded, except insofar as they bear directly on a correlation of experience and known aspects of nerve physiology.

Despite the fact that many of the unique properties of vision or visualness are dependent upon total brain organization, the ability of the eye and the rest of the visual pathway to deal with light provides for the organism's precise and detailed response to the external world. Our interest lies in consolidating the information which pertains to how the visual pathway does this. The preceding remarks have partaken of the nature of a reconnoitre. The general nature of vision is outlined and some of the problems confronted are implicitly suggested, granted the survey has been at all realistic. Now we are faced with the question of how to proceed.

**Experiments on the organism as a whole.** As the first step, a survey of the methods which are being used might be profitable. In a classification, all those means whereby the behavior of the organism-as-a-whole, whether intact or reduced by brain oblation, is sampled or systematically tested should come first. Experiments of this sort can be arranged with one of two things in mind: either to determine what must be happening in some segment of the optic pathway; or to ascertain the nature of possible sensory phenomena themselves.

Assuming that this general category is clear, experimentation may be classified into the following groups:

(1) Experiments in which reaction time or some other property of overt response in an animal species is measured as light intensity or duration is varied. This has been one of the methods used by the photochemist to determine the role played by the photoreceptor cell. Simple animals in which the reactions were very slow in beginning were chosen, in which case it was deduced from a number of facts that most of this latent period was used by the photoreceptor processes and very little in the remainder of the pathway to the final muscle response. Consequently it is the temporal features of photoreception that are being studied, though the whole animal is used for the tests.

(2) Human sensory experiments in which the behavior of the sense-cell is also being deduced from the quantitative relation between stimulation and sensation. In simple situations, certain features of sensation run parallel with formulations already made for the photochemical processes in the sense-cells, hence it is believed by some that their photochemistry largely determines the nature of vision.

(3) Human sensory experiments in which the relations between stimulation and sensation are either related to the retina as a system or to the properties of more central parts of the nervous system. This, with the following type, constitutes a great fraction of the experiments from which deductions of how the optic pathway functions can be made.

(4) Human experiments in which intermittent stimulation (flicker) is employed. This group does not differ greatly from the last, but in terms of the amount of work done by use of this method, it stands alone.

(5) Animal experiments in which some characteristic of overt reaction is taken as the index of flicker recognition. The results here compare well with those obtained in the human experiments, and humans placed under the circumstances required in the animal experiments provide data which are identical to those obtained under the conventional conditions.

(6) Exploratory procedures conducted to determine the role of various parts of the brain. These are comparative tests on

intact, operated and injured individuals to ascertain the modifi-
cations of behavior due to removal of parts of the brain, or to
its injury.

(7) Other types of sensory exploration.   In earlier academic
psychology much less was known even as to the more general
features of the outcome under various stimulus conditions.   Ex-

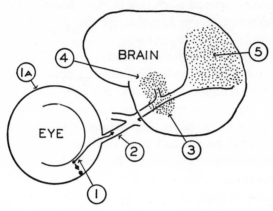

FIG. 5.—A diagram to indicate the various loci at which electrical records are
taken along the optic pathway.   1. Activity of single ganglion-cell fibers.   2.
The optic-nerve discharge.   3. Activity of the lateral geniculate body.   4. Activity of the superior colliculus.   5. Activity of the optic cortex.   1A. Retinal
activity.   The retinogram taken at this place is an integrated record of retinal
events and consequently not so clearly interpretable.

perimentation then partook of the nature of exploration rather
than control.   Some work is still of that kind.   The production
of the appearance of movement from stationary objects once
upon a time was a discovery, although nowadays experimentation with it is partly a matter of quantification.

(8) Conditioning experiments in sub-human species to determine the visual capacities of animals.   A conditioning experiment consists in presenting a stimulus eliciting a definite response,
closely allied in time with one which originally does not.   After
some repetition, the originally ineffective stimulus presented alone
is reacted to, much as was the initially effective one.   Stimuli
which the animal can differentiate from the "conditioned" one

will not elicit a response. Thus visual discrimination tests may be set up on this basis.

**Part-preparation methods.** The remainder of the ways by which vision may be studied employ preparations composed of parts of the optic pathway.

(1) Preparations in which the sense-cells can be isolated either to study their electrical discharge or the photochemical behavior. The preparations of the Limulus eye are good examples of the former.

(2) Preparations of the eye whereby ganglion-cell fibers are isolated prior to their collection into the optic nerve.

(3) The measurement of the electrical potentials from the surface of the eye. Such records are known as electroretinograms, and due to the course of the isopotential lines in connection with the geometry of the eye and points of recording, the records are not nearly as definitive as might be desired.

(4) Recording of the optic-nerve discharge. The only technique satisfactory for this has specific requirements which are successfully met in the preparation as described in the chapter on the optic-nerve discharge.

(5) Recording from the superior colliculus and the lateral geniculate body. This also requires specific conditions for success.

(6) Recording from the surface and layers of the optic cortex of the cerebrum.

Each one of the fourteen methods has already yielded a definite contribution to our knowledge of vision, many of the details of which will become apparent from chapter to chapter.

# II

# FORMS OF BRIGHTNESS DISCRIMINATION

## BRIGHTNESS DISCRIMINATION

**Thresholds.** It has already been pointed out that such features as stimulus intensity and size are determining factors in the sensory outcome. This implies that there are minima below which these cannot fall without becoming ineffective. These minima may be thought of as *boundaries* below which sensation does not occur and above which it does. It was also demonstrated that as the values of some stimulus factors were increased in the range above this minimal effective point, sensation not only increased in certain ways but new sensory properties one by one emerged and old ones disappeared, giving rise to additional *boundaries.*

Psychophysics, less than a century old, in instituting the quantitative study of sensation made use of the idea of thresholds and from then on they gained wide attention among investigators.

Thresholds, or limens, are measured by the minimum quantities of stimulation which will result in sensation under specified conditions. The weakest illumination and the smallest brightness difference between two areas of illumination which can be detected are examples. The conditions for just reaching a boundary are called threshold conditions.

Thresholds may be grouped into two classes, those which measure the minimal total stimulation required for arousing sensation, and those which measure the minimum detectable difference between two objects or two parts of a single object. The former is known as the absolute limen or *absolute threshold,* the latter as the differential limen or *differential threshold.* It is also called "the just noticeable difference" or j.n.d.

We can do no better than begin our quantitative consideration of vision by becoming acquainted with the way certain thresholds behave. The limen is not to be considered a simple product of some minimum *intensity* of illumination or a certain minimal difference between two surfaces, for intensity is but one of the factors involved. The area of the stimulus-object and the duration of stimulation and the level of the surrounding field conspire with intensity to bring about the result.

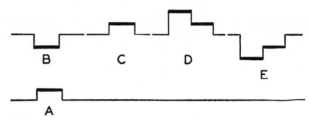

Fig. 6.—Diagrams to indicate the various kinds of thresholds. Distance from the bottom line to the upper ones represents brightness, thus different positions of the upper lines represent different brightness levels. The bottom line represents the level of the dark background. Thus A is the absolute threshold, B, C, D, and E differential thresholds, B with an undifferentiated test-object below the field level; C the same, but above the *field*. In D and E the test-object is *bipartite,* and judgment is made between the two parts.

In the usual experiment in determining the absolute threshold, duration is made indeterminately long and so ceases to be an experimental variable. Intensity and area alone remain for consideration in such cases. But when short durations are used, the values of the other two factors must be manipulated to compensate. The point at which duration becomes just short enough to become a variable is called the *critical duration,* a duration which is involved not only in measurement of thresholds, but in responses above it.

The threshold is a strict quantitative affair when using durations below the critical one. As long as area is *neither* extremely small nor quite large, the amount of energy required for threshold is a constant. That is to say, the effects of the product of area and intensity are a constant, except beyond certain limits in either direction, where quantity needed for response becomes greater.

The effects of the product of duration and intensity are also a constant when short durations are involved.

**Inconstancy of threshold and other weak sensations.** There are quantitative characteristics of the threshold that are not brought out in the data arising from the usual techniques whose results are soon to be described. These properties, nevertheless, are important in an understanding of the function of the organism and should be made known here.

The matter may be introduced to the reader by first saying that weak sensations fluctuate in intensity and very weak ones may periodically disappear and reappear. This has a bearing on the concept of the threshold.

The most recent and most complete study of this matter was made by Guilford who determined the monocular limens of his observers by calculating the average of observations taken during one hour on each of six days. To make the readings, the observers reported when a small disc in a dark room became just perceptible as its intensity was increased, and when it disappeared as its intensity was lowered from an easily observable level.

Using a series of values clustering around the limens, Guilford had his observers determine what fraction of the time the disc was perceptible, by signaling when the disc appeared and disappeared. He found that the fluctuation of weak sensations was definitely related to the limen, that the relative amount of their visibility was a direct outcome of stimulus intensity and appeared to follow the *phi-gamma* hypothesis. The hypothesis states that when a series of set values is used (method of constant stimuli) the percentage of trials in which sensation will be elicited will bear a systematic relation to intensity. The percentage is low for the weak, higher for the stronger and highest for the strongest. When frequency is plotted against intensity the curve is ogive or S-shaped. The limen itself has a definite theoretical position on it, the value represented at the 50 per cent point, though seldom does this happen to coincide with any of the actual values used in experimentation.

Guilford found that the average period of perceptibility varies directly with stimulus intensity; that the average time the disc is not visible varies indirectly as some function of intensity; and that the fluctuations are most rapid near the limen, becoming less frequent as the illumination is made more or less intense.

The limen then is, as well as being the point where the stimulus has a 1:1 chance of appearing in any trial, the point at which the fluctuations are most rapid and the stimulus is visible one-half the time. This is to say, the factors which control the threshold control the fluctuations, and it might well be added here that this is an example of the fact that all measurement of performance is of a statistical nature.

**Ricco and Piper's laws.** Some years ago, two laws describing the relationship between size of the stimulus and its intensity at threshold were independently proposed. The one formulated by Ricco states that the product of area and intensity is constant for threshold excitation in the human fovea. The other, by Piper, says that in peripheral vision the product of intensity and the square root of area is constant for threshold excitation. The experimentation underlying both of these formulations was limited in range, and it has been found that they do not hold throughout a wide enough range to have the significance required of them. It has been shown that Ricco's laws hold for both the fovea and periphery if the visual angle subtended is less than 10 minutes. Piper's law holds in the periphery for visual angles between 2 and 7 degrees. The implication is obvious that it is much easier for two formulations to coincide when the ranges are limited than when they possess a reasonable extension. Consequently these laws leave much to be desired with regard to telling what the threshold relations really are.

**More extended determinations.** Recently Graham, Brown and Mote were convinced that investigations on the area-intensity problem up to now had one or more serious shortcomings and that the matter needed reinvestigation.

Under conditions obviating these difficulties they set out to determine more accurately the stimulus relations at threshold by providing for (1) the extension of the test range and the inclusion of many measurements within it, (2) fixed distances between the eye and test-object avoiding the manipulation of distance to vary the effective test-object area, (3) the use of homogeneous parts of the retina, and (4) adequate fixation.

With test-objects ranging in diameter from 1.86 minutes to 1 degree for the fovea and diameters ranging from 1.86 minutes to 25 degrees and 6 minutes for the periphery the results are as

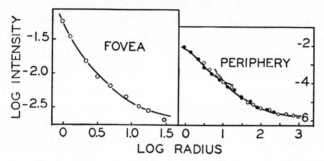

Fig. 7.—Curves showing the foveal and peripheral intensity thresholds as functions of the radius of the test-object. The foveal curve follows Graham, Brown and Mote's data and equation (5). The peripheral curve consists of two sections, the right-hand one being computed from the above authors' equation (6), which holds for areas greater than 10 min. in radius. Intensity in millilamberts. (*Graham, Brown and Mote.—J. Exptl. Psych.*)

follows. If the logarithm of intensity is plotted against the logarithm of radius of the stimulus object the curves for both fovea and periphery are not linear but increase in slope while passing from the smallest to the largest area. Throughout the ranges tested for both fovea and periphery the increase is consistent and becomes asymptotic for the largest areas.

Since the significance of the results especially for the periphery depends on their being obtained from a homogeneous retinal area, the investigators tested the areas they used in the following manner. One-half of the largest area was covered and the threshold of the remaining area tested and then with the same fixation the threshold of the other more lateral half was also obtained. An insignificant difference between the thresholds for the two halves of the circle was found and it was concluded that the large test-object was stimulating a region of the retina characterized by no significant threshold gradient. This indicated that the drop in threshold they obtained by including more and more area was not due to the incidental inclusion of more and more sensitive elements.

**The cube-root formula.** Elsberg and Spotnitz studied the area-intensity relationship for threshold response in the fovea, using small squares whose visual angles covered a range from 8 to 36 minutes. They found a constant logarithmic relation between area and intensity over this range, the conclusion being that the product of the cube root of the area and threshold intensity is constant. They then complicated their test-object by using white squares with inner black areas. In which case the product of the cube root of the area of the large object and its intensity, minus a certain correction, is a constant. This correction is the quantity found by multiplying the intensity by the cube root of the black area divided by the cube root of the large white area.

When the cube-root formula is applied to the data of Graham, Brown and Mote, for the fovea, it will be found to fit them only through a range of from 5 to 25 or 30 minutes, out of the total range of 1.86 minutes to 1 degree, a range not unlike that originally used to derive the formula. And when the cube-root formula is applied to peripheral data, it also fits only through a middle range, or in the neighborhood of 1½ to 16 degrees.

The cube-root formula as applied to the visual threshold under variations of intensity and area was a part of a series of studies in which cube roots, square roots, and their multiples were found to apply, at least approximately, to conscious behavior just as to many physicochemical volume and surface reactions, respectively, outside the body. Elsberg and Spotnitz accordingly suggested that threshold discrimination is dependent upon *volume* reactions in the nervous system.

**Interrelations between area, intensity and time.** For brief flashes and small areas, the product of duration and intensity is a *constant for threshold response.* That is, as duration is increased, intensity must be decreased in order that the response remain at

threshold value. This reciprocity soon breaks down when duration is made long so that further increases in it have less and less
effect in compensating for decreased intensity. The point at
which this begins to occur and the constancy breaks down, is
called the *critical* duration. Beyond it, intensity alone becomes
the effective variable.

The departure from strict constancy may be gradual or abrupt
depending upon the properties of the system in question. Though
strict reciprocity holds over only a very narrow range, in the
measurement of sensation, the departure is only gradual as duration is extended. It applies for a flash of less than 50 milliseconds
(ms.), but needs modification for longer durations. Notwithstanding, Blondell and Rey, by the insertion of two constants
into the equation showing the relation of the stimulus factors
to each other, made it describe flashes up to 3 seconds.

Graham and Margaria, among the latest to investigate these
relations, confirmed the previous workers' essential findings.
They applied their stimuli to the peripheral retina, varying area
from 2 minutes to 3 degrees in four steps. Their flash durations
extended from 31 to 640 ms. In addition to finding that for
short durations, the product of intensity and time must be constant for threshold effect; that duration finally becomes an indifferent matter; that for longer durations more energy is required; that the intensity threshold increases as area decreases;
they found that small areas produce a more abrupt transition
from the state described by It = C to I = C. That is, they found
critical duration to terminate more abruptly.

Crozier finds that the relation between threshold intensity and
exposure time can be quantitatively accounted for by the deduction that the reciprocal of the threshold yields a probability integral when the logarithm of time is used. He states that it is
unnecessary to presume that the reciprocity law has any sensible
application in this situation, for it does not follow from the measurements that the sensory effect at threshold is a constant, or
that it is related to a fixed amount of photochemical change.

**Utilization time.** Critical duration may be understood in light of the concept of "utilization time." In many systems there is a limited time during which excitation can accumulate to produce a given effect, so that the excitation accumulating within this time must reach a certain amount or else be too little to produce a threshold response. In other words, at threshold, the quantity of excitation is just sufficient before it is too late to be utilized. This seems to be true in the visual sense-cell and in more complex segments of the nervous system. In the former, utilization time is determined in one of the processes which must occur before the sense-cell is made to discharge, the outcome in such a system being an abruptly terminating *critical* duration. On the other hand, in the more complex systems underlying sensory acts, values for critical duration cannot be accurately fixed, for the deviation from strict reciprocity between duration and intensity of stimulation is diverged from very gradually. This is what would be expected were the utilization time of no single unit the sole determining factor in the production of the end-result. It is the outcome from a system in which a number of factors combine, either one after another or simultaneously to determine the response.

Hence, the character of the critical duration would seem to be a criterion of whether or not the response studied is determined by a single critical factor or by a number of them.

Undoubtedly the utilization time of the sense-cell itself is involved in determining the sensory outcome of the intact organism. If some of the later events which are also factors could be eliminated, it is likely that the termination of the critical duration would become more abrupt and thus more nearly like that of the sense-cell itself. It is interesting to note that as the area of the stimulus is reduced critical duration terminates more abruptly. Since area reduction seems to work toward making critical duration more abrupt and thus more nearly like that of the sense-cell itself, we might suppose that the reduction in area tends to remove some of the steps in reaching the final outcome. It might take considerable analysis to determine whether the so-called "steps" must be serial or whether they simply represent the reduction in complexity in the pattern of activity occurring at any one instant.

**Differential thresholds.** The amount by which two areas must differ in brightness in order for the difference just to be perceptible is the differential threshold. The simplest is that in which a homogeneous test-object is made brighter or darker than the surrounding background. Such a ground in the simplest cases extends over the whole visual field. Thus in this case, measurement is made of the threshold between the object and ground. It is also common for the test-object itself to be divided. The background around such a test-object may be illuminated or left entirely dark. The two common divided test-objects are the bipartite or bisected disc, and the disc-annulus pattern.

The differential threshold is often expressed as a fraction, the numerator of which is the difference in brightness of the two parts of the test-field, and the denominator the absolute brightness of one of them. This is often known as the Weber fraction. In some instances the reciprocal of the Weber fraction is used.

Figure 8 shows the relation of $\Delta I/I$ to log I, when a homogeneous test-object is used. It can be seen that the fraction grows smaller as the general level of the background is raised, although the rate of decrease finally bcomes practically zero. Certain earlier investigators obtained a final rise in the curve, denoting an increase in the fraction. This is not to be taken as the general rule, but rather as an outcome dependent upon the specific conditions of their experiments.

Some of the latest measurements of the relation of $\Delta I/I$ have been made by Steinhardt, using a simple test-field on a large background. In the main, the measurements corroborate previous workers' findings. He finds that the fraction decreases as intensity increases but without increasing again at high intensities. Instead it decreases steadily and approaches a finite limiting value depending upon the size of the test-field and upon the brightness of the surrounding field. The data for test-objects under $2°$, when logarithmically plotted, show that $\Delta I/I$ shifts uninterruptedly when intensity is varied, while the data for larger test-fields exhibit a break in the curve in the section where $\Delta I/I$ decreases rapidly. Test-objects below 2° show higher values of $\Delta I/I$ for all intensities, as compared to larger fields. Such test-objects differ from one another mainly in the low intensity side

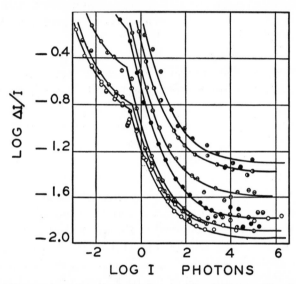

Fig. 8.—Human intensity discrimination as dependent upon illumination and size of test-object. ·Each curve is for a separate test-object; the visual angles subtended are as follows, reading from the upper to the lower curves in order: 23.5′, 31′, 56′, 2° 14′, 5° 36′, 17°, and 24°. *(Steinhardt—J. Gen. Physiol.)*

of the break. With very bright fields, $\Delta I/I$ is quite sensitive to alterations in brightness of the surrounding field, except for large test-fields which in effect provide their own surrounds. This sensitivity is exceptionally marked for fields under ½°. Even though the effect is most outstanding for high intensities, the surround-brightness appears to affect the relation between variables as a whole, except in very small fields where the absence of a background of sufficient brightness produces distortion in the theoretical relation otherwise obtained.

The two halves of the test-object need not be strictly adjacent.

They may be separated by progressively greater and greater intervals in order to determine the effect. The value of $\Delta I/I$ changes
as the two fields (each having a visual angle of 20′) are moved
farther apart. In one set of monocular experiments, in which
$\Delta I/I$ was plotted against log I, the relation $\Delta I/I$ increased
progressively as the separation increased from 4′ 15″ to 30′. The

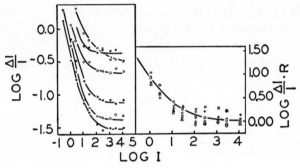

Fig. 9.—Two sets of curves to show the influence of area on foveal intensity
discrimination. Each curve in the left-hand graph is for a separate radial value
of test-object. Reading from the top down, the radial values in minutes are
2.0, 3.3, 6.0, 10.0, 16.3, and 28.0. The right-hand curve shows the relation
between $\log \dfrac{\Delta I}{I}\cdot R$ and log I. R represents radius and the curve is theoretical.
The symbols represent radii varying from 2.0 to 28.0 min. Intensity in millilamberts. (*Graham and Bartlett—J. Exptl. Psych.*)

results were exhibited as a family of parallel curves. With binocular determinations in which the one field was exposed to one
eye and the other field to the other eye, the two being separated
visually by only a narrow dark space, the outcome was the same
as for the narrowest separations of the two fields seen monocu-
larly. As yet no explanation has been given these phenomena,
aside from the statement by the investigators that they demonstrate some kind of summation.

**Threshold as dependent on duration.** Graham and Kemp analyzed brightness discrimination as it is influenced by the duration
of $\Delta I$. With durations ranging from 2 to 500 ms., they found the
following.

$\Delta$I/I values at constant intensity are highest for the shortest duration and they decrease with an increase in duration up to the limits of a critical exposure time. At durations longer than the critical duration the ratio $\Delta$I/I remains constant. The critical duration is a function of intensity, decreasing as intensity increases.

Within the limits of critical duration, the product of $\Delta$I and exposure time is constant for any value of prevailing intensity, I. This is the Bunsen-Roscoe law. With greater than critical durations, the law is superseded by the relation $\Delta$I = *Constant.*

**Differential sensitivity and area.** The work of Steinhardt, for example, has indicated that differential sensitivity increases as area is made greater. In the family of curves in which he plotted log $\Delta$I/I against log I, in photons, the curves lay lower and lower toward the abscissa as their areas represented visual angles from 23.5 minutes to 24 degrees. The results of other workers agree.

Holway and Hurvich plotted log $1/\Delta$I against the log of the visual angle.* Their data showed a linear relation between the two for a variety of intensities varying from 0.000625 millilamberts (ml.) to 500 ml. Heinz and Lippay had previously attributed a similar result to the increase in the number of activated elements as area was increased. The former investigators point out, however, that with a fixed retinal area, $1/\Delta$I varies inversely with illumination. Thus it would appear that sensitivity decreases when the number of active elements is increased.

Hence the claim that differential sensitivity is a direct linear function of the number of excited elements does not, in general, hold true. To account for the outcome in both cases by one mechanism, Holway and Hurvich suggest what they call the *availability principle.* They say that differential sensitivity is governed by the excitation potentially available for the task. In any retinal area there is a limit to the number of nerve fibers which

---

* The differential threshold is designated by $\Delta$I. When the threshold is low, indicating marked sensitivity, $\Delta$I is small. Thus the size of $\Delta$I and the degree of sensitivity are inversely proportional. To remedy this and to provide a numerical measure which varies directly with sensitivity the reciprocal of $\Delta$I or $1/\Delta$I is used.

can be activated as illumination is raised.  An additional factor, the maximum frequency at which these fibers can discharge, also participates in defining the total excitation potentially available. This minus the amount of excitation at any moment is the poten- tially available excitation.  It is obvious then that the actual ex- citation and the potentially available excitation are complements. For any given image an increase in intensity will increase the actual excitation and decrease the potentially available excitation remaining.  Since $1/\Delta I$ decreases with increase in intensity, it and the available excitation are correlated.  If the size of the image is doubled, let's say, on the fovea where there is supposedly a fairly equal distribution of elements, and where homogeneity exists in other respects as well, the amount of excitation is prob- ably doubled.  If the total potentially available excitation is also doubled, then the available remainder is doubled.  According to this, $1/\Delta I$ would be expected to increase.  They reason that since the expectation is fulfilled, they have demonstrated their hypothesis.

**Differential sensitivity and mode of perception.**  In most stimu- lus situations, whether simple or not, a part of the visual field can be regarded as *figure,* and that which remains, as the *ground* field.  In some of these, the figure-ground relations may be re- versed at will; in others this relation alternates spontaneously, in which case the pattern is spoken of as ambiguous.

It is said that when a given area is seen as figure it may have one brightness and when seen as ground, another.  The fact that a given area does vary in brightness in keeping with its place in a geometrical pattern is not to be denied.  The question of whether the outcome is dependent upon the figure-ground mode of perception or upon the geometric relation is the one to be decided.

Fry and Robertson investigated this question by using a pat- tern in which the photic stimulus conditions were held constant but in which the brightness of a part of the field was tested both when it was included and excluded as a part of the *figure.*  Under such conditions they found no real difference in brightness.

In other cases, it has been reported that the *threshold* is dependent upon the figure-ground mode of perception. To get such results, Gelb and Granit used a dark cross on a bright ground and also another design in which the figure was light and the field dark. A red dot was seen as part of the patterns, being added to them by reflection, and was used as the fixation point. The threshold value was found for each of its positions, one on the figure and the other on the ground in each pattern. Since the dot had a higher threshold on the figure whether light or dark, they deduced that it had such a value on the figure because it was the *figure*. But they did not rule out certain other factors which could have been responsible.

Fry and Robertson point out that the order of the readings favored the higher thresholds for figure inasmuch as the thresholds for both light and dark figures were ascertained immediately after the critical retinal area had been modified by exposure to a bright stimulus whereas the grounds were ascertained under opposite conditions.

Fry and Robertson obviated this error by using an ambiguous pattern, whose parts could be seen as figure or ground without alteration of stimulus conditions in which case the threshold difference between figure and ground was absent. Though these investigators have not shown that the difference cannot happen under any legitimate circumstances they have kept the burden of proof on those who have already alleged the difference.

Another kind of experiment has led to the postulation that seeing white as figure as compared with seeing it as ground has a direct effect upon the retinal output as if the brightness had been increased. The experiment used as the basis for this was the rate of succession of short exposures necessary for the two parts of a Rubin cross to fuse. It was found to be higher when the white cross was seen as figure than when ground.

Fry and Robertson, using an artificial pupil, obtained results throwing a different interpretation on the phenomenon. They found that though the critical flicker frequency was higher when the white cross was seen as ground, the difference disappeared when an artificial pupil was employed, or the iris and lens muscles were immobilized by drugs. It would seem then that when attempting to see the white cross as ground the pupillary aperture is made greater, allowing more light, hence making it brighter. But it is also true that the white cross *can be seen either as figure or ground during the use of the artificial pupil or the drugs in the eyes, without a change suggesting a difference in brightness.*

**The construction of a brightness scale.** The organism's response to intensity not only involves distinguishing between small just detectable differences, but also in judging the brightness relations between surfaces differing considerably in intensity. Thus adjusting the intensity of a surface until judged equal in brightness to a standard surface is not the only method of quantifying reaction to photic intensity. When two surfaces are quite different in intensity, one of them may be adjusted until it looks, let's say, one-half as bright as the other. This procedure is called *fractionation* and has been used to construct a brightness scale. The unit of measurement in this case is the bril. One hundred brils is the brightness seen when luminosity is 1 millilambert.

Information from various intensities throughout the usable range, provides a curve relating brils to millilamberts.

The traditional method of scaling merely used a series of standard intensities covering a usable range and step by step determined just noticeable differences (j.n.d.'s). Each j.n.d. was a just perceivable difference in brightness. The method alone does not determine whether all j.n.d.'s are equal, whereas with the fractionation procedure (ratio scaling), all units are equal. Comparisons have shown, however, that brils and j.n.d's do describe essentially the same curve.

**Summary.** We have dealt with thresholds, for in their measurement lies the initial recognition that the visual field before us is not homogeneous but contains differentiations of light and shade. Thresholds have meant to us measurements in the appreciation of minimal amounts of these differences. They can also be looked upon as the measurement of narrow regions in the intensity scale in which sensory qualities change and in which new entities emerge. They represent also stations on a curve of function, the whole curve being the object of discovery as well as the particular points upon it, transforming what would otherwise be the mere study of isolated functions into a study of human experience and thus legitimate psychology.

## VISUAL ACUITY

**Visual acuity by measurement of interspace.** Response to intensities of stimulation takes on another aspect in addition to the behavior which has been called brightness discrimination. It is called visual acuity, though it is really a form of brightness discrimination in which spatial factors are the focus of investigation. Visual acuity is the ability to perceive the interspace between two objects when it is very small or the ability to see a very narrow line when its length is great enough to cease being a critical factor in the total stimulation. Visual acuity is defined as the reciprocal of the just resolvable visual angle measured in minutes of arc. Often the logarithm of this is used for plotting against the logarithm intensity or some other variable. It is obvious that visual acuity is a form of brightness discrimination when it is recognized that the brightness not only of the two objects whose separation is to be perceived but also the brightness of the interspace must be discriminated. The very same mechanism which is brought into play when two adjacent surfaces of differing intensities confront the eye is also to be utilized when the surfaces are slightly separated.

It is the objective then in studying visual acuity to determine what role the intensity relations of all parts of the nearby visual field play in governing the minimal separable distance between two objects. This study includes not only the brightness of the objects but their areas as well.

One of the simplest geometrical patterns used to investigate visual acuity is a pair of parallel bars. The background which surrounds them may be either dark or illuminated. If the latter, the bars themselves may be darker or lighter than the background or "surrounds."

In addition to this pattern there are several others which have been used, as, for example, an incomplete circle, or letter *c,* or a grating of alternate dark and light bands surrounded by an illuminated field.

When the surrounding field is illuminated, its level is usually varied to obtain the relation between visual acuity and illumination. As in many other experiments, an artificial pupil is sometimes employed as a means of control.

**Visual acuity under the more general conditions.** Shlaer determined the relation of visual acuity to illumination over a range of 8 log units for a grating and also for a C-shaped figure when they appeared on a field 30° in visual angle. Naturally the test patterns involved a contrast between black and the level of the illuminated field. The curves for each test-object exhibited a break at an acuity of 0.16. This was interpreted as meaning that the values below this are dependent upon one type of sense-cell and the values above by another. Inasmuch as the nature of the retina and the differences in the behavior of its two kinds of sense-cells have not been discussed, no comment will be made upon the interpretation.

The grating provides for higher visual acuities under about 30 photons and lower acuities above this illumination. The greatest acuity possible with the grating is 30 per cent lower than with the C. *Furthermore, Shlaer shows that with an aperture of less than 2.33 millimeters (mm.) the pupil is the limiting factor in the resolution of the grating, whereas when the aperture is larger than that the size of the central cones governs it.* Cobb had previously shown that the size of the pupil affects retinal image formation and thus visual acuity. Since the data on visual acuity gained by a number of other workers prior to Shlaer suffer from the lack of artificial pupillary control or from the use of a variable distance between test-object and observer which affects accommodation, his work will

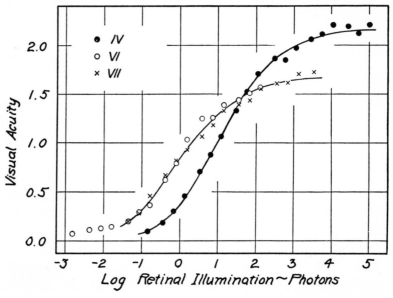

FIG. 10.—Visual acuity as dependent upon retinal illumination. The filled circles represent the outcome with the C. The open circles and the crosses represent the outcome with the grating. (*Shlaer—J. Gen. Physiol.*)

be taken as the standard for the more general conditions. On the other hand, marked departures from the conditions specified by Shlaer have been used.

**Visual acuity with a dark field.** It has been a policy with a number of careful workers, including Shlaer, to insure a stable state of adaptation of the eye for their work by using illuminated surrounds of considerable size. Wilcox did not follow this procedure and was criticized for it. In one case, he used two tiny illuminated bars on a dark field and in another two dark bars on a lighted field. Hecht and Wald feel that Wilcox measured a *glare phenomenon* * instead of the relation of visual acuity and the level of illumination prevailing on the retina. No fault could be found with the situation in which the black bars appeared on an illuminated field. Regardless of whether the former is to be called a case of glare, it is still a legitimate test situation. We have a right to know what the outcome will be. Interpretations of the results, like any other, must be made with due caution, and these we shall examine later. First, the results themselves must be presented.

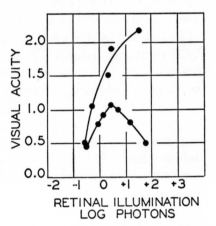

With light bars on a dark ground, the threshold is very high at low intensities. That is to say, the separation of the bars must be relatively great. In absolute amount, they must be in the neighborhood of 130 seconds of arc apart under the conditions used by Wilcox. As intensity is gradually increased the threshold separation decreases but only until a

Fig. 11.—Curves showing visual acuity measured by parallel bars. The curve which ascends throughout its whole length indicates visual acuity determined by dark bars on a light background. The other curve represents the results with bright bars on a dark background. (*Modified from Wilcox.*)

certain minimum is reached, after which it increases. Visual acuity in terms of the reciprocal of this separation is pictured in Figure 11. This dispels the prevailing idea that increased intensity is always favorable for visual acuity.

With dark bars on a bright ground, the outcome is different.

* It is difficult to define a term which another individual has used. But from the general trend of the discussion, it would seem that a glare phenomenon is one in which the retina is weakly illuminated with focused light, except for a small-sized bright image. This image is so different in intensity from the surrounds that one cannot speak of the general illumination or the general adaptive state of the retina. If we take into account entoptic stray light discussed in the next chapter, we will be aware of further complications.

In this case the threshold decreases without reversal as intensity increases, although the rate becomes gradually less. Thus the intensities of test-object and ground do not act similarly in their roles in visual acuity. Wilcox believes that it is impossible to state a simple law expressing the relation between visual acuity and intensity. To explain the results, he employs the concept of irradiation which will be discussed in the chapter on contour.

**Visual acuity as affected by the illumination of remote regions.** Fisher measured visual acuity for a grating in a 2 degree foveal area when the illuminations of the area were 0.193, 10.07 and 318 photons. Monocular fixation with a 2 mm. artificial pupil was used while the other eye was confronted with a uniform field of low intensity. Annular surrounds varying both in subtended visual angle and in intensity were also employed for the measurements. The radial widths of the annuli were 2.5, 5, 7.5, 12.5 and 20 degrees, while their intensities varied from 0.0566, 0.193, 10.07, 318 and 8560 photons.

Under these conditions the results were as follows. When the annulus was brighter than the test-object, visual acuity became poorer with increase in the size of the annulus. When the annulus was dimmer than the test-object, visual acuity became finer with increase in the size of the surrounds. When the two were equally bright, changing the size of the surrounds had no consistent effect upon visual acuity. This latter condition was similar in principle to one of Shlaer's experiments.

Fisher believes that the explanation of none of his results can be made on a neural basis inasmuch as neural interaction does not cover the large visual angles which were involved in his experiments. Further discussion of the matter will have to wait for a later chapter.

**Visual acuity in some of the lower animals.** The visual acuity of the bee has been measured by Hecht and Wolf, the fiddler crab by Clark, and the Drosophila by Hecht and Wald. In each of these forms, visual acuity is poor at low intensities and improves with log intensity in a typically sigmoid * fashion. In

* The curve describing the relation of visual acuity to the logarithm of the intensity of the stimulus field is somewhat S-shaped.

the bee the minimum visual angle that can be resolved is between 0.9 and 1.0 degrees. In the Drosophila, visual acuity is still poorer, the minimal angle being about 9.28 degrees. The ratio between the fineness in resolution in these two forms and man is 1 to 9.4 to 1110.

With the conditioning technique, Smith obtained discriminatory responses with the cat, which shows that its resolution reaches at least a fineness of 5.5 minutes of visual angle. This indicates no great difference between it and the monkey as tested by Klüver in a comparable way.

**Visual acuity as a function of time.** Duration of stimulation is one of the factors determining the smallest separation between two objects that can be perceived. Graham and Cook investigated the relation between time of exposure, interspace, and intensity by use of a series of seven gratings, and a series of seven different exposure times varying from 2 ms. to 500 ms.

The following is the broad outcome. With all durations of stimulation, visual acuity increases with intensity. This, of course, is a confirmation of other studies that have gone before. With fixed intensity, visual acuity increases with the logarithm of stimulus duration in a sigmoid fashion. For short durations and for all separations of bands (sizes of grating), intensity and time are reciprocal for a constant acuity. For longer durations of stimulation time becomes less influential in governing acuity. That is to say, there is a critical duration in the determination of acuity as in the determination of other responses. Critical duration decreases as intensity is increased.

Critical duration, or the range within which the product of intensity and time is a constant, is made most obvious by plotting total energy (log I x t) as the ordinate, against the logarithm of the duration of stimulation. In such a graph, a slope of zero indicates that intensity multiplied by time equals a constant. The extent of the horizontal section of the curve then shows the range of the critical duration. If the curve leaves the horizontal at an identifiable point, or if its inflection covers but a small range before the curve takes on a fixed slope, critical duration is much more tangible. It also indicates that the utilization of excitation is confined to a single neural locus.

As it happens, the visual-acuity curves for the conditions the above workers used, show a fairly abrupt termination of critical duration, suggesting its dependence upon activity at one point. Since anatomy is possibly the limiting factor it is likely the sense-cell.

**Visual acuity without employment of interspace.** It happens that the resolution of the eye can be measured not only by finding the minimal perceptible separation between two objects such as lines or bars, but also by use of a single line. This is made possible by the following facts. The receptor surface of the eye (retina) is a mosaic, or sheet of active units which may be likened to an emulsion whose grain determines its fineness of resolution. The finer the grain the smaller the possible separation between spatial differences which are recordable.

When this analogy is applied to the eye it is obvious that the size and separation between the elements of the retinal mosaic will determine visual acuity. If a line could be so fine as to cast an image which would occupy only a part of the space between two rows of retinal elements it would not be observed. Several factors make it impossible for that to happen. First of all, all the elements are not arranged in perfect rows, secondly, the optical system of the eye produces images which are slightly blurred and thus never so sharp in contour as the lines they represent.

These facts, nevertheless, do not prevent the retinal mosaic from being the limiting factor in determining visual acuity (except when the pupil is small). Thus when the minimal perceptible separation between two bars is to be determined, the outcome bears a definite relation to the mosaic. And when a single line is to be resolved the way the blurred light is distributed with reference to the spatial distribution of the elements of the mosaic is the limiting factor. The scheme in Figure 12, represents the conditions that are conceived to exist.

The most recent measurement of the resolving power of the

eye making use of a single line is that of Hecht and Mintz who used a dark line on a circular field subtending an angle of 12.6 to 19 degrees. The resolution threshold varied from about 10 or 11 minutes when the background brightness was 0.00000603 ml. to about 0.5 second (sec.) when it was 30.2 ml. A significant

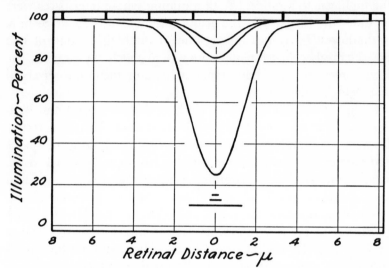

Fig. 12.—The distribution of the light in retinal images of fine wires. The width of the geometrical images is shown as the three lines at the bottom of the figure. The calibration at the top indicates the retinal mosaic of cones. It is to be noted that the distribution of light in the retinal and geometrical images are quite dissimilar. (*Hecht and Mintz—J. Gen. Physiol.*)

feature of the curve depicting this relation is a break such as is found for various other visual functions when intensity is varied from a high to a very low level.

The range represented by the measurements is 1200 to 1, a scale 10 or 20 times greater than ordinarily obtained with other types of test-objects such as gratings or broken rings. With them the resolution lies generally between 20 and 30 minutes of arc at the lowest intensities, and between 0.5 and 1 minute (min.) at the high, covering an overall range of 1 to 60. It is obvious that the difference in the two ranges has to do mostly with the higher light intensities where the value with single lines becomes about 60 times as fine as with a broken ring or with a grating.

Such differences in visual acuity have also been found in animal experimentation. Ehrenhardt with a grating whose spaces and lines were of equal width obtained a resolution in the lizard of one degree at the lowest intensities and about 11.5 min. at the high, a 1 to 5 range. With a grating whose interspaces were 30 times the line width, the acuity threshold was about 30 min. at the lowest intensities and 1.3 min. at the high, a range of 1 to 25. Here also the absolute values were much the same at the lower intensities for both types of measurement but diverged at the higher levels.

Comparison of the results of Hecht and Wolf (1929) and Buddenbrock (1935) indicates the same discrepancy between results from the line and grating methods. With a grating of spaces and bars of equal widths, the threshold is an angle equal to the smallest ommatidial * separation. With a single line, it is reduced to an angle covering only a quarter of one ommatidium.

**Visual acuity and sense-cell size.** Hecht and Mintz's finest resolution of 0.5 sec. represents greater acuity than that found by Hartridge (1922) for single lines. They attribute the difference to the uniformity of the background they used.

The geometric image of a line subtending a visual angle of 0.5 sec. would be scarcely .04 $\mu$ wide, or about $\frac{1}{60}$ of the width of a single foveal cone which has been estimated as 2 to 2.6 $\mu$. It is important to note that such calculations of retinal images are only hypothetical. One reason among others is that they are too small to be handled in the simple terms of geometrical optics. Because of diffraction at the pupil and other imperfections of the optical system, the image of a line is not a sharp dark shadow subtending only a small part of the cone, but a blurry shadow extending over several cones.

---

* The compound eye of certain lower animals is composed of a mosaic of tube-like structures all of which stand on end, forming a layer. Each of these tubes is a separate sensitive element and is called an ommatidium. Light enters at one end and its direction must be nearly enough parallel to the long axis of the tube to reach the opposite end, the sensitive part. Light falling on one ommatidium does not affect its neighbors. The size of the cross-section of a single ommatidium conceivably could determine the fineness of visual resolution.

**Visual acuity and the perception of contours.** The study of visual acuity has taken us to the verge of the investigation of the conditions for the recognition of contours. Since there are a number of additional factors yet to be considered, contour construction cannot be discussed here. It deserves extended treatment of its own, and is therefore reserved for a later chapter which follows the consideration of a number of preparatory phenomena.

**The nature of intensity discrimination.** Visual acuity reduces to being a type of intensity discrimination. What Crozier and Holway have to say with regard to intensity discrimination applies to it as well as to the determination of thresholds. They assert that the sensory ability to distinguish between two nearly equal intensities is governed by the fact that the just perceptible difference, or the differential threshold, is directly proportional to the standard deviation of the intensity which is experimentally varied. The characteristics of the experimental results of brightness discrimination accrue from the statistical nature of the basis for comparison between the physiological effects of the fixed stimulus intensity and the varying ability of the organism to produce a statistically distinguishable effect as a result of the exposure to another intensity at the same time.

They further point out that this relation is not vitiated regardless of whether the technique is that of simultaneous or successive exposure of the two intensities; whether the discriminable difference is changed by altering the area of the test-object; whether a background illumination or artificial pupil is used; regardless of which one of the psychophysical methods is used; or whether the discrimination is made by increasing or decreasing the second intensity relative to the first. Despite the quantitative differences in the results in the several cases, the law remains the same (the differential threshold and its standard deviation are proportional); the law holds equally well in vision and audition and when the exposure time of the stimulus and the minimal distinguishable increment both systematically change.

The above workers also claim that the determination of the

differential threshold is independent of any intrinsic properties of a specific peripheral or central sensory mechanism. That is to say, the various senses are all controlled alike by a statistical mechanism which is an expression of the central nervous system itself. This is vastly different than the assertion met with so often, that the photochemistry of the sense-cells is the primary determinant of the quantitative feature of brightness vision. It is essential then that the reader become aware of the two opposite ways of attempting to handle the data of brightness vision. The one school attempts to start with the receptor and determine just what it is capable of doing and then build onto its simple pattern the endless varieties of sensory complications in behavior by the method of accretion, the introduction of new constants, etc., to the original formula. The conviction seems to persist that more and more refinement in the notions of receptor behavior will produce the explanations needed. The other school utilizes the very same sense-cell data, the same data from human experimentation, but has found certain traits in them that show they cannot be the expression of the receptors alone but possess instead the nature that Crozier and Holway have just outlined. Bartley, dealing with different discrimination data, has come to the conclusion that they show that the nervous system patterns the sensory outcome.

### BINOCULAR VISION

**Binocular measurements.** Thus far in the present chapter, discussion has pertained to the way the retinal segment of the optic pathway functions. In all of the experiments employing human observation, monocular vision was used. Knowledge of retinal function is made possible not only by use of monocular vision in which the modifying effect of the interaction of the pathways from the two eyes is held at a constant minimum or in a sense eliminated, but also by comparing the results of employing one and both eyes.

In the cases in which a particular sensory outcome is dependent upon whether one or both eyes are used, a different kind of a process or a different ultimate pathway for the activity of a single eye is suggested than when the shift from one to two eyes brings about no essential change. The critical distinction must lie beyond the retinae themselves and it has become standard procedure to recognize this.

Although some investigators have pointed out that an object seen binocularly appears more brilliant than when viewed with one eye, certain aspects of the situation have remained in controversy. The fact itself seems to have become confused with the details concerning the mechanism of its accomplishment. That is, the issue of just where functional convergence of the separate pathways from the two eyes takes place has been confused with the question of interaction and summation themselves. Sherrington in his renowned experiments on binocular flicker found many of the quantitative aspects of monocular and binocular vision to be about the same, and concluded that there was a surprising degree of independence between the pathways from the two eyes. In his way of stating it, binocular fusion which results in a unitary perception from the elaboration from the two eyes is psychical rather than physiological. This puts that question out of the realm of the experimental, and does not clarify the question of summation. What might better have been said was that under the conditions he used, little or no interaction could be demonstrated, despite the unitary outcome on binocular perception, though logically some physiological basis for this unity cannot be escaped.

Subsequent investigators tended to rest upon Sherrington's view, ignoring the significance of facts obtained under other conditions which, both before the time of Sherrington and since, have shown that the brilliance of an object seen with two eyes is greater than when seen with one.

When once the subjective summation or subtraction is admitted, the hypothesis of physiological independence loses one of its essential supports. Hence it is and always has been a matter of primary importance to determine whether or not binocular interaction occurs. It may occur in one set of experimental conditions and not in another. But its absence in any case does not disprove its existence as a mechanism of the visual system.

The question of binocular summation does not rest entirely upon the findings in the flicker experiments as arranged by Sherrington. The results pertain only to the conditions used and no sweeping generalizations should have been made from them. Experiments in which precise timing is not a factor are much simpler and do not necessitate the experimenter having to find by accident or otherwise, the right temporal arrangements for producing the various results. That is to say, the simple matching of two fields, one seen by a single eye and the other by both of them, provides the most suitable methods of determining whether or not the two eyes work together to produce a different outcome than one alone.

**Fechner's paradox.**    One of the earliest binocular phenomena to be reported is that now known as *Fechner's paradox*. It consists in this, that if a given area of one of the retinae, say the right retina, is stimulated with a certain intensity and the corresponding area on the left retina is more weakly stimulated, this feeble stimulation of the left retina adds nothing to the net brightness, but instead diminishes it. The end-result of interaction here is subtraction. If summation were operative, the feeble stimulation of the left retina should combine with the stimulation of the other eye to form a greater total brightness. Despite the fact that this has been a long established phenomenon, exception has been commonly taken to the statement that the pathways from two eyes interact.

**Variable reduction of light reaching one eye.**    If one of two equally bright squares lying side by side is seen by one eye and the other is seen by both eyes it looks brighter, though not twice as bright. De Silva and Bartley studied this situation by measuring the subjective brightness of the square when only part of the light coming from it to the second eye was obstructed.

The actual procedure was as follows. To begin with, view of the two squares (the test-square and the standard) was unobstructed for both eyes, and the brightness of the right-hand square was adjusted until the two appeared equal. Then an episcotister mounted on a track at right angles to the line of regard was brought in from the left until interposed between the left eye and its view of the left square. When revolving above critical fusion frequency, the episcotister reduces the flux by a

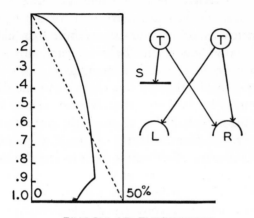

BINOCULAR EXPERIMENT

FIG. 13.—A diagram showing the optical system and the results in De Silva and Bartley's binocular experiment. T and T are the test-objects, light from both of which reaches the right eye (R) unobstructed. Light from the right test-object reaches the left eye (L) unobstructed while light from the left test-object is partially obstructed by an episcotister or by an optical wedge, or is totally obstructed by a diaphragm. If an object were to seem twice as bright when viewed with both eyes as when viewed by only one eye, the left-hand test-object would seem only half as bright as the right-hand one when the obstruction at (S) is complete. In order to determine the actual difference, the intensity of the right-hand test-object is reduced until the two test-objects match in brightness. The results of such a procedure with various amounts of partial obstruction at (S) are indicated in the graph whose ordinate, reading downward, shows various fractions of obstruction, and whose abscissa shows the amount of subjective reduction. The range of the scale is from zero to 50 per cent, and if the subjective reduction were an arithmetic subtraction it would follow the broken diagonal line in the graph. The solid curve shows what actually results when the light from the left test-object to the left eye is obstructed by each of several amounts. Slight obstruction reduces the brightness more than anticipated and obstruction of a considerable fraction of it reduces brightness less than the anticipated, or arithmetical amount.

predetermined amount. The left square now looks less bright than the right one, and to compensate, the actual intensity of the right one is reduced. This, however, reduces the flux from it to both eyes.

Since it would be expected on the basis of simple arithmetic subtraction that a patch seen by one eye would be only half as bright as when seen by both, it would be expected that if the second eye were allowed to receive some of the light from the patch, the patch would now be seen as more than half as bright.

Figure 13 shows how bright the test-square looks as the second eye is allowed to receive various amounts of light from it. In the beginning when the test-square and the standard provide their full quotas for both eyes, they appear equally bright. According to the figure, if $\frac{1}{16}$ of the light from the test-square to the left eye is obstructed, the square is more than $\frac{1}{16}$ less effective. This extra effectiveness in reducing the brightness of the square continues until about $\frac{1}{2}$ of the light to the left eye is obstructed. Then further reductions in the amount of light received by the left eye become less and less effective in lowering its subjective brightness. When all of the light from the left square to the left eye is blocked out, the square looks much more than $\frac{1}{2}$ as bright as the standard. Stating the matter in terms of the test-square (the square seen by only one eye), it must be made from 1.27 to 1.44 times as bright as the standard which is seen by both eyes in order that they be seen as equal.

Fry and Bartley, as a part of their study of binocular vision and contour, performed the following experiment, the results of which are shown in Figure 14. Two bright rectangles were produced on a dark background by cutting out suitable apertures from black cardboard. The illuminations furnished the two eyes passed through the apertures and were separately controlled. The lower of the two rectangles was illuminated from a broad field so that it appeared equally bright to both eyes. The part of the illumination of the upper which reached the left eye was controlled by an episcotister and the portion reaching the right eye was otherwise controlled.

The brightness of the upper rectangle as seen by the left eye (AL) was set at each of a number of levels and the observer adjusted the brightness of the other rectangle (B) so that A and B matched. The figure shows the results when A as seen by the right eye was dark. It shows that, depending upon the absolute brightness of B, AL must be some value between equality and double the intensity of B to appear equal to it. From

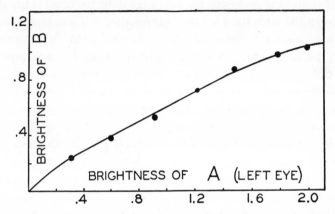

Fig. 14.—A graph showing the intensity of an object B seen binocularly must compare with the intensity of an object A seen with one eye when they appear equally bright. Units in c/ft.² (*Fry and Bartley—Am. J. Ophthal.*)

the shape of the curve it is to be expected that AL would have to be made even more than twice as bright as B, if the intensity of B were to be further increased.

These very few examples of comparison between monocular and binocular vision serve to demonstrate that the two differ, and that the magnitude of the difference varies from situation to situation. In some cases it is slight and in others considerable. But in keeping with the rule that the actual amounts of intensity difference can only be determined by the matching technique, it is unsafe to rely on the statement that binocular and monocular results differ but little in cases where they are not measured in this way.

The results of these experiments showing binocular interaction suggest that had Sherrington used some means of measuring the "slight" differences between the monocular and binocular outcomes in his experiments he might have found them to be greater than he had supposed. Since he used no equating method which is the only one by which intensities can be properly measured, the results in those particular experiments are still in doubt.

**Binocular intensity threshold.** Graham showed that the absolute threshold is no lower for two eyes than for one. This is not incompatible with the idea that summation at a common cerebral pathway occurs. There are two thresholds to be considered. First, the minimum amount of light necessary for a response in either of the two converging pathways, and second, the minimum frequency of impulses arriving at the common cerebral pathway to pass the synapses there. It is conceivable that in the case of either one of the two converging pathways there must be a certain minimal frequency below which it will not respond at all to stimulation of the retina by light. If this threshold frequency is sufficient to elicit a discharge in the common cerebral pathway, there would be no occasion for adding a stream of impulses by way of other converging pathways. If some such situation as this exists, Graham's finding can be interpreted as a consequence of the absolute threshold depending entirely upon the threshold at the retina, and therefore cannot throw light upon the problem of the threshold at the common cerebral pathway. This would show that the mechanism which operates to determine threshold response is not necessarily an indication of what may be expected when supraliminal inputs into the neurological circuit are to be considered.

**Other binocular effects.** In addition to showing that the intensity of a given surface is modified by including the second eye in its observation, there are several other binocular effects to be pointed out.

Binocular observation increases the depth effect of a complex scene, the mechanism of which is in part a matter of optics and in part the result accruing from the lack of strict spatial correspondence in the two hemispheric projections of activity.

By use of instrumentation (various types of stereoscopes) separate pictures either of different objects or slightly different views of the same object can be presented to the two eyes, in which case one of four results will occur. If the two pictures are not quite properly placed, the two will stand apart and not quite become a unified pattern. Convergence of the two eyes is involved in the achievement of proper binocular fusion, and this is gradual enough to be readily observed. In which case, the two pictures standing apart laterally gradually move together.

When the proper convergence is accomplished, one of the remaining three results will occur. The outcome will either be a single pattern exhibiting enhanced perspective; or one picture may be seen behind the other, or the two fields may fuse to form a new result. The latter occurs when two homogeneous surfaces of different colors are presented.

Two of the salient features of binocular vision achieved by presentation of separate pictures, or, as we might say, stereoscopy, are binocular rivalry and binocular luster. When two eyes are presented different colored surfaces, they do not always fuse into a new color, but one or the other will dominate for a time. Soon, however, it will be displaced by the other, this alternation or rivalry continuing indefinitely. When a bright field is presented to one eye and a dark field to the other, a peculiar glitter or luster is often the result. While at other times it is as if the black lay behind the light surface.

Some of these effects, though most usually obtained under stereoscopic conditions, are not exclusively binocular phenomena. Bartley reported that in slow intermittent stimulation in which the flickering field was surrounded by a bright annulus, the dark phase seemed to lie behind the bright, and under critical conditions the luster or glitter found in stereoscopy emerged. This demonstrated that the two eyes were not required for obtaining these results and that the effects were the results of critical timing. Accordingly, the results when obtained by binocular observation may also be a matter of the temporal organization of the impulses from the two eyes reaching a given cortical region.

The range of flicker frequencies producing glitter lies in the region of the alpha rhythm (see Chapter XIII). No simple connection between this inherent cortical rhythm and the present sensory phenomena may yet be made, though it is reasonable to suppose that if other brightness phenomena are dependent upon this rhythm (see Chapter VI), luster may also be.

**Brightness vs. quantity.** Though no doubt the reader is aware of the essential difference between brightness and light flux, some discussion of the two with regard to response is necessary at this time. It will have been noted that the chapter heading is that of brightness discrimination rather than response to quantity of light. If the two were correlated the matter would be much clearer than it is.

If two equal-sized areas equally distant from the eye emit the same quantity of white light they will look equally bright. Naturally, for the best comparison, they should both be in the field of vision at the same time. In such a case, brightness and light quantity or flux are equal.

This is not always the case, and the circumstances under which it is not, are not to be considered exceptions. For example, if one of the original areas is brought closer to the eye than its neighbor, it may or may not continue to appear equal in brightness. Ordinarily it will, for the mode of perceiving the two areas is that of alternately glancing at them. Perhaps the successive comparison may be mingled with momentary fixation so that they lie to opposite sides of the line of regard.

When the two objects are at unequal distances from the eye, they no longer subtend equal angles on the retina, that is to say, their retinal images will differ in size, though the flux per unit area is compensated in such a way as to remain equal. Since subjective brightness remains equal in the two cases, it would seem that brightness is correlated with flux per unit retinal area and that the total area is non-consequential.

On the other hand, if the observer, instead of glancing back and forth, fixates so that the two areas lie to opposite sides of the line of regard, and more or less relaxes accommodation, the nearer of the two areas will then appear to be brighter. In such a case, the flux per unit area does not correlate with brightness, but instead it is the total flux.

We are able to refer to our measurements in this chapter as brightness discrimination primarily because we always refer back to the brightness measurements obtained with the photometer. The fields of the photometer are perfectly adjacent, being either side by side, or one inclosed by the other as a disc and annulus, and measurements are based on obliterating the boundary between the two nearly equal areas.

The question arises as to whether the responses obtained from the *physiological* preparations are measures of brightness or flux, and it must be said that they are the latter, even though intensity is the variable, and the experimenter speaks of manipulating brightness.

**Summary.** The present chapter has included a discussion of the psychophysical studies, from which the fundamental nature of response is to be gained; namely, the studies of the absolute threshold, brightness discrimination and visual acuity. These demonstrate the fact that there is a definite lower limit both in space and in quantity to effective stimulating; that two areas may be compared in their effect, on the basis of total flux or on flux per unit area, and that the distance between two areas can be too small to be observed. These principles and their associated details begin to characterize sensation in a way which is usable in correlations with nerve physiology.

## REFERENCES

Bartlett, N. R., and R. M. Gagné. On binocular summation at threshold. *J. Exptl. Psych.,* 1939, 24:91-99.

Bartley, S. Howard. Some factors in brightness discrimination. *Psych. Rev.,* 1939, 46:337-358.

Cobb, Percy W. The effect on foveal vision of bright surroundings: II. *Psych. Rev.,* 1914, 21:23-32.

Cobb, Percy W. Further observations on the speed of retinal impressions. (*Light Res. Lab. Nela Park, O.*)

Creed, R. S.  The physiological integration of sensory processes within the gray matter of the nervous system: A critical review.  *Brain,* 1931, 54:29-54.

Crozier, W. J.  On the sensory discrimination of intensities.  *Proc. Nat. Acad. Sci.,* 1936, 22:412-416.

Crozier, W. J.  The theory of the visual threshold.  *Science,* 1939, 90:405.

Crozier, W. J.  The theory of the visual threshold: I. Time and intensity.  *Proc. Nat. Acad. Sci.,* 1940, 26:54-60.

Crozier, W. J., and A. H. Holway.  On the law for minimal discrimination of intensities: I.  *Proc. Nat. Acad. Sci.,* 1937, 23:23-28.

Crozier, W. J., and A. H. Holway.  On the law for minimal discrimination of intensities: II.  *Proc. Nat. Acad. Sci.,* 1937, 23:509-515.  III. 1938, 24:130-135.

Crozier, W. J., and A. H. Holway.  Theory and measurement of visual mechanisms: I. A visual discriminometer. II. Threshold stimulus intensity and retinal position.  *J. Gen. Physiol.,* 1939, 22:341-364.

Crozier, W. J., and A. H. Holway.  Theory and measurement of visual mechanisms: III. $\Delta I$ as a function of area, intensity, and wave-length for monocular and binocular stimulation.  *J. Gen. Physiol.,* 1939, 23: 101-141.

Crozier, W. J., Ernst Wolf, and Gertrud Zerrahn-Wolf.  On the duplexity theory of visual response in vertebrates.  *Proc. Nat. Acad. Sci.,* 1938, 24:125-130.

Crozier, W. J., and Ernst Wolf.  On the duplexity theory of visual response in vertebrates: II.  *Proc. Nat. Acad. Sci.,* 1938, 24:538-541.

De Silva, H. R., and S. H. Bartley.  Summation and subtraction of brightness in binocular perception.  *Brit. J. Psych.,* 1930, 20:241-250.

Elsberg, Charles A., and H. Spotnitz.  The sense of Vision. I. A method for the study of acuity of vision and of relative visual fatigue.  *Bul. Neurol. Inst. N. Y.,* 1937, 6:233-242.

Elsberg, Charles A., and H. Spotnitz.  The relation between area and intensity of light and the size of the pupil, with formulas for pupillary reactions.  *Bul. Neurol. Inst. N. Y.,* 1938, 7:160-164.

Elsberg, Charles A., and H. Spotnitz.  The sense of vision. II. The reciprocal relation of area and light intensity and its significance for the localization of tumors of the brain by functional visual tests.  *Bul. Neurol. Inst. N. Y.,* 1937, 6:243-252.

Fisher, Bruce M.  The relationship of the size of the surrounding field to visual acuity in the fovea.  *J. Exptl. Psych.,* 1938, 23:215-238.

Fry, G. A., and S. H. Bartley.  The brilliance of an object seen binocularly.  *Am. J. Ophthal.,* 1933, 16:687-693.

Fry, G. A., and V. M. Robertson. Alleged effects of figure-ground upon hue and brilliance. *Am. J. Psych.,* 1935, 67:424-435.

Graham, C. H. The relation between area and intensity of visual thresholds. *Am. J. Psych.,* 1930, 42:420-422.

Graham, C. H., and N. R. Bartlett. The relation of size of stimulus and intensity in the human eye: II. Intensity thresholds for red and violet light. *J. Exptl. Psych.,* 1939, 24:574-587.

Graham, C. H., R. H. Brown, and J. R. Smith. Brightness discrimination for varying durations of the just discriminable increment. *Psych. Rec.,* 1937, 1:229-233.

Graham, C. H., R. H. Brown, and F. A. Mote, Jr. The relation of size of stimulus and intensity in the human eye: I. Intensity thresholds for white light. *J. Exptl. Psych.,* 1939, 24:555-573.

Graham, C. H., and Carolyn Cook. Visual acuity as a function of intensity and exposure-time. *Am. J. Psych.,* 1937, 49:654-661.

Graham, C. H., and E. H. Kemp. Brightness discrimination as a function of the duration of the increment in intensity. *J. Gen. Physiol.,* 1938, 21:635-650.

Graham, C. H., and Jacob Levine. The latency of visual after-effects as a function of the intensity of illumination on an adjacent retinal region. *Am. J. Psych.,* 1937, 69:661-665.

Graham, C. H., and R. Margaria. Area and the intensity-time relation in the peripheral retina. *Am. J. Physiol.,* 1935, 113:299-305.

Graham, C. H., and John Paul Nafe. Human intensity discrimination with the Watson-Yerkes apparatus. *Pedag. Semin. & J. Genet. Psych.,* 1930, 37:220-231.

Graham, C. H., and L. A. Riggs. The visibility curve of the white rat as determined by the electrical retinal response to lights of different wavelengths. *J. Gen. Psych.,* 1935, 12:279-295.

Guilford, J. P. 'Fluctuations of attention' with weak visual stimuli. *Am. J. Psych.,* 1927, 38:534-583.

Hecht, Selig. A theory of visual intensity discrimination. *J. Gen. Physiol.,* 1935, 18:767-789.

Hecht, Selig, and Esther U. Mintz. The visibility of single lines at various illuminations and the retinal basis of visual resolution. *J. Gen. Physiol.,* 1939, 22:593-612.

Hecht, Selig, James C. Peskin, and Marjorie Patt. Intensity discrimination in the human eye: II. The relation between $\Delta I/I$ and intensity for different parts of the spectrum. *J. Gen. Physiol.,* 1938, 22:7-19.

Hecht, Selig, and George Wald. The visual acuity and intensity discrimination of drosophila. *J. Gen. Physiol.,* 1934, 17:517-547.

Helson, Harry, and Elizabeth V. Fehrer. The role of form in perception. *Am. J. Psych.*, 1932, 44:79-102.

Holway, Alfred H. On the precision of photometric observations. *J. Opt. Soc. Am.*, 1937, 27:120-123.

Holway, Alfred H., and Leo M. Hurvich. Visual differential sensitivity and retinal area. *Am. J. Psych.*, 1938, 51:687-695.

Kravkov, S. V. Effect of indirect light stimulation as a function of the intensity of a direct stimulus. *Acta Ophthal.*, 1937, 15:96-103.

Kravkov, S. V. Illumination and visual acuity. *Acta Ophthal.*, 1938, 16:385-395.

Lowry, E. M. Some experiments with binocular and monocular vision. *J. Opt. Soc. Am. & Rev. Scient. Instru.*, 1929, 18:29-40.

Luckiesh, Matthew, and Frank K. Moss. Supra-threshold visibility. *J. Opt. Soc. Am.*, 1940, 30:62-69.

Shlaer, Simon. The relation between visual acuity and illumination. *J. Gen. Physiol.*, 1937, 21:165-188.

Smith, Karl U. Visual discrimination in the cat: IV. The visual acuity of the cat in relation to stimulus distance. *J. Genet. Psych.*, 1936, 49: 297-313.

Smith, Karl U. Visual discrimination in the cat: V. The post-operative effects of removal of the Striate cortex upon intensity discrimination. *J. Genet. Psych.*, 1937, 51:329-369.

Smith, Karl U. Visual discrimination in the cat: VI. The relation between pattern vision and visual acuity and the optic projection centers of the nervous system. *J. Genet. Psych.*, 1938, 53:251-272.

Smith, Karl U., and John Warkentin. The central neural organization of optic functions related to minimum visible acuity. *J. Genet. Psych.*, 1939, 55:177-195.

Smith, J. Roy. Spatial and binocular effects in human intensity discrimination. *J. Gen. Psych.*, 1936, 14:318-345.

Steinhardt, Jacinto. Intensity discrimination in the human eye: I. The relation of $\triangle I/I$ to intensity. *J. Gen. Physiol.*, 1936, 20:185-209.

Wald, George. Area and visual threshold. *J. Gen. Physiol.*, 1938, 21:269-287.

Warkentin, J., and Karl U. Smith. The development of visual acuity in the cat. *J. Genet. Psych.*, 1937, 50:371-399.

Wilcox, Warren W. The basis of the dependence of visual acuity on illumination. *Proc. Nat. Acad. Sci.*, 1932, 18:47-56.

# III

# ENTOPTIC STRAY LIGHT

**Sources of entoptic scattered light.** One of the eye's primary functions is focusing the light received so as to form an image of the environmental field before it. Though the eye is often likened to a camera, it deviates from the ideal camera in several respects. It is not light-tight, its inner surfaces are reflective, and the image formed is blurred.

In everyday situations the image covers the whole retina, for the individual moves in a lighted environment. The image is also complex since the eye is generally regarding a world of things or intricate geometrical forms. In such cases, to speak of the image is either to speak of the image of a single one of the objects in the visual field, or the image of the whole field of view.

In the laboratory, the visual field is simplified. No more than a small fraction of it is used as the test-object. The remainder of the field is homogeneous, either dark, or at a controlled level of homogeneous illumination. The image then is that of the test-object, and it is useful to speak of the region of the image and the remainder of the retina as two separate things.

As was hinted above, the focused light forming the image is not the only retinal illumination. That is to say, the remainder of the retina receives light even when the visual field around the test-object is dark. This is unfocused and is called stray or scattered light.

Since the stimulus pattern in the visual field and the distribution of light on the retina do not even approximately coincide, examination of the stimulus itself does not directly indicate what the distribution of retinal illumination is, thus the principles of the entoptic treatment of the light by the eye must be learned and taken into account.

As we have already said, the factor which distorts the gross distribution of light is that of scatter. It arises from three principal sources: diffraction and scatter in the internal media; passage of light through the sclerotic coat surrounding the cornea; and reflection from the image to all other parts of the retina. Since the fundus of the eye is a hollow globe, it acts like a photometric integrating sphere.*

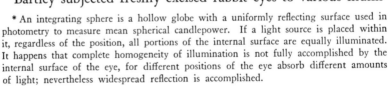

artificial pupil

light passing the sclerotic

diffraction and scattering in the media

reflection from image

Under many conditions the level of stray illumination is a considerable fraction of the intensity of the image itself. This is ably demonstrated by the use of an excised rabbit eye. An albino eye shows this best, due to the fact that it allows more of the light to pass outward through the coats for the external observer to measure.

**Photometry of the external globe.** It is possible to measure the brightness of the two parts of the external globe, the brighter area produced by the image and the dimmer level of the remaining region. This

FIG. 15.—A diagram of the eye to show the various sources of scattered light. An artificial pupil, the half of which is shown in the upper right-hand part of the figure, eliminates one of the sources of unfocused or scattered light, the light passing through the sclerotic coat of the eye. (See text for discussion of the other sources.)

forms a direct method of studying stray light, though there are additional ways of demonstrating its presence and ascertaining its physiological and sensory roles.

Bartley subjected freshly excised rabbit eyes to various illumi-

* An integrating sphere is a hollow globe with a uniformly reflecting surface used in photometry to measure mean spherical candlepower. If a light source is placed within it, regardless of the position, all portions of the internal surface are equally illuminated. It happens that complete homogeneity of illumination is not fully accomplished by the internal surface of the eye, for different positions of the eye absorb different amounts of light; nevertheless widespread reflection is accomplished.

nating conditions. For example, a test-object intensity varying from 342 to 2750 candles per square foot ($c/ft.^2$) was admitted to the eye through a 5 mm. artificial pupil. The resulting image as photometered from outer surface of the globe varied from 9.5 to 78 $c/ft.^2$ and the average brightness of the rest of the retina from .0266 to 2.12 $c/ft.^2$ The area of the test-object was varied in eight steps from the largest (46°) taken as unity down to about 0.034 of it (5.5°). In this case the brightness of the scattered light outside the image varied in proportion to the area of the test-object.

It is of interest to know what the ratio of the scattered to the focused light is under sample conditions. In the first experiment above, the ratio was 1 to about 36, without the restriction of an artificial pupil. The albino eye confronted by a test-object subtending a visual angle of 46°, exhibits a ratio of about 1 to 12, whereas, with a 7° stimulus, the ratio is about 1 to 700.

In other experiments the rabbit's eye was masked by use of small opaque discs, one just covering the pupil, and the others covering still more of the eye. With no light entering the pupil, the retina was illuminated to a noticeable level by a 7° test-object at 1500 $c/ft.^2$ As a way of demonstrating the effectiveness of this illumination, cortical responses were elicited. This means that the level is far above the response threshold.

In still other tests, stimulus intensities necessary to obtain threshold cortical responses to an evenly lighted retina, and to a retina on which a small bright image was added, were employed. The image added little or none to the size of the response, and shortened its latency only slightly. For details of the technique see the chapter on the response of the optic cortex.

**Additional methods of detecting or measuring stray light.** In addition to the direct photometry of stray light such as just described, there are other ways of either demonstrating its existence or of gaining an estimate of its amount.

The methods are of the following kinds: (1) The measurement of stray light in the human eye by using a peripheral light source to determine its effect on the differential threshold of a foveal test-object; (2) its measurement by use of flicker methods in which the critical flicker frequency (c.f.f.) curves of the test-object and that of the field at a given distance from the fovea are compared; (3) its indication by using two bright test-objects which alternately appear and disappear in opposite phase, on a dark ground. This can be demonstrated in the human observations, and also in electroretinogram experiments to be described in a later chapter; (4) its existence and function in experiments in "apparent" movement; (5) blurredness of the retinal image.

**Measurement of stray light by its effect on the differential threshold.** This method of measuring stray light in the eye may be briefly stated as follows: A bright object is placed in the peripheral part of the visual field and the amount of stray light falling on the fovea is measured by the change produced in the differential threshold between two parts of a disc-annulus test-object stimulating it. The change in threshold produced in this way can be compared with that produced by directly illuminating the region of the fovea with a veil of light of known intensity in addition to the test-object, called the "substitute stray light" by Bartley and Fry, who measured stray light in this way.

The observer's task in measuring the threshold consists in increasing the brightness of the central disc until it becomes just distinguishable from the annulus. The results of varying the brightness of the peripheral object upon the differential threshold are shown in curve A, of Figure 16, when the angle between it and the test-object is kept at $5°$ and the brightness of the annulus at .05 $c/ft.^2$ In the graph, the values given as differential thresholds represent the brightness differences between the annulus and the central disc. One may compare these values with the results of using the "substitute stray light" given in B, of the same figure. The two situations have been found to produce the same effect on the differential threshold. As intensity is increased, the threshold rises and at about the same rate in both cases.

Such a comparison shows that the intensity of the scattered light falling on the fovea when an object of 2220 $c/ft.^2$ subtend-

ing a visual angle of 1° and 14 min. (′) projects its image upon
the retina 5° from the fixation point, is equal to an illumination
of .34 c/ft.² admixed to the original level of the test-object by
the "substitute stray light." Since an artificial pupil of 1 mm.
in diameter is used the intensity of the stray light is 2.87 photons.

The intensity of stray light which a bright object produces is
specified in terms of three factors; its brightness, the solid visual

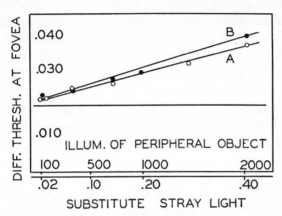

Fig. 16.—The relationship between the illumination of the peripheral object
(curve A) and the level of the substitute stray light (curve B) and the
differential threshold at the fovea. The two scales of the abscissa are for
the two curves. Units in c/ft.²  (*Bartley and Fry—J.O.S.A.*)

angle which is subtends, and also its distance away from the
retinal image where it is measured. In the present case the
peripheral light produces .00408 photons of stray light per square
foot of brightness and per unit of solid visual angle (milliste-
radian) 5 degrees from the retinal image. Calculations made
from the direct photometry of the external walls of an excised
rabbit's eye compare quite favorably with the present one.

Bartley and Fry also investigated the effects due to the existence of a peripheral glare source on the differential threshold
of a bisected disc test-object. They duplicated the essential conditions of Geldard by using a test-object whose diameter fell well
within the fovea, and a glare source located about 5 degrees

from the fovea. In both investigations the intensity ratio of the two halves of the bisected disc test-object was 0.59, the differential threshold being measured in terms of the intensity level of the brighter half of the disc when the difference in the two halves was just perceptible. Accordingly a drop in the brightness level required for this indicates an increase in differential sensitivity.

The curve showing Bartley and Fry's results exhibited a very marked drop when a dim peripheral object was injected. This was greatest when the object supplied a retinal illumination of about 2000 photons. In this respect, they corroborated Geldard. But when the brightness of the peripheral object was increased, differential sensitivity began to rise. This difference was evidently brought about by extending the range of conditions.

The fact that the disc-annulus test-object and the bisected disc test-object gave different results was attributed to a difference in interaction. They assumed that the glare source acted on the borders in the test-objects in keeping with the way they were oriented with reference to it and, in the case of bisected test-object, the orientation aided the formation of the threshold border. This will be made more explicit to the reader in the chapter on contour.

Figure 17 shows the outcome of varying the distance of the peripheral object from the fovea. The annular part of the test-object is .05 c/ft.$^2$ and the peripheral object is 2220 c/ft.$^2$ The intensity of stray light falls off rapidly as the peripheral object is moved from 5 to 10 degrees away from the test-object, and from there on it shows only a little diminution. The peripheral object can be seen by the observer to possess a halo which diminishes rather rapidly between 3½ and 5 degrees. As the peripheral object is displaced more and more, it is made to fall on the blind spot which in the examination of the fundus appears brighter than its environs. Owing to the fact that much of the stray light is reflected from the image, it might be expected that the amount of stray light caused by casting the image on the optic disc would be greater than when other parts of the retina are used. In keeping with this, we find a rise in the curve at the place representing the optic disc (16°).

To summarize, it may be said that Bartley and Fry's use of the two different test-objects along with their other experiments resulted in definitely distinguishing between the effects due to

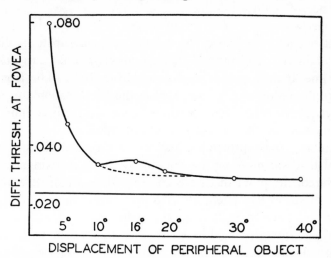

DISPLACEMENT OF PERIPHERAL OBJECT

F͟ɪɢ. 17.—The relationship of the displacement of a bright object and the stray light falling at the fovea as indicated by the change in the differential threshold. The displacement is expressed in terms of the visual angle sub-tended by the center of the test-object and that of the peripheral object. It will be noted that in the region of 16° the curve exhibits a hump. This is the region of the optic disc, and since it is lighter in color than the rest of the fundus it might be expected to reflect more light. If so, it accounts for the hump. Units in c/ft.² (*Bartley and Fry—J.O.S.A.*)

stray light and to retinal interaction, and enabled them definitely to measure the amount of the former.

**Stray light demonstrated by field flicker.** If a series of flashes is delivered at a high rate, flicker which is the sensory result with a slow repetition is replaced by a subjectively steady illumination. This point is often called the fusion point and the flash rate required to produce it is the critical flicker frequency (c.f.f.). Ordinarily the image of a test-object subtending but a few degrees of visual angle is used, and the properties of flicker are studied as if the image of the test-object constituted the entire illumination of the retina. What we have already demonstrated by use of the excised eye and the differential threshold shows without a doubt that this is not the case. Accordingly, the flicker method may be employed as another means to show the existence of scattered light.

Properly directed observation shows that not only the test-object but also the entire visual field may participate in flicker. Flicker in the field outside the test-object may be measured in the same manner as it is in the test-object itself. The first rule regarding flicker is that the weaker the illumination the lower the frequency necessary to produce fusion. On this account c.f.f. is a measure of the intensity of illumination.

Utilizing these principles, Bartley investigated flicker in the visual field surrounding the test-object. Since its existence there is assured, the problem that is confronted is one of determining what produces it. There are two possibilities in accounting for its origin; namely, scattered light as he supposed; or some sort of retinal interaction. His study was undertaken with the assumption that the shape of the curves of c.f.f. for the test-object and surrounding fields as intensity and area are varied would provide a means of distinguishing between the two possibilities.

He found that the c.f.f. frequency curves for the field were a constant fraction of those representing the test-object as would be the case were flicker due to scattered light. This is to say that lower flash frequencies were required to bring about fusion in the field than in the test-object. Such a result does not rule out interaction but strongly suggests stray light as the origin. As the area of the test-object is a factor in determining the c.f.f., it was also a factor in determining the fusion point for the field. This would hardly be the case were retinal interaction responsible for field flicker.

It was also found that the field could flicker after the test-object had reached the fusion point. This would seem to be further proof that the origin of the flicker in the field originates there and thus is due to scattered light falling on the field as a whole

rather than to an effect transmitted laterally through neural connections from the test-object to remotely outlined regions of the
retina.

When the image of the test-object instead of being cast on the
fovea is placed on the peripheral retina, a curve representing

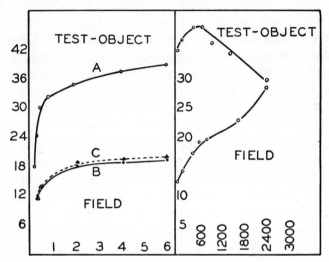

Fig. 18.—Critical-flicker-frequency curves for test-object and surrounding
field. Left-hand graph, (A), test-object when fixated; (B), field when the
test-object is 16° from fixation point; (C), field when test-object is the same
distance from the fovea as in the latter case, but its image now falls on the
optic disc. Right-hand graph showing a curve for the field and one for the
test-object when the illumination is so bright that the c.f.f. for the test-object
is declining. Under such circumstances the c.f.f. curve for the field is still
rising. The two curves may cross, and the c.f.f. for the field be higher than
for the test-object. In the present graph, the test-object is 1° and an artificial
pupil of 4.9 sq. mm. was used. In both graphs the ordinates represent c.f.f.
and the abscissae represent candles per sq. ft. (*Bartley—J. Exptl. Psych.*)

fusion at the fovea under a series of intensity conditions can be
obtained. If instead of the image falling on an active part of the
retinal periphery, it is placed on the optic disc, flicker can still be
seen at the fovea. This constitutes still another proof of flicker
in the field being due to stray light, since as yet no sense-cells
have been discovered in the optic disc to account for retinal inter-

action. The curve in the two cases virtually coincides as would be expected if stray light were responsible.

**Stray light demonstrated by two flickering discs in opposite phase.** Fry and Bartley used another means of demonstrating not only the existence of entoptic stray light but its efficacy. The experimental conditions were as follows. Two bright discs of light were made to appear on a dark background. They were so timed that as one appeared the other disappeared. Despite the fact that their appearance and disappearance constituted a flicker situation, the outcome as a whole was different than when a single test-object is used.

As a basis for appraising the situation, it is to be recognized that the alternate appearance and disappearance of a single disc of light at a slow rate such as 3 or 4 per second (p.s.) sets up vigorous field flicker and is outstanding in the amount of discomfort caused the observer. When the two discs alternate as described above, field flicker is absent and the discomfort never arises. This is what is to be expected if stray light is responsible for field flicker and the annoyance just described.

A moment's reflection shows us that by use of the two alternating discs, scattered light is held virtually uniform, though the discs in their appearance and disappearance provide for flicker as far as they themselves are concerned. Since the rate of alternation is far below fusion, the lack of flicker in the field is not a question of rate. This may be shown by momentarily masking out one disc, whereupon field flicker appears. The flash rate involved in such a case is much less than half the frequency needed for fusion. This method was also used to determine whether the retinal elements excited by the image of the test-object or the elements more feebly activated by stray light over the whole retina were responsible for the electroretinogram. Details relative to this are reserved for a later chapter.

**Blurredness of the retinal image.** The discrepancy between the distribution of the light in the stimulus object and on the retina takes on not only the form of a widespread scatter which has already been discussed, but also blurredness of the retinal image itself. That is to say, an homogeneously bright object with sharp contours will not produce an image with identical characteristics. The transition from illumination in the image to darkness outside of it is not abrupt, but gradual. It is important to know the nature of this transition. Previously it has been calculated from the laws of chromatic and spherical aberration and defraction, but the method is laborious and takes into account blurredness under static conditions only. That which is due to minute rapid fluctuations in fixation occurring even when the best of rigidity is attempted is not taken into account in such calculations. Fry and Cobb, on the other hand, have demonstrated a method which gives an overall measure of blurring produced by the various sources.

Since it is known that the threshold of visibility of a long narrow line depends upon its width as well as its brightness, it is evident that there is a spread of light in the image. It would be expected that the image would be brightest in the center and that the threshold of visibility would be determined by a certain minimal intensity in this region. Reducing the width of the object, when it is already very narrow, would be expected to lower the intensity at the center, due to the blurring.

Fry and Cobb's investigation rested on the original assumption that the distribution of illumination across the image of a very narrow bar is described by the Gaussian equation

$$(\text{I}) \qquad Y = \frac{\text{I}}{\sigma\sqrt{2\pi}} e^{-\frac{x^2}{2\sigma^2}}$$

where Y is the intensity at a distance x from the mean and σ, the standard deviation or the mean square deviation from the mean of the distribution. The area under the curve between the extremes of plus and minus infinity is unity. The problem of these investigators was then the measurement of the value of σ. Using white light and an artificial pupil having a diameter of 2.33 mm. and a well accommodated eye, they found σ to be equal to 44 seconds (″) of visual angle, though under other conditions it would undoubtedly be different. The use of mono-chromatic light, for example, would obviate the defects of chromatic aberration, and eliminate one of the factors producing the blur. If the pupil size were altered, the defraction and chromatic aberration would also be changed.

To find $\sigma$ it was necessary to obtain the brightness thresholds for two bars, $B_1$ and $B_2$, the width of the former $W_1$ so great

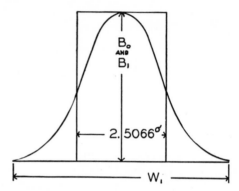

Fig. 19.—Diagram to indicate the dimensions dealt with in Fry and Cobb's experiment. (*Modified from Fry and Cobb—Trans. Am. Acad. Ophthal. and Otolaryngol.*)

that further increase did not reduce its threshold and the width of the latter, $W_2$, so small that brightness and width were reciprocal. Investigation showed that any width greater than $242''$ was sufficient for the former and any width less than $30''$ for the latter. $\sigma$ is then obtained by the following formula:

$$(2) \qquad \sigma = \frac{1}{2.5066} \frac{(B_2 \ W_2)}{B_1}.$$

We can construct diagrams of the two retinal distributions, the one which would exist if the image was a perfect replica of the stimulus object, and the other the Gaussian distribution which is being tested for its validity. Since the total amount of light in the image is the same regardless of its distribution, certain relations between the two are known. The two diagrams are shown in Figure 19, in which the height of the rectangle and of the

Gaussian curve is the same. They are so constructed because it was assumed that the intensity in the center of the image should be the same regardless of distribution. It is known that when the rectangle and the Gaussian curve are the same height and contain the same area, the width of the rectangle is equal to 2.5066 $\sigma$. We shall call the height of the rectangle indicating intensity $B_0$, and the width of the rectangle $W_0$. This means that $W_0$ is 2.5066 $\sigma$. We shall call the width of the base of the Gaussian curve $W_1$ and its height $B_1$. It is evident that $B_0$ equals $B_1$. $B_2$, as we have assumed, is the brightness of a width of bar so small that brightness and width are reciprocal, and $W_2$ is the width of such a bar. Thus, according to the hyperbolic relations,

$$(3) \qquad B_0 \ W_0 = B_2 \ W_2.$$

Since $B_0 = B_1$ and $W_0 = 2.5066 \ \sigma$, equation (2) is obtained when these values are used in equation (3).

Fry and Cobb obtained the threshold of a bar 3000″ long and 192″ wide, and also the thresholds for a number of narrower bars down to one in which width and intensity were reciprocal. By substituting in (2) the value of $\sigma$ was obtained. Theoretical values of thresholds for the various widths of bars using the $\sigma$ which had been obtained coincided with the empirical thresholds and this was taken to mean that the distribution of light in the image caused by blurring follows the Gaussian equation whose $\sigma$ value is 44″ for an infinitely narrow bar under the particular optical conditions tested. It also validates the assumption that the intensity at the center of the retinal image remains constant for various bar widths at threshold.

Using the fact that the light in the image of an infinitely narrow line is distributed in keeping with the Gaussian equation, it is possible to determine the light distribution for objects of various widths and to demonstrate how width affects the intensity at the center of the image. Intensity and width increase almost proportionally at first, but the relation slowly changes to one in which increase in width finally fails to raise intensity at all. The strength of illumination for any object wider than 242″

is 1 photon per sq. mm. of pupillary aperture and for each candle per sq. meter of brightness of the external source.

**Eye pigmentation.** On the basis of what has already been said about the sources of stray light, eye pigmentation would be expected to play a role in visual function, if it acted as an obstruction to light passing through the sclera and if it reduced reflection from the retinal image.

Helson and Guilford studied the absolute threshold for both

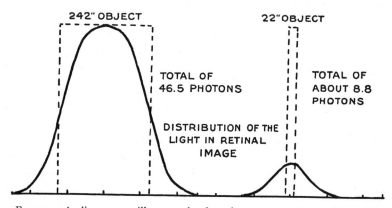

Fig. 20.—A diagram to illustrate the fact that a very narrow object and a wide one of equal intensity do not produce retinal images of equal intensity. The visual angle of the left-hand object is 242 seconds, while that of the right-hand object is 22 seconds.

Negroes and whites, the latter being divided into three groups according to darkness of iris pigmentation. Their results showed that the threshold was higher for the poorly pigmented eyes. It is not certain how much this bears on the problem of stray light, but nevertheless, it suggests that a similar study be conducted on visual acuity with a range of supraliminal light intensities where stray light most certainly plays a role.

**Summary.** This chapter indicates that the eye is stimulated by two kinds of light, focused and non-focused, and that the latter plays a material role. Though there are situations in which it plays no material part, the possibility of it is always to be considered. This will be demonstrated, for example, in the chapter on adaptation phenomena.

## REFERENCES

Bartley, S. Howard. The comparative distribution of light in the stimulus and on the retina. *J. Comp. Psych.*, 1935, 19:149-154.

Bartley, S. Howard, and Glenn A. Fry. An indirect method for measuring stray light within the human eye. *J. Opt. Soc. Am.*, 1934, 24:342-347.

Fry, Glenn A., and S. Howard Bartley. The relation of stray light in the eye to the retinal action potential. *Am. J. Physiol.*, 1935, 3:335-340.

Fry, G. A., and P. W. Cobb. A new method for determining the blurredness of the retinal image. Am. Acad. Ophthal. and Otolaryngol., 1935, pp. 1-6.

# IV

# SENSE-CELLS AND THE RETINA

## THE SENSE-CELL

**Kind of sense-cell studies.** The study of vision basically begins at two points; namely, at the sense-cell and at sensation itself. Sensation with its manifold phenomena provides the data that are to be accounted for. The sense-cell represents the element which is directly acted upon by light.

It is apparent that a knowledge of the behavior of the sense-cell as a mediator between radiant energy and nervous processes should first be sought in accounting for visual sensation. In actual practice, it has turned out that interest in it has not failed to develop but has motivated a constant effort on the part of some investigators to show that what happens in the sense-cell accounts for the end-result in sensation. Today we have in the work of Hecht and his colleagues a very good conceptional framework of photoreception.

It must be kept in mind from the start that most of the studies on the sense-cell apply to it as an abstracted unit rather than one of a group of functioning receptors. In fact, as yet, we have little or no knowledge of the behavior of one sense-cell affecting the activity of others, as do the elements in the visual pathway beyond. We do not know whether such an interaction is possible, not to say probable.

Notwithstanding, a general humoral factor has in a few cases been postulated as a means of accounting for widespread interaction effects declared impossible through neural channels. This supposition is based on interpretations of various experiments on spatial summation. The humoral substance was supposed to be released under specific conditions and to raise the general level

.

of retinal activity rather than merely that of a limited area, as might be accomplished through spatial summation.

The investigation of the first events in the visual process has been pursued mainly by studying, (1) the latency and vigor of light reactions in simple animals, (2) the nature of the photo-chemical substances of the sense-cell *in vitro*, (3) flicker phenomena and dark adaptation in humans, and (4) single sense-cells in simple animals having compound eyes which can be reduced to a single active element. Thus there are two broad aspects of the problem of vision as applied to the sense-cell; its photochemistry and the relation of its rate of discharge to various stimulus conditions. The first three of the investigations just mentioned try to answer the former, the fourth to answer the latter. Each of these methods is valid when used in light of the findings of the others and when mindful of its limitations, some of which will become obvious in later sections. It is remarkable that deductions about the behavior of the sense-cell can be made from such a variety of data.

**Limulus studies.** Most of the direct studies on the behavior of the visual sense-cell have been made on the Limulus eye on account of its well-suited anatomy. The eye is embedded in the shell of the animal, a part of which surrounding can be used for mounting the preparation for experimentation. The fibers leading from the individual sense-cells collect apparently without synapsing to form the long optic nerve bundle extending to the central nervous system of the animal. Thus the eye itself is composed of only a collection of independent sense-cells as contrasted to the vertebrate eye with its nervous complications. As an experimental arrangement, it is as if the rods and cones and their processes were lifted from the subsequent part of the retinal pathway of the vertebrate eye for study.

In recording, light is usually focused on a few of the ommatidia and the optic nerve bundle is teased apart until the activity of only one or a very few sense-cells is recorded. Prior to this reduction in activity, one electrode may be put on the front of the eye, which we might call the "cornea," and the other electrode placed on the optic nerve bundle.

The electrical potential representing the response of the total eye to a very short flash (.020″) is a monophasic fluctuation last-

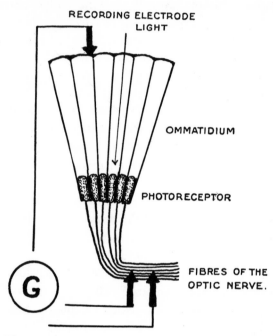

FIG. 21.—Diagram showing a section of a compound eye and the way electrical records are taken from it. Light enters each ommatidium as indicated by the arrow and reaches the sense-cell at its base. The recording electrode at the top of the diagram rests against the outer surface of the eye. The lower two electrodes support the delicate optic nerve which is composed of fibers from the sense-cells. G is the recording instrument. If the upper and one of the lower electrodes are used, the potential recorded is across the eye from front to back, and is often called a retinal potential. If the two lower electrodes are used, an optic-nerve record can be obtained.

ing about a fifth of a second with a latency of .08″. If both electrodes are placed on the nerve itself, the response is of a much different nature. When the activity of only a very few fibers is being recorded, a series of very abrupt discharges results. With fewer and fewer active elements the picture becomes more and more simple. With one active sense-cell, the temporal distribution of the discharge spikes is quite uniform, and they are all of nearly the same size, in contrast to the original volley where they were quite irregular both in size and distribution.

The response of the sense-cell to illumination consists of a series of the brief discharges ranging from a very few (p.s.) up to perhaps 130 p.s. There is reason to believe that in the human it may reach perhaps 150 to 200 p.s. The variables in the functioning of the sense-cell, which are useful to study, are those of discharge frequency including temporal pattern and the latency of various points in the discharge pattern.

Increasing the intensity of a flash of fixed duration contracts the latent period of the response of the single sense-cell, and increases the frequency and the total number of impulses discharged. Extending the duration of a flash of fixed intensity has a similar effect, when flashes shorter than the latent periods are considered. Intensity and duration are reciprocal in their effect. To elicit a given constant effect it is necessary that the energy of the stimulating flash be constant. This is strictly true for all aspects of the response if their duration is shorter than the latent period. This shows that the Bunsen-Roscoe law applies to the photosensory mechanism.

The reciprocity relationship will appear to fail if this restriction should be unrecognized, and then the condition for constant response will be that of constant intensity. For both initial and maximum frequency of impulse discharge, the reciprocity relationship fails, and is replaced by the constant I requirement at a critical duration which is *definitely shorter* than the time of appearance of the particular feature of the response. Hartline interprets this as indicating that the impulses are determined within the sense-cell at a time which is appreciably earlier than their appearance under the electrodes.

The succession of impulses discharged by the sense-cell assumes a temporal grouping depending in part upon stimulus intensity. The onset of intense illumination produces a burst—a group of impulses at high frequency. This is followed by a continued discharge at a much lower rate. Under some conditions, the initial burst is followed by a pause or "silent" period before the lower rate sets in. If the sudden increase in illumination from zero or from some other preexisting level is slight, the burst will be absent. The response will begin with a discharge rate, little if any greater than the one to be maintained throughout the duration of the illumination.

The eye of Limulus provides a structure in which it is possible to study "the area effect" in its simplest form. In experiments measuring the latent period of nerve response as a function of the number of ommatidia illuminated it was found that the latent period of two or three central ommatidia is the same whether they are illuminated alone or accompanied by a large surrounding area. This holds good over intensities ranging from 1 to 10,000.

Experiments also demonstrate that the magnitude of the *retinal* potential is directly proportional to the number of ommatidia illuminated up to the total of one-half of the eye, beyond which the size of the response increases less rapidly with increase in number of ommatidia. This is due, probably, to the angular displacement of the more peripheral elements with respect to the direction of the stimulating light.

These facts are a functional demonstration of the conclusions from anatomy that in the Limulus eye there is no interaction between the sense-cells of adjacent areas and making sure that interpretations in other experiments on the Limulus actually apply to single cells.

**Differentiation of sense-cells and ganglion-cell discharge.** All sense-cells do not act alike with reference to changes in illumination. In the eye of the Pecten there are two sense-cell layers, the cells in one discharging to the onset or increase of illumination and the other to its cessation or sufficient reduction.

If other animal forms have two types of sense-cells, they are not segregated into two discrete layers but are indistinguishably intermingled. The existence in this species of two functionally different sense-cells suggests their possible existence elsewhere.

The visual sense-cell of the vertebrate cannot be isolated. The preparation employing the most direct recording of its action is that in which single active ganglion-cell fibers are isolated and their actions recorded. The result has been the discovery of three different types of discharge. We shall call them Y, X, Z. About 50 per cent of the fibers discharge with a rapid burst of impulses at the onset or increase of illumination, sink into quiescence and burst into action again at the reduction or cessation of illumination. Others (20%) fire with a burst at the onset or increase of

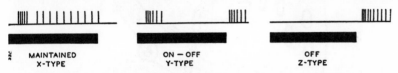

| MAINTAINED X-TYPE | ON – OFF Y-TYPE | OFF Z-TYPE |

Fig. 22.—A diagram showing the 3 types of ganglion-cell-axon discharge in the vertebrate retina. The heavy horizontal lines represent the light. The relation between its onset and cessation, and the distribution of the impulses in the response is hereby made evident. (*Bartley—Psych. Rev.*)

illumination and settle down to a more or less steady lower rate throughout its duration. The third kind (30%) fire only at the cessation or substantial reduction of illumination. It would seem from this that during steady illumination a maximum of only 20 per cent of the fibers can be activated.

The three modes of fiber response may be due to one of three causes: (1) That they are produced by three essentially different types of sense-cells, or (2) that the retinal layers between the sense-cell and the ganglion layer produce them, or (3) that they are due to functional differences between ganglion cells. Decisive evidence for any one of the alternatives is still lacking, except in the Pecten.

**The receptive field of an optic-nerve fiber.** An optic nerve fiber responds to stimulation of any point within a limited retinal area which is termed the *receptive field* of that fiber. The limits of the receptive field can be mapped by a very small spot of light whose location can be accurately manipulated. The retinal location of any receptive field is fixed and its area depends upon the intensity and area of the exploring spots and upon the adaptive state. The receptive field is smallest under threshold stimulation. It is then about ¼ to ½ mm. in diameter, approximately doubling with intensities of 100 to 1000 times the threshold. The effective-

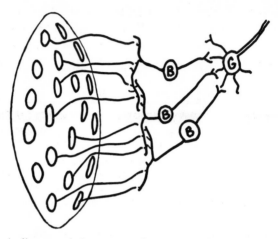

Fig. 23.—A diagram of the receptor field of a single optic-nerve fiber. The large circle in perspective is the field on the surface of the retina. The small circles within it are the sense-cells. Their fibers lead to the bipolar cells marked B, upon whose receiving branches they converge. Note that more convergence occurs within the center of the receptor field than at its periphery. The axons of the bipolar cells converge on the ganglion cell (G). Light falling anywhere within the receptor field is effective in producing an ultimate response in G.

ness of a small spot of light depends on its position in the receptive field, the more sensitive central region of the field responding most vigorously.

The larger the area of a spot falling within the receptive field, the greater the response. Two spots illuminated concurrently are more effective than either one alone, indicating summation.

Ganglion fibers responding at both *on* and *off* or at *off* only, respond to movement of a spot of light or of a shadow within the receptive field. The *off* fibers, however, respond only when the spot of light moves to a less sensitive region of the receptive field. In general, any change which abruptly reduces the amount of excitation produced by light is accompanied by an off-response in such a fiber.

Off-responses are abruptly terminated by re-illuminating either the same spot of the retina used to evoke them or some adjacent region within the receptive field. The inhibition is complete if the strength of re-illumination equals or surpasses the one eliciting the response, and if a region of the receptive field of similar or greater sensitivity is re-illuminated. Likewise the larger the area re-illuminated, the more complete is the suppression of the discharge. From this it would seem that the effect produced varies in keeping with the number of sense elements involved and the number of interconnections available.

All of the findings indicate physiological convergence upon the ganglion cell. This convergence is not only one of facilitation but of inhibition for the inhibitory effects due to illumination converge upon the ganglion cell from all parts of the receptive field, and are integrated in the total inhibition produced. The inhibitory process is most effective shortly after the onset of re-illumination. The latency is about .1 second. Inhibition subsides in several seconds to a lower level and continues throughout illumination.

**Events within the sense-cell.** Concerning the events which underlie the sense-cell discharge, Hecht begins with the most general notions. First, there must be a sensitive substance to absorb light and be changed by it into one or more active products. Second, a supply of this original photosensitive material must be maintained to sustain the process. Finally, the direct or indirect end-result of the primary light reaction must institute an impulse from the sense-cell.

Hecht suggests the following system. He postulates photosensitive substance S. Let light of intensity I fall on it, producing the photoproducts P, A, etc., whose concentrations at the moment are given by x. The velocity at which this *primary light reaction* ← P + A proceeds will be proportional to I and to the concentration $(a - x)$ of sensitive material. To describe the situation more fully, two more factors, the order of the reaction and a velocity constant must be included, though in simply obtaining a bird's-eye view of the matter these need not concern us.

He makes the additional assumption that the primary process in photoreception is something like a reversible photochemical reaction where P, A, etc., can reunite by themselves or with the help of additional substances or energy to reform the original sensitive substance S. The rate of this primary dark reaction $S \leftarrow P + A$ will be proportional to the concentrations x of the photoproducts.

When light impinges upon such a system the two reactions proceed concurrently until their rates become equal, and the system reaches a *stationary state*.

Visual discrimination, visual acuity, and flicker phenomena under certain limited conditions behave as if they were determined by just such a simple system as described by the stationary-state equation.

It is to be pointed out that the concentrations a and x of the primary light reaction may be considered as the various levels or intensities of the rise and fall of the "excitatory" process. Such a view changes only the details of the mechanism; the quantitative relationships will remain the same.

Hecht indicates that it is even unnecessary to refer either to a photochemical reaction or to an excitatory process, but to the measurement of light and dark adaptation (see Chapter VIII). It is found by direct measurements that the course of dark adaptation may be described quite empirically by an expression in which x, instead of being the concentration of S, the original photosensitive substance, transferred to form a corresponding concentration of P and A, refers to measurements of reaction time, or of intensity thresholds. The course of light adaptation may also be measured, though not directly, wherein x will be some function of the reaction time or of the threshold intensities. The algebra follows exactly as before, so that in terms of light and dark adaptation, one may predict the occurrence of such events as described by Talbot's law.

It is assumed from the ability to predict Talbot's law and from the other correlations between photoreception and sensation that the latter is quantitatively dependent upon the sense-cell as if the intervening nervous system in the retina were, in effect, only a simple conductor of the impulses of the sense-cell on the way to the brain.

This is exemplified in Hecht's use of the fact that the maximum sense-cell frequency of discharge is below the maximum impulse frequency possible for the nerve fiber. From this he argues that it is the sense-cell that determines the sensory outcome and not the fiber.

It is to be granted that the fiber properties do not determine the sensations in question, but on the other hand, it is to be recognized that the nervous system is composed of synaptic layers whose activities are slower in rate than maximum fiber discharge and function in an organizational capacity rather than as simple conductors.

In the case of the eye, the retinal synaptic layers begin immediately to determine the optic-nerve discharge and give to it far different characteristics than could be predicted from the discharge rates of the various individual sense-cells of the retina. On this account it is difficult to see how predictions from photochemical activity of the sense-cells to sensation are possible. In fact we know that correlations or parallelisms of any kind between the two sets of events are possible only in some instances.

## THE RETINA

**Function and plan.** The retina is a very complicated neural structure. It is not only a layer of sense-cells but a part of the central nervous system. The number of functions attributed to it are many. It is not only the discriminator for brightness, it is presumably the mechanism for distinguishing color, for providing for visual acuity and contour, and for adaptation to a million-fold range of illumination. In view of this it deserves attention both from the standpoint of the contribution of its individual sense-cells, and from the standpoint of its neural organization.

The impulse which originates in the sense-cell passes inward along a series of three neurons; namely, the cone or rod, the bipolar cell, and the ganglion cell whose axon is one of the fibers of the optic nerve. Involved in this transmission are several collateral elements, the amacrines, the transverse or horizontal cells. Through these as well as the arborized transverse processes of the serial elements, crosswise interconnections are made so that

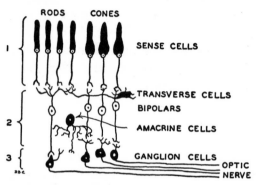

Fig. 24.—A cross section through the retina showing the essential elements, including the frontal pathway (1-2-3) through it and the lateral connections. (*Bartley—Psych. Rev.*)

any one part of the retina can modify the nervous activity of others. As a consequence, the output may be only in the most broad aspects anything like the input.

**Rods and cones.** The sense-cells of the vertebrate retina histologically fall into two groups, the rods and the cones. In some cases the morphological distinction between the two is quite poor, and furthermore not all vertebrate eyes are provided with similar proportions of them. Some contain cones exclusively; others only rods.

To distinguish between a rod and a cone would seem to be a relatively simple matter, but in reality the great variety in form of these cells in different species of animals has frustrated a clear-cut classification. Verrier interprets her recent observations so as to regard the rods and cones as variants of a single photoreceptor cell, dispensing with the concept of structural and physiological duality in the retina.

Typically a cone is an element with two major components. The outer segment is conical and is the distinguishing feature. The inner segment typically possesses an ellipsoid and a myoid element, and sometimes a highly refractive globule, the paraboloid. A spherical oil drop is located at the distal end of this inner segment.

The rod is typically cylindrical and possesses a refractive disc in a position corresponding to the oil drop in the cone. Many types of rods possess an ellipsoid and some a paraboloid. Both rods and cones have a myoid element extending through the external limiting membrane.

Though the conical-cylindrical structural differentiation between the two cells is used, the mode of centripetal connection with the bipolar cell is also said to be the basis for distinguishing them. All cones are supposed to have dendritic endings, and the rods to have knob-like endings. The situation is by no means this simple.

Diurnal birds have sense-cells which from their gross form should be called rods and are so-called by Franz, though they possess dendritic terminations. On this basis, Pütter declares all reptiles have only cones. Notwithstanding, some groups of reptiles such as certain lizards and snakes are nocturnal in habit. Their sense-cells do, however, have all the other structural features of rods.

It is commonly known that the human foveal cones are long cylindrical elements appearing more rod-like than cone-like. They are nevertheless called cones because their physiology fits in with the traditional traits of cone vision.

In many fishes, amphibians, and birds, which possess both types of sense-cells, a distinction can be made in spite of their ambiguous shape on the basis of their inverse photomechanical responses to light. Some cells shorten in the light and elongate in darkness. Others elongate in the light and shorten in the dark. The former are classed as cones and the latter as rods.

The sense-cells of mammals, however, do not exhibit such re-actions.

Nocturnal reptiles such as the Gecko are cone-free. Crocodiles are rod-rich, the cells each having light-reflecting tapetum. Many other forms have a complete or relative absence of cones, and begin their activity as dusk approaches.

On the same basis, birds are divisible into nocturnal and diurnal forms. Some birds, for example, migrate only at night. Mammals in general have mixed retinae. Among the lemuroids and tarseoids which are nocturnal, the retinae are devoid of cones or of a fovea.

In the typical nocturnal animal, the cornea has a marked curvature. In the Lemurs and some others, it comprises one-third of the globe; whereas, in the human it is only one-fifth or one-sixth. The lens in the Galago, one of the Lemurs, as compared to the whole globe, is enormous. Its relation is 1:1.63; whereas, in man, the relation is 1:9. In the Galago the ciliary muscle is extremely large, being four times as great as in the rhesus monkey and man.

Insofar as the retina is concerned, an animal's capacity for detailed vision is apparently dependent upon its structure. In this sense it is quite similar to a photographic plate. The fineness of detail it can register is dependent upon the fineness of the emulsion. If the particles are small and close together much greater detail is obtained than when they are large and farther apart.

A low visual acuity in the retina signifies that the distance between the sense-cells is large; whereas, a high visual acuity indicates that the distance is small. It is interesting to note that the vertebrate retina exhibits striking variations in this respect. Inasmuch as the number of sense-cells is structurally fixed, it is certain that the number of elements per unit area must vary functionally so as to mediate the great range in visual acuity known to result from changes in the level of illumination.

Typically the sense-cells are more numerous per unit area near the visual axis than toward the periphery. In some of the pure cone retinae, such as in the turtles, there is a small area in the optical axis where the cones are decidedly smaller and more plen-.

tiful. This increase causes a thickening of the external nuclear area. It is called the *area-centralis retinae* and is possibly the forerunner of the central fovea. The collection of many fine receiving units in this area represents a structural condition conducive to greater visual acuity.

If one compares the highly developed foveas of certain reptiles with that of man, it is easy to believe that in the former the conditions for finely detailed vision are better met than in human beings. The cones in the Chameleon fovea are slender and compactly arranged. As compared with the monkey and man, the fovea is much deeper.

Walls has put forth certain ideas regarding the foveal depression. Whereas it has been commonly thought that the thinning or displacement of the retinal layers in the fovea represents a situation whereby light may reach the foveal cones without passing through the retinal layers, Walls points out that in the turtle's afoveate area-centralis, the retina is thickened but despite this the resolving power is greater. This suggests that thinning of the retina to admit light is not the objective. If it were, man and monkeys would be superior to reptiles and birds, for in the latter though the fovea is deeper it is not nearly so broad.

Walls, on the assumption that the retinal refractive index is greater than that of the vitreous, believes that the limiting membrane of the foveal clivus (slope) is a refractive surface. The highly convexly sloping surface broadens the retinal image by the time it reaches the cones, bringing into play a greater number of them.

On this basis the steeply convexiclival fovea of birds and lizards is superior to the broader but less steeply sloping fovea of man and monkeys. Though this concept appears to give order to the facts, it remains to be seen whether it is workable.

In this connection it may be noted that some birds have developed a temporal fovea as well as a central one. The unusual visual acuity of these birds is notorious. Walls states that the hawk fovea contains a million cones per square millimeter. This would require a solid packing of elements $1 \mu$ in diameter. In contrast to this, the human fovea is made up of cones no closer than 2½ $\mu$ from center to center, an arrangement requiring about 160 thousand elements per sq. mm.

In the human eye, the center of the retina, the fovea, is occupied exclusively by cones, while the remainder of the retina is populated by rods and cones, with rods becoming predominant toward the periphery. The central area of about 1.5° is entirely rod-free, while a slightly larger area, 2° in diameter, contains so few rods that it may be considered virtually rod-free. Progressively the cones become fewer and fewer toward the periphery of the retina and the rods become more and more plentiful, though the total combined population is less dense. According to the most recent estimates there are between 110 and 125 million rods and between 6.3 and 6.8 million cones in the human retina.

As was stated above, the neural connections of the sense-cells in the retina are of two general types, the one-to-one, and the multiple. The cones presumably are provided with a one-to-one connection with the ganglion cells, while the rods are much more collectively hooked up. The afferent processes of a whole group of rods converge on a single bipolar, and several bipolars may likewise converge on a ganglion cell. The highest figure given for inward convergence is 80 rods for each optic nerve fiber leaving the periphery. In speaking of the cone and rod connections in this way, it must not be forgotten that the arborizations of adjacent elements intermingle so that the connections specified are by no means the exclusive ones.

**The duplicity theory.** Very little information can be dealt with in connection with the vertebrate eye without in some way or another involving what has long been known as the duplicity theory. The conception was first suggested by Schultze in 1866 and later developed by von Kries. In essence it is to the effect that in keeping with the population of the retina with two kinds of sense-cells, vision shows two ranges of function, one mediated by the rods and the other by the cones. Cone vision provides for a high degree of visual acuity and for the perception of color as well as intensity, while rod vision mediates the lower range of intensities and is achromatic and relatively gross in discrimination.

The distinction between the two sets of facts must be at once pointed out. There is first, the sense-cells with the presence or absence of definite morphological distinctions. There is next, the animal's response. The data that have accumulated with reference to it fall into two classes; (1) the animal's living habits, whether they be nocturnal or diurnal, and secondarily, whether from their behavior they seem to have good or poor visual acuity, (2) the animal's behavior in experimental situations such as in tests for flicker recognition. In these situations the curves that are constructed from the data evidence either a tendency to segment into two parts (in one case three), or else to represent a continuous function.

Possession of these two sets of facts, the duality of sense-cell types, and the duality of visual functions when experimentally examined, has led to the desire to directly correlate the functions with the rods and cones as two distinct types of sense-cells.

The works of Hecht and colleagues and Crozier and his colleagues have been the primary present day sources showing duality in the quantitative achromatic functions of many forms of retinae, and providing the data from which the existence of two functionally discrete populations of sense-cells is deduced. These in some cases have been identified as the rods and the cones. In others the total range of visual function has simply been divided into two kinds, photopic (light adapted) vision, and scotopic (dark adapted) vision without identification with specific structures.

The outcome of testing such functions as visual acuity, flicker discrimination, and dark adaptation has led to treating the human eye not as a single organ but as a double one. There is one set of relationships between function and intensity for low, and another for high, illuminations. This is exhibited by a break in the curves representing them. The shift occurs at an illumination of about 0.1 meter candle (m.c.) or in a field whose brightness is about .003 c/ft.[2] It is not known whether or not the cones are fully responsible for vision above this level and rods below it.

The difference between afferent neural interconnections of the rods and cones precludes the direct measurement of the intrinsic distinctions between them. Part of the extra sensitivity of the rods may accrue from their richness in this respect and a way has not yet been found to show definitely whether or not that is the case.

To say the least, it has not been shown that an animal devoid of rods lacks vision at very low illumination levels, for a comparison of the critical flicker frequency curves of a rod-free animal and one possessing both rods and cones, shows that their range can well be quite similar. This would indicate that at least some structures labeled as cones are sensitive at very low levels of illumination.

The following is an example from the work of Crozier and Wolf to show the kind of unexpected results that are encountered when assignment of limited ranges of function to each of the groups, rods and cones, is undertaken. According to the duplicity theory, one might expect for a pure rod retina, a critical flicker frequency curve rising to a low peak and then declining, all parts of which would represent low flash intensities.

It turns out from experiment, however, that the rod retina of the Gecko, as well as the pure cone retina of the turtle, exhibits a smooth curve which describes a probability integral. The two curves begin together at the top, having been corrected for the same maximum c.f.f., and follow each other quite well. It is surprising that the range of intensities covered by the two is the same. It also turns out that the values for the standard deviation of the logarithm of the intensities are more nearly the same than those of two genera of fishes.

From these results it is to be concluded that the rod retina does not necessarily function best at low intensities nor less well at higher levels of illumination than a cone retina. The results throw considerable doubt upon the propriety of identifying structural appearance and functional ability.

Another way of attempting to answer the question is to consider what is to happen to the rods at high illuminations. If the rods play no part in vision above .003 c/ft.$^2$, it is surprising, for they are far more plentiful than cones over a large part of the retina, and this would be equivalent to saying that they are useless over a greater part of the range of everyday illuminations.

In further pursuing the question, we may recall that visual purple has been related to rod functioning. Light bleaches it, and in darkness it regenerates. Total bleaching might be considered an index of rod inactivity. Examination of eyes exposed to illumination many times above the critical level we have mentioned show less bleaching than might be expected. Tansley's albino rats confronted with an illumination of 2000 m.c. for considerable time still retained some visual purple. Lythgoe exposed frogs to an estimated illumination of 50,000 m.c. for 40 minutes and found the visual purple to be only ¾ bleached. This is to be viewed in light of the fact that in frogs visual purple can be masked from light by migrating pigment epithelium.

Granit's experiments show that the electrical response of the retina under some conditions is very small if visual purple drops below 50 to 60 per cent of its top value. At the same time the work seems to indicate that there is considerable visual purple left after exposure to 50,000 m.c. If we still assume that the rods play no role at the higher illuminations, we must, like Granit, conclude that the visual purple present can produce no stimulation, although bleachable, and therefore evoke no sensation.

**The water beetle optic-ganglion discharge.** The electric discharge of the optic ganglion of the water beetle is a demonstration of how stimulus conditions modify the way cells work together. The results of such a study were reported by Adrian in 1937. Inasmuch as the results have to do with the optic system and inasmuch as we are to discuss from time to time how the retinal cells must act, this study is pertinent here.

In a fresh preparation, a regular rhythm is recorded only when the eye is exposed to very bright light. Such stimulation evokes waves at 20 to 40 p.s., declining with time. In contrast to this, medium light causes the disappearance of the waves.

In an older preparation, a rhythm of 7-10 p.s. appears in the electrical record, when the eye is in total darkness. If dim illumination is provided, the rhythm ceases. Though this "dark" rhythm is an abnormal reaction, as is shown by the fact that it can be instituted by injury, it can be used in the analysis.

Since the conditions under which the beetle eye functions are neither those of absolute darkness nor dazzling light, some of the conditions imposed by the experiment are abnormal. But it is only under these circumstances that the great mass of cells act in sufficient unison to give definite rhythm to the record, while under everyday conditions for the animal they respond more nearly independently and, due to algebraic cancelation, little activity can be seen in the record. Ganglion activity is attested to despite the lack of definite waves, for under dim light an irregular discharge exists in the optic nerve.

That the waves in a continuous record appear only at one of two relatively fixed rates (dark or bright rhythm) raises the question of whether there are two types of cells responsible. A train of waves of declining frequency may follow the cessation of bright light, so it is clear that the two rhythms are not due to two entirely independent groups of elements with fixed response rates. There seems rather to be a single set of units able to respond over a wide frequency range, and the relatively fixed rhythms we have just alluded to represent the rates at which synchrony is possible.

The separation of the observable rhythms into two fixed ranges may be due to the fact that the population of receptors varies considerably in response frequencies at low and medium intensities of stimulation. Such a diversity in discharge rates militates against synchrony. With maximum stimulation this is not true. All receptors tend to respond more nearly at the same top frequency and synchrony is thereby favored. With no stimulation, heterogeneity of discharge frequencies would again be eliminated, for the spontaneous discharge rate would tend to be nearly alike for all cells. This would favor synchrony of cell discharge when the eye is in darkness.

The question of whether the dark rhythm represents an off-discharge is another way of asking whether the elements responsible for the dark and bright rhythms are separate. In some water-beetle preparations a small off-discharge was observed, but

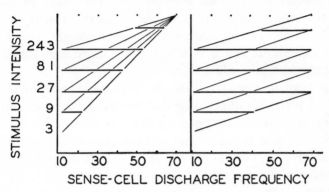

FIG. 25.—Schema to represent the relative heterogeneity of discharge frequencies dependent upon diversity of threshold. As stimulus intensity is increased more and more additional elements are activated. The various thresholds are indicated by the lower left-hand origins of the diagonal lines. As intensity reaches the maximum either all of the elements are discharging at the same high rate as indicated in the left-hand figure or else all elements have reached their maxima which are not represented by the same discharge frequency. This is indicated by the right-hand figure. The heavy horizontal lines crossing the diagonal indicate by their length the diversity of frequencies of discharge produced at various given stimulus intensities. Thus for example, in the left-hand figure when the stimulus intensity is at an arbitrary value of nine units, discharge frequencies cover a range of perhaps 10 per sec., whereas, when the intensity is at 81 units the range of difference in discharge frequency is about 45 units. Under such conditions there is supposedly little or no chance for synchrony. With either the very highest or the very lowest intensities there is maximum opportunity for synchrony.

in most, cessation of illumination elicits no increase in activity which could be likened to an off-discharge of newly active elements. The activity is composed only of an irregular discharge of small impulses, from which it is supposed that the dark rhythm evolves. The extinction of the dark rhythm by weak light would be the result of their enhanced but non-uniform activity. On this assumption it would be expected that the abolition of the rhythm

by light would be accompanied by an increased impulse discharge in the optic nerve. This was found to be true in every
preparation tested.

Another sign of this increased activity is the existence of a
sustained negativity of the ganglion which increases in amount
with the level of illumination. The negativity reaches a maximum with illuminations sufficient to give the bright rhythm, and
outlives the light which is followed by an after-discharge, but
disappears abruptly when there is none.

It is evident, however, that the impulses accompanying the
ganglion potentials during bright illumination are on the average
larger than those appearing in the dark rhythm, so that some elements contribute to the former and not the latter. But the continuous drop in the rate of the rhythm following the onset of
darkness testifies against the complete independence of the contributing elements.

As the frequency of the waves in this after-discharge declines,
the impulses superimposed on the ganglion waves are of all sizes,
but progressively the large spikes disappear until the final rate of
the dark rhythm is reached, when they are found only very
infrequently, if at all. It is entirely possible that these large
spikes represent not large nerve fibers but several of a smaller
size acting together. If this be true, we have no evidence from
the diversity of spike size that the activity during darkness is
due to a special group of elements analogous to those responsible
for the off-discharge in other animals.

**Summary.** It was intended that the reader should gain from
this chapter the information of how the sense-cell performs,
mainly from the electro-physiological, but also a little from the
photochemical standpoint. He should have gained the idea that
a ganglion cell output is originated at the cessation of stimulation
as well as its onset, that all sense-cells do not act alike, and that
the vertebrate retina is often populated by two more or less distinct types, the rods and cones. He should have discovered the
essentials of the *duplicity theory* which outlines especially the
dual functioning of the human retina, and finally assimilated the

idea that the many cells of the retina must somehow act together. This was intimated if not strongly suggested, and an example of it was given in the synchronous activity of the cells in the water-beetle ganglion.

## REFERENCES

Graham, Clarence H. The relation of nerve response and retinal potential to number of sense cells illuminated in an eye lacking lateral connections. *J. Cell. & Comp. Physiol.*, 1932, 2:295-310.

Graham, C. H., and H. K. Hartline. The response of single visual sense-cells to lights of different wave-lengths. *J. Gen. Physiol.*, 1935, 18: 917-931.

Hartline, H. K. Intensity and duration in the excitation of single photo-receptor units. *J. Cell. & Comp. Physiol.*, 1934, 5:229-247.

Hartline, H. K. The discharge of impulses in the optic nerve fibers of the eye of Pecten irradians. *Proc. Am. Physiol. Soc.*, 1937, p. 72.

Hartline, H. K. The response of single optic-nerve fibers of the vertebrate eye to illumination of the retina. *Am. J. Physiol.*, 1938, 121:400-415.

Hartline, H. K., and C. H. Graham. Nerve impulses from single receptors in the eye. *J. Cell. & Comp. Physiol.*, 1932, 1:277-295.

O'Day, Kevin. A preliminary note on the presence of double cones and oil droplets in the retina of marsupials. *J. Anat.*, 1936, 70:465-467.

O'Day, Kevin. The visual cells of the platypus (Orinthorhyncus). *Brit. J. Ophthal.*, 1938, pp. 321-328.

Riggs, L. A. Recovery from the discharge of an impulse in a single visual receptor unit. *J. Cell. & Comp. Physiol.*, 1940, 15:273-283.

Riggs, L. A., and C. H. Graham. Some aspects of light adaptation in a single photoreceptor unit. *J. Cell. & Comp. Physiol.*, 1940, 16:15-23.

Walls, Gordon L. The reptilian retina: I. A new concept of visual-cell evolution. *Proc. Assoc. for Res. Ophthal.*, 1934, p. 10.

# V

# THE BLIND SPOT

**Retinal anatomy produces a blind spot.** It can be easily shown that under some conditions the field of vision contains a blind area. Its existence in the normal eye has been known for almost three hundred years. Despite this long history, the controversy over the significance of the phenomena involved has not completely terminated even yet.

The anatomical basis for the experiences included as "blind-spot phenomena" is the optic disc. In one part of the retina all of the outgoing fibers which are to constitute the optic nerve collect. In this region there are said to be no sense-cells as in the other parts of the retina. This is known as the optic disc. Since no one has observed sense-cells there, it is assumed by most investigators that the light falling on it produces the effects which are to be enumerated, by transference of the light to surrounding regions of the retina and that the sensory end-result is much as if the stimulation took place in the optic disc. Light falling on it does not at best provoke clear vision as when cast elsewhere. Under some conditions it provokes no vision at all, and under still other circumstances the area and the rest of the retina function as a total field, so that no "blind spot" exists. The subjective results under a variety of fundamental sets of conditions seem to form one of the best demonstrations we have of the field nature of the mechanism providing for vision. The failure to recognize this has led to a great amount of confusion.

It must be pointed out at the beginning that the emergence of vague sensation under limited conditions when light is cast on the optic disc, although it can be accounted for under a field hypothesis, has led some to hope for a direct sensory basis such as finding a few scattered sense-cells there or that nerve fibers themselves are sensitive to the amount of light used. The way must always be left open for possibilities as rare as these, but in the meantime it appears that the instruments for successfully accounting for the phenomena are in our hands, and should be used. Were either of the above hopes concerning the sensitivity

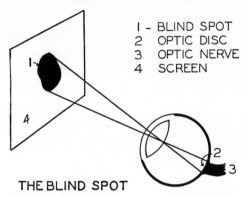

1 - BLIND SPOT
2   OPTIC DISC
3   OPTIC NERVE
4   SCREEN

THE BLIND SPOT

Fig. 26.—A diagram showing the eye with its optic disc and the blind spot in the visual field. Note that the blind spot of the visual field is cone-shaped, including a progressively larger cross section as distance from the eye is increased.

of the optic disc to be realized, it still would not vitiate the principles which we shall set forth.

**Location and size.** The optic disc is 16 to 20 degrees nasal to the fovea, the region of clearest vision. The blind spot is in the temporal half of the visual field about on the level of the line of regard or a little below it. It subtends a visual angle of from 5 to 7 degrees, thus its absolute linear dimensions vary with the distance from the eye. The binocular field then possesses two "blind" areas. They do not occupy positions from which light would stimulate corresponding retinal points, and thus in no way do they subjectively overlap. In binocular vision, every point in external space which is "blind" for one eye is seen by the other. The total space in the external environment from which light originating would fall on the optic disc, is represented by two cones whose apexes begin in the eyes and whose bases lie in infinity.

The visual outcome from light arising from anywhere in these cones may demonstrate a blind spot, a region filled with a diffuse haze, or a situation in which nothing seems amiss, there being no gap or area qualitatively different from its surroundings.

**The method of presentation of material.** There has been so much controversy over the means whereby sensation is aroused when light is cast on the optic disc, so many experiments which are essentially similar but differ in certain details, so many conflicting reports with reference to quite similar tests, that separate consideration cannot be given to the work of the various recent investigators without hopelessly confusing the reader. On account of this, it has been thought best to present my own theory and apply it to the gamut of essential conditions under which sensation is aroused by optic-disc illumination. The treatment given in this chapter will orient the reader in the basic matters pertaining to experiment and theory and he may later consult individual works as he wishes.

**The sense-cell adjacency principle.** Current theory has it that visual acuity is dependent upon the density of the population of the retinal sense-cells, that the limit of resolution has to do with spaces represented by the widths of cones and their distances apart. *This is to say that any light which would fall between two rows of cones, not touching either, would be unperceived.* Over practically all of the retina the elements are so close together that for practical purposes no light can fall between them and some of it not fall on the cells themselves  As far as the retina in general is concerned, then this situation is never realized. The idea stands only as a hypothetical construct. Nevertheless it is one which is perfectly straightforward and convincing.

It is only logical that this idea be applied to the optic disc. *Here the sense-cells have, as it were, been pushed aside.* At least we have reason to believe that the disc is an area devoid of them. Sense-cells begin to exist only at its boundaries, and from all indications, they are scarce even there. They only become more dense in population as we go farther from the center of the optic disc. Various measurements which are similar in their results to the effects obtained as the periphery of the retina is approached indicate this. There is then this one essential difference between our hypothetical gap and the optic disc, namely, that instead of the latter being abrupt in transition it is graded. This very fact

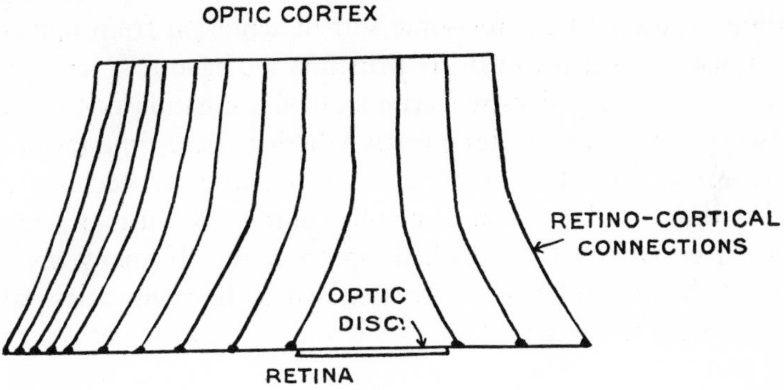

OPTIC CORTEX

RETINO-CORTICAL
CONNECTIONS

OPTIC
DISC

RETINA

Fig. 27.—A device to illustrate the point-to-point relations of the elements in the retina and the receiving elements in the cortex. The sense-cell layer in the retina is pushed aside in one region by the nerve fibers as they collect in leaving the eye. No such disturbance in the regularity of the projection area of the cortex is known to exist. Since representation of space depends upon density of sense-cell distribution, the gap known as the optic disc produces some peculiar results in vision. (See text.)

is one of the several producing results which have helped confuse investigators not recognizing the principles set forth here.

Since there is a considerable space between the sense-cells lying on one side of the area and on the other, light can, under limited conditions, be made to fall within the area without a threshold amount escaping to them. The two factors involved in realizing this non-stimulation of nearby sense-cells outside are low intensity and restriction in area of the patch of light cast onto the disc. At the other extreme, it is possible to cast a patch of light onto it bright enough to illuminate the whole retina a supra-threshold amount. If the image is nearly as large as the optic disc itself, light will more easily escape to sensitive areas outside.

**Sensitive-disc theories.** There are those who fail to see how sensation can be elicited if the optic disc is not sensitive. Accordingly they postulate one of the two theories previously alluded to. The first one is that a few sense-cells exist there despite the fact that they have not yet been found. The idea that a few sense-cells are scattered over the optic disc, an area which if normally populated would contain myriads of them, though providing a rational basis for some sort of sensation from optic-disc illumination, still involves the principle we have first laid down. It is that sensation does not arise from illumination of the retina between sense-cells. Consequently whether there are a few sense-cells in the optic disc, or none at all, is only a matter of degree rather than a difference in principle. Surely cells, if many, would not have remained overlooked up to now. If many are still missed they would have to be assumed to be pigmentless structures failing to react to staining technique. This is not a promising outlook.

The second alternative postulate regarding optic-disc behavior was to the effect that the ganglion-cell fibers collected there are sensitive to light, a suggestion which has developed in view of the rare possibility of finding sense-cells in the optic disc. Granting that nervous tissue, such as the fibers, might be sensitive to light, we can be sure that it would require high intensities. The use of such would involve sufficient light to spread beyond the optic disc through the optical properties of the tissues themselves. Widespread sensitive areas would be involved and hopelessly complicate results. Though we cannot entertain the possibility that moderate or weak light would activate the optic-disc fibers themselves, a serious objection would arise if it could. The principle of eccentric projection would be violated in the attempt to make such stimulation account for blind-spot vision.

**The principle of eccentric projection.** The principle of eccentric projection is simply a rule stating the basis of the orderly connection between points in space, the stimulation of the retina, and the recognition of the location of objects. It states that every point in space stimulates a predictable point on the retina inasmuch as the eye is an optical instrument and follows the simple law of lenses. There is first of all image formation so that the illumination pattern on the retina is a fair copy of the environment which the eye confronts. The physiological processes underlying the experience of vision use the image as material and retain in principle the same orderliness so that there is usually little confusion between where an object is seen to be and where it is found to be by means other than direct vision.

If the vision accruing from the illumination of the optic disc were dependent upon the excitation of the fibers which collect there, the orderliness that is required in everyday vision could not be provided. The observer could not say just where something were seen. In fact the stimulation would have the character of diffuse whole field stimulation. This would be due to the fact that geometrical patterns which would be cast on the optic disc would find the fibers, in their radial convergence into the disc, lying at right angles to the pattern instead of having their terminations ending in a sheet-like mosaic upon which the focused pattern is cast. As a consequence the image would have no orderly connection with the fibers, a violation which could not be tolerated.

Hence the notion that the direct stimulation of the ganglion-cell fibers might account for blind-spot phenomena finds nothing to stand on. In its stead, the proposition that the exclusive illumination of the optic disc gives rise to no sensation will be put in its place. This means focused illumination so weak that any scatter from it is sub-threshold when falling on sensitive areas surrounding the disc.

**Eccentric projection applied to blind-spot phenomena.** Sensory phenomena arising from the usual illumination of the optic disc are a special case of the principle of eccentric projection. Since areas within the disc are insensitive, they themselves cannot be differentiated one from the other by exclusive illumination of them. All illumination which escapes from the disc falls on sense elements immediately surrounding it as well as more distant ones and the impression produced is one of continuity. The result is as if any other adjacent cells were activated.

If the simple geometry of the situation instead of the principle of sense-cell adjacency were to be the determining factor, the stimulated sensitive area around the optic disc being a ring would produce the impression of a ring of light. This at the same time would create a dark area within the ring, or in other words demonstrate a failure of the blind spot to fill in. We know, however, that these results do not occur under these conditions. The sensory impression is, on the contrary, a continuous patch of light for the same reason that the stimulation of adjacent cells anywhere gives the impression of continuity.

Likewise, with practically uniform illumination of the retina as in viewing a homogeneous field, no gap is discernible through direct sensation. Obviously enough, if dark objects are then so placed to fall within the blind spot they disappear when monocular vision is used. Directly sensed gaps in the field of vision are in fact an absurdity. Gaps are only deduced. They arise from the fact that the experimenter or observer knows illumination has been thrown on a limited portion of the retina and no sensation has resulted, whereas illumination cast elsewhere in the immediate vicinity or over the remainder of the retina produces a visual impression. The gap then is not a direct sensation but a derived conviction. Helmholtz was criticized for entertaining such a view. He said the gap was a product of judgment. His error was not in saying this. He failed in not making the matter more explicit. But this was hardly possible without first utilizing the principle set forth in this chapter with reference to light and the distribution of the sense-cells. The full significance of this relation for the various features of vision was not recognized in his day, and it is fair to say that we do not yet see all that is implicit in this arrangement.

The principle of sense-cell adjacency answers Helson's objection to the non-sensitive disc theory, the objection being that in order to explain blind-spot phenomena, the illumination would have to be transferred from the disc to the sensitive elements at its borders to result in a seen object. Then this seen object would have to be transferred back into the area of the disc to be seen in its proper spatial relationship to its surroundings. This is an absurd way of attempting to adhere to the principle of eccentric projection and is unnecessary. It is a total misunderstanding of what is to be expected of retino-cerebral representation.

**Mapping the blind spot.** We now come to the matter of mapping the blind spot. It is based on the principle of the disappearance and reappearance of objects carefully moved in the proper section of a uniform visual field.

A large upright screen, often a cardboard square about a yard in width, is used. If it is white, the exploring object is black; if black, the latter is white. The exploring object is a small disc attached to the end of a thin rod or wire. When the observer whose head is held rigid by a support is seated three to five feet from the screen, the experimenter asks him to signal when the disc appears and disappears. The observer, of course, uses only one eye and maintains a steady fixation. The disc can only be seen "out of the corner of his eye," but the places of disappearance and reappearance are easily enough discerned. The experimenter after preliminary exploration may wish to construct a set of meridians on the screen, along which to move the disc, or he can continue to move it slowly back and forth in directions suggested by previous reports of the observer.

The experimenter upon completing his explorations will have one or two concentric rings of dots on the chart. If both sets, one indicates the places where the disc disappeared, and the other where it reappeared. These dots are connected by lines to give two rings. A new ring may be made in between the two as an average or else the inner or outer one may be chosen, depending upon the purpose in mind. When the distance between screen and observer is 4 or 5 feet, the horizontal dimension of the blind spot is on the average about 5.5 to 6.8 inches, while the vertical dimension is somewhat greater. The usual shape of the area is generally more nearly an ellipse than a circle. If the original position of the observer can be resumed any time later at will, through the use of a reliable support for the head, the original mapping may be used over and over again.

To use transmitted light for an experiment, the outline of the blind spot is cut from the screen and the aperture is covered by opal glass. Through this, light of the desired color or intensity is delivered to the eye, and any restricted portion of the total blind spot can be used by blanking out the portions not wanted.

It is obvious then that the mapping conditions are particularly suited for demonstrating the "gap" in the visual field.

**Sensation without an intensity gradient across the boundaries of the optic disc.** It will make it much easier for the reader to follow the basic experimental results if they are given in an order dictated by a rational scheme rather than by the order dealt with in the experiments of the several investigators.

We wish first to know the outcome when the optic discs are illuminated at the same level as their surrounds. In most cases one is unable to note any subjective intensity differences whatsoever in the total field and thus is entirely unaware of a gap or any other particulars such as we are describing. But under special conditions a noticeable differentiation appears.

If both eyes are fixated upon a gray screen moderately or weakly illuminated, two dark rings may appear and then disappear. If one eye is quickly closed, it is said that both blind spots will be observable, the one a dark disc with a bright surrounding glow and the other a bright disc with a dark halo, the closed eye being responsible for the latter disc. These phenomena were observed by both Köllner and Helson. Under the usual conditions, discs are seen. Charpentier was able to see green discs after stimulating the rest of the retina with red. Brückner says we can see what appears to be both blind spots by looking at the blue sky. The discs will be seen as brighter than if only a single eye is used.

In explaining these phenomena, we shall follow the proposition laid down in the beginning by attributing them to areas surrounding the optic discs. It will be noted that one of two things are seen, rings or discs, though generally the latter. To account for either one, it must be remembered that the sense-cell population immediately around the optic disc proper is much more sparse than in more remote regions. On this basis the observed intensity of the light would tend to be different, just as brightness at the edge of the visual field differs from brightness at the fovea, since at the outer periphery of the retina the cells are less thickly distributed. The objects seen in the region of the blind spot are disc-like according to the principle of sense-cell adjacency already laid down. When rings are seen, they can be expected to be due to some sort of brightness-contrast phenomena involving the areas adjacent to the disc and those further away. This is attested to by the fact that what is sometimes called a ring is at other times in the same report, called a disc with a halo. The halo signifies that the subjective space occupied by the phenomenon extends indefinitely outward from the fixation point. That the ring and the halo are of contrasting brightness need not burden the particular hypothesis we are using for under any theory this would be a matter of brightness contrast to be explained by the laws thereof which are as yet unknown.

We may conclude that the disc-like areas which are seen when confronted by a uniform field are not the optic discs but are the results of differential stimulation of the regions closely surrounding them. Since adjacent sense-cells when stimulated give rise to a continuous field in consciousness, disc-like areas result. Rings result when brightness-contrast conditions arise.

**Sensation when the intensity gradient is in favor of the surrounds.** When the surrounding field is more highly illuminated than the optic disc, or some part of it, the conditions for this are satisfied. The mapping set-up was one of this kind, and the dark exploring disc was small relative to the blind spot.

Under such conditions, nothing is seen. The whole field is simply uniform and we can say with Helmholz, that there is not even a gap. It is understandable, when he states that were a gap visible it would have to show some quality of visibility, and that the discovery of the gap is not a sensation but a "judgment." The space corresponding to the blind spot subjectively does not exist.

There are several special cases in which the surrounds of the optic disc may be more highly illuminated than it. The two most important have already been mentioned; namely, when a ring of light is thrown on the retina around the disc but which by chance allows a few sensitive elements to intervene between it and the disc proper, and when the ring coincides precisely with the edge of the disc. In the first case there is an inner ring-like area between the illuminated one and the optic disc. In the second, the bright ring is small enough so as not to allow any sensitive area between it and the disc. In the first case a ring will be seen and in the second a disc or solid patch of light. These appear, in part, by virtue of the fact that the rest of the retina is also only dimly illuminated. The dark center, when a ring is seen, is not due to the "gap" (blind spot) itself, but due to the fact that there are sense-cells within the ring of light which are not intensely stimulated. The blind spot never functions as a positive *dark* area. The observer merely identifies the dark central area with the gap by deduction. The dark area is located the only place it can be; namely, centripetal to the stimulated areas, and it is not a ring (as some might expect), but a solid patch due to the fact that all the sense-cells adjacent to the gap represent in consciousness a unitary area.

The following is a third variation of the illuminating conditions. Helson arranged a pattern of light around the blind spot so that it became increasingly brighter nearer and nearer to the edges of the blind spot itself. Sometimes the illumination was extended so as to fall within the blind spot. The result was a patch of light which had no central core. This is to be explained by the operation of the sensitivity differential of the area around the optic disc. Even though the illumination gradient *ascended* as the blind spot was reached, the sensitivity gradient *descended* as the optic disc proper was neared. It is reported that one observer reported a gap where the rings ceased. We still do not know what a *gap* is, nor do we know whether this report was made when light fell directly on the optic disc or not. When illumination boundaries are to coincide with the margins of the optic disc, anything less than perfect fixation results in all sorts of unpredictable phenomena.

**Sensation when the intensity gradient is in favor of the optic disc.** When the illumination of the optic disc is above that of its surrounds, various phenomena emerge. These form the bulk of the experimental material over which controversy has continued these many decades. Like the case in which a shadow is thrown on the optic disc, the bright spot thrown on it may be much smaller than the total disc area. If so, it will not have a chance to disturb areas outside the disc so much as if larger. Nevertheless, its smallness may be more than compensated for by its intensity. There are, however, two differences in the effect on surrounding fields between the large and small spots cast onto the disc. They are dependent upon the fate of light falling on the retina.

It can be shown quite directly that the retina immediately around a bright image is more intensely illuminated than more remote regions, by viewing an excised rabbit eye as described in Chapter III. This probably arises from scatter in the tissues, even when it can be said that the image itself is sharply focused. Ordinarily this illumination is of little effect due to the low ratio between it and the image, but when it is the only light reaching sensitive areas it need not be at all great to account for sensation.

When the image cast on the optic disc is very bright but small this scatter will reach beyond the borders of the disc. When the image area approaches that of the disc, the light reaching the sensitive surround per unit of total light flux in the image will be greater, and have a different distribution than before, due to the fact that the scatter source is nearer to sensitive tissue.

**Need for rechecking incoherent results.** The results of actual experimentation with various shapes of bright objects whose images were cast on the optic disc are next to be considered. But one caution is to be noted throughout, namely, that any finding which does not fall in line with the bulk of the evidence will have to be reserved for further examination, for it is possible the conditions of observation are not as exact as assumed. This conviction follows from some unpublished experiments in which the observer knew what he was looking at. It was found that a great variety of results, depending upon slight faults in fixation, occurred, and that by deliberately shifting slightly from the original good fixation in which the direct illumination undoubtedly fell within the bounds of the optic disc, the variety of results reported by different observers could be repeated. Thus by using a "knowing" observer, a more extended set of correlations between conditions of observation and sensory outcome was possible. Previous experiments of other recent investigators depended largely upon the skill of the observers themselves, and provided no real check upon whether the particular protocols obtained were those which represented results under perfect fixation alone.

**Irregular images within the optic disc.** (1) When the image of a half-moon shaped object was cast on the optic disc (o.d.), one of Helson's observers reported a ring-like object, but which was not fully complete. The same observer reported two squares as a rectangle. Helson interprets this as diffusion in the blind spot over a distance greater than from either stimulus to the edge of the blind spot. The implication he wishes to bring out here, remember, is based on the assumption that the optic disc itself is sensitive and that light which perchance falls on sensitive surrounds cannot account for the results.

These two examples fall in line with our original assumptions. The semi-disc being seen as an incomplete ring is in keeping with expectations when the sensitive surrounds are responsible for the sensation. If the illumination from the semi-disc had been centered on the optic disc the result possibly would have been a nearly circular bright patch. When the image is shifted perceptibly to one side of the optic disc, the stimulation of the sensitive edges though separated by the o.d. tend to give the impression of continuity. Due to the shape and location of the image, the part of this sensitive ring that is much less stimulated than the remainder has its effect in holding the "closure" partly in check.

The two squares separated by an interspace, in producing a subjective rectangle, is also in line with the principles first laid down. *Their unification into a rectangle does not depend upon diffusion between them but upon stimulating sensitive elements adjacent to opposite sides of the o.d.* They are as in all cases

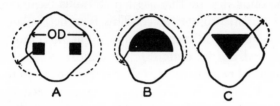

FIG. 28.—Three examples of the effect of placing complicated patterns of illumination on the optic disc. The irregular solid lines represent the boundaries of the optic disc. The two squares, the semi-disc, and the inverted triangle are the patterns of illumination within the optic disc. The broken lines represent the boundaries of the light extending from the disc to the surrounding areas.

seen as adjacent. Both of these experiments are pictured in Figure 28.

The third case is that of reporting a cross as an irregular cross. According to theory it would simply be a doubling of the rectangle effect just described. It happens, however, that the observer's drawing of what was seen showed the whole thing to be rather blurry and irregular, perhaps due to the tendency toward fixation instability.

Another case is that in which a second observer reported a triangle, base upward, as a vertical object with the lower end narrower. Diagram C, Figure 28, makes the mechanism of this apparent. The same observer also, after not being able to tell the shape of a cross, except that it was a non-round figure, reports the same two squares used on the first observer as two spots. This is an illustration, first, of the variability of the results obtained in blind-spot experiments and, second, of a report which is obviously "too good," the implication being that the proper fixation was not held. Eye movements would be expected to "cut" the rectangle into two spots.

Another experiment was performed in which the stimulus which was a bright area the shape and size of the blind spot was covered by a card practically its size so that only a little stray light surrounding it was visible. In which case the blind-spot observer sees a unitary patch of dim haze, whereas stimulation of the optic disc by the original stimulus produced a bright patch with a still brighter core. This is to be explained simply on the basis of the difference in total light flux and the way it was distributed on the optic disc surrounds.

**The length of exposure.** It is very important to note the effect of the length exposure. Helson's observers agreed that during the very first moment of exposure form was best, though it did not endure long enough to be reported upon. This has been interpreted as evidence for form perception mediated by the optic disc, and that the disc adapts rather quickly. The results are better interpreted as indicating that the observers were not able to maintain fixation during the instant of exposure onset, but "righted" their fixations as best they could and as soon as possible after the first flare of stimulation. *This very inability to maintain perfect fixation at the onset of the stimulation is one outstanding feature even of practised observers, and there are many reasons to believe that it is next to impossible to obtain proper fixation at the critical instant of stimulus onset.*

**Scattering of light in the optic disc and elsewhere.** The amount of scattering in the eye is proportional to the light flux. Helson made experiments with a number of trained observers to ascertain whether the subjective scattering varied in different parts of the visual field, especially near the boundaries of the blind spot. The contours of objects seen near the borders of the blind spot are seen as moderately sharp and do not diffuse into the blind spot. *We should not expect them to do the latter, for the light falling there is not seen.*

It is declared that on the basis of a scatter theory, the amount of scattered light to account for the known phenomena would have to increase tremendously around the blind spot, and in fact reach a magnitude beyond belief. One error in connection with this attitude about scattered light is that light falling on the optic disc must be scattered from there to the surrounds and back again so as not to violate the principle of eccentric projection.

Helson's search did not reveal much subjective scatter occurring under the conditions used. But let us consider what these conditions were. They consisted in presenting bright objects on dark grounds. If the objects are very bright we know there is a glare. Common experience has decided that. If the illuminations are less bright, it is also known that very little illumination is observed around the seen object. It is so slight as to be overlooked. But the very same amount becomes very evident, however, under intermittent illumination as shown in the chapter on stray light. The particular kind of scatter involved in the blind-spot phenomena, we shall see, is the very kind responsible for flicker around the test-object, but which had received little or no attention until Bartley's studies on stray light.

When light is cast on the optic disc the situation is reversed. The intense light falls on an insensitive area and only the scatter reaches the sensitive surrounding area. *It is thus not masked in any way by the extreme brightness of another area. It alone is there to be perceived.*

**Color phenomena as critical for blind-spot theory.** It has been reported that two colors can be simultaneously seen in the blind spot. Or restated in terms neutral to any theory, two colors may be seen when two different-colored images are cast on the optic disc.

This result has been reported when the conditions have been of two essentially different kinds. The first was the placement of the images of two squares of color, small and quite widely removed from each other and from the boundaries of the optic disc. The second was the use of a central patch of light surrounded by a ring of a different color.

The explanation of the perception of two separate colors in the first case is easy and follows the accounts that have been given for the other stimuli that have been placed within the optic disc. The explanation of the second is possible but more complicated, and one for which there is as yet less collateral evidence. That is to say, it possibly carries less conviction for those who are inclined to be skeptical of the position we have taken. Nevertheless, it does form a possible way out and eliminates the belief that the seeing of two simultaneous colors can be accounted for only by positing sensitivity of the optic disc itself.

Recent attempts to see the two complementary colors which were concentrically projected onto the optic disc were not successful. This does not prove that the original reports were in error but it does at least emphasize the fact that the conditions are most critical for the production of a two-color result. Helson did point out also that short exposures were better than long for the attainment of the two-color perception. This calls for the need of the caution that was previously given, namely, that the results which depend upon only momentary exposures (1 second, or less) are to be suspected of being due to improper fixation, or eye movements. Bright stimulation suddenly appearing tends to cause the eye to turn toward it in direct fixation. Naturally it is the task of the observer to avoid doing this. For most patterns his eye moves only an insignificant amount. Unless the stimuli lie very near the edge of the optic disc, this movement is not at all critical and the reports can be taken without any hesitation. The nearer the stimulation approaches the sensitive area of the region around the optic disc proper, the more necessary it is to have perfect fixation.

*We know that all other types of perception are characterized by more clearness if given more time. Here we have a contradiction of that in the fact that with more time the thing that is seen is more diffuse.* The explanation that has been offered is that the optic disc itself provides the color experience and that it is a region that adapts very quickly to stimulation. We must also note that the spatial relations wane in their clarity as well. Mere adaptation ought not to bring this about. If it were adaptation, as alleged, there should be a waning only of the color, leaving the same spatial pattern simply reduced in saturation.

The other possible explanation aside from the suggestion that the glimpses of two colors, one enclosed by a ring of the other,

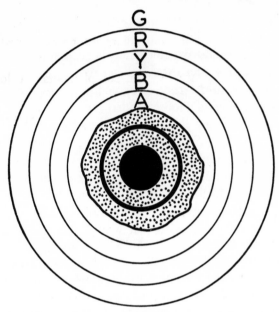

Fɪɢ. 29.—The color zones of the retina surrounding the optic disc. If two colors can be separately localized when one is presented as a ring enclosing the other, it would be expected that these color zones would function in the achievement of it. (See text.) The stipled area is the optic disc. The black disc and ring are the images of the two parts of the test-object falling within its boundaries.

is due to a glimpse of the pattern during the very first instant of observation before the fixation of the eye had righted itself, is given in the following.

In the first place, a number of investigators have found that the color zones of the area around the optic disc have some of the same properties as at the periphery of the retina. That is to say that one color can be perceived by the aid of the sensitive elements closer to the optic disc than certain others. Thus there is a color gradient from the edge of the optic disc outwards in all directions.

It is possible that this might provide for seeing one color enclosed within another when the intensities of each happened to be properly adjusted.

Since the boundary of the blue zone is closer to the optic disc than is the red zone, blue would be seen if the scatter of the two colors were equal and extended only a moderate distance from the disc. If their scatter extended somewhat farther a blue area would be seen within a ring composed of a mixture of red and blue. If the scatter of blue extended farther than the red, blue might be seen as lying beyond the red and separated by a transition zone of a mixture of the two. The relative intensities of the light in the ring and the inner disc would determine the distance of the individual scatterings. There may be in addition to the color-zone factor, a number of others having to do with such things as the relative effectiveness of the two colors in scattering through the tissues, which would also play critical roles in determining the outcome. This we do not know, but at least it seems plausible that if we are to grant that the two colors can be separately perceived when so presented, as in Helson's experiment, the basis lies in the excitation of the areas around the optic disc. *This alternative seems much easier to credit than the existence of undiscovered sense-cells in the optic disc or differential color stimulation of the optic nerve fibers themselves.*

As was said, an attempt to repeat this type of experiment with complementary colors has thus far ended in failure. Non-complementary colors as were used in the original experiment have not been used. The failure may have been due to not finding the right intensity relations, but it is more likely that it was on account of the complementariness of the colors, red and green, that were used. We should expect that their zone boundaries on the retina would be more nearly coincident than those of non-complementary colors, and thus not provide for the analysis we have outlined. Furthermore, we should expect them to give some sort of a fusion of the two colors with a lessening of the saturation. The color resulting was of this very nature and depended upon the proportions of the two stimulating intensities. Helson's theory would predict the seeing of red and green separately just as some of his observers saw red and blue.

**Perception of movement.** The outcome when stimuli which elsewhere arouse the perception of movement are made to fall on and around the optic disc is another matter of interest in studying the blind spot. For this purpose a small light was moved about in the visual field coinciding with the blind spot to study the effect of a real moving stimulus. For the study of apparent movement two stationary spots were alternately presented under controlled conditions of time and spacing.

All of Helson's observers perceived real movement when moving illumination was cast on the optic disc. The two observers which he used for apparent movement reported that they observed it. One of them was not sure whether he had directly sensed it or inferred it. Other investigators previously had reported that the perception of movement is easily aroused by stimulation on or around the optic disc. Opponents of scattering and irradiation state that it is inconceivable on the basis of scattering and irradiation theories how light leaving the optic disc to surrounding retinal elements could set up a "movement" process. They declare that such theories would require one to assume not only that individual points lying in the blind spot are subjectively localized there through their stimulation of neighboring points outside the optic disc, but that these rational points produce a movement process over a region not localized to the places actually excited, but to the blind spot.

The consideration of real or apparent movement in connection with illumination of the optic disc must first include the nature of the thing seen moving. *When the optic disc is illuminated, that is, when stimuli lie within the blind spot, a contoured object is never seen as a result.* Instead, a patch of light with a very ill-defined boundary is seen. This is naturally localized with its center somewhere in the blind spot, for reasons already given. The patch is ill defined because its limits depend upon the crude distribution of illumination arising from scatter in the tissues. It is larger than the original object would warrant if its image fell directly on sensitive areas capable of fine resolution. In addition to the spread to the regions adjacent to the optic disc, there is general entoptic scatter. It was shown that reflection from a small bright image illuminates the whole retina to an appreciable degree. This illumination becomes recognizable especially under conditions in which the stimulation is changing, either as to intensity or position on the retina, so that it along with shifts in the more intense illumination on the sensitive region around the optic disc combines to give the usual conditions for *phi* and optimal movement. (See Chapter VII.)

With the stimulation arrangements such as described by Helson, there is a functional amount of stray light cast on the retina as a whole. When the light is moved about in the blind spot the scatter on the various sides of the optic disc is varied accordingly and this obviously shifts the position of the patch which is seen. When two stationary spots are alternately presented within the blind spot their images on the optic disc produce an alternate shift of illumination in the sensitive areas adjacent to the opposite sides of the optic disc. In connection with this, just as in producing apparent movement by stimulation elsewhere in the retina, shifts in stray light add to the realism of the total effect.

**The spatial properties of the visual field.** The question arises as to whether all pairs of points subtending equal visual angles are subjectively equally separated. We have evidence that they are not. If visual acuity, the resolution of two points or lines, depends upon the density of population of the sense-cells involved, *we might suppose that subjective space in its grosser characteristics would also depend upon the distribution of sense-cells.*

It has already been assumed in our discussion that the distribution of sense-cells around the optic disc proper is less dense than in retinal regions more remote. Observers report that patterns whose images involve the optic disc and its environs are subjectively smaller than when their images are shifted to an adjacent region. That is to say, for example, four bright patches forming the corners of a square, so separated that their images fall just outside the optic disc, will be seen as lying closer together than when observed by use of another part of the retina. The comparison can be made by alternately shifting the eye in properly predetermined directions. In such cases the difference in the separation of the spots is easily recognized.

If the properties of the visual field are dependent upon the density of sense-cell population and a sparse population gives rise to a subjective "contraction" of the visual field, it can be seen how the wide separation of sense-cells such as occurs in the optic disc will provide for the total absence of a psychological gap in the visual field. This is only stating the same thing differently than we did at the beginning of the chapter. There it was pointed out that no subjective reality could emerge from the illumination of the retina between two adjacent sense-cells. This implied that it did not matter what the actual distance between these sense-cells was. It could be a matter of microns or millimeters. *The difference would only show up as some sort of a discrepancy between the geometrical environment of the individual and his subjective organization of space.*

We have no reason to suppose that subjective space as sensorily built up from a brain field often called the cortical retina has non-functional area in it to compare to the optic disc in the retina. It should simply be thought of as a continuum, the pushing aside of the sense-cells in a small portion of the retina to form the optic disc being a mere mechanical accident. Binocular vision has happened to function well enough that such an incidental event as the production of a tiny insensitive spot in the retina is of little practical consequence. Nevertheless, we have found it of importance in formulating notions about subjective space.

### REFERENCES

Brückner, A. Ueber die Sichbarkeit des blinden Flecks. *Arch. f.d. ges. Physiol.*, 1913, 136:610-657.

De Silva, H. R., and Alden Weber. The responsiveness of the blind spot. *J. Exptl. Psych.*, 1932, 15:399-415.

Feinberg, N. Experimentelle Untersuchungen über die Wahrnehmung im Gebiet des blinden Flecks. *Psych. Forsch.*, 1926, 7:16-43.

Ferree, C. E., and G. Rand. The spatial values of the visual field immediately surrounding the blind spot. *Am. J. Physiol.*, 1912, 29:398-417.

Garvey, C. R. Is the blind spot blind? *J. Exptl. Psych.*, 1933, 16:83-97.

Helson, Harry. The effects of direct stimulation of the blind spot. *Am. J. Psych.*, 1929, 41:345-397.

Helson, Harry. How do we see in the blind spot? *J. Exptl. Psych.*, 1934, 17:763-772.

Scofield, C. F. Perception in the region of the optic disk. *Am. J. Psych.*, 1930, 42:213-234.

Stern, A. Die Wahrnehmung von Bewegungen der Gegend des blinden Flecks. *Psych. Forsch.*, 1926, 7:1-15.

Werner, H. Untersuchungen über den blinden Flecks. *Arch. f. d. ges. Physiol.*, 1913, 153:475-490.

# VI

# REPEATED STIMULATION: FLICKER

## STUDY OF CRITICAL FLICKER FREQUENCY

**Significance of repetitive stimulation.** Thus far we have been primarily concerned with sensation which is the result of uniform stimulation for indefinite periods of time. Phenomena which were not dependent for their existence upon a critical stage in some rapid but measurable transition process were the type singled out for study. In most of these cases, small differences in time did not produce significant differences in sensory outcome.

Now we come to the phenomena which are dependent either for their very existence as qualitatively unique experiences or for their quantitative features primarily upon the time factor as a variable. In this group are the phenomena which arise as the result of the more or less frequent repetition of brief periods of stimulation. The chief qualitative characteristic of the sensation produced is its undulatory nature. In the touch and pressure senses it is called vibration, in vision it is called flicker. In such sense, there is a considerable range within which repetitive stimulation possesses this vibratory character. Below this range, the individual periods of stimulation are each perceived as separate, and even may be so far part as to seem unrelated. Above it the rate is so high that the separate stimuli are indistinguishable; it is as if stimulation were perfectly continuous.

With repeated stimulation, the intervals during which no stimulation is being delivered are as important as the stimulation periods themselves, for recovery becomes as important as stimulation. Perception is continuous even though stimulation is intermittent, and the observer's report is either upon the "quiet" period and the stimulation period, or else if only upon the latter, the result is still determined in part by the former. As intermittent frequencies rise, the outcome, though still an undulatory sensation, is one dependent upon the *differences* in the level of physiological processes occurring in the two phases. The sensory outcome depends upon the process of intensity discrimination and continues to do so until fusion is complete, that is, until the levels of the physiological processes during the two phases are so nearly alike as no longer to permit of this discrimination.

As was said, repeated stimulation need not be sensed as such. The rate may be too high for the separate stimuli to produce discrete impressions, with the result that sensation is of a uniform state. Repeated light flashes, when their rate is slow, produce the sensory effect called flicker, which becomes much less vigorous as the rate is increased. The rate just producing the impression of steady illumination is spoken of as the fusion point, or in terms of the flash rate, the critical flicker frequency (c.f.f.). Experiments involving the use of repeated flashes of light are known as flicker experiments, and the employment of such technique is called the flicker method.

In flicker experiments the c.f.f. is the most common object of determination. In producing it there are several outstanding factors, namely, intensity of illumination both of the flash and the field in which the flash appears; the area of the object that is flashing; and the ratio between the durations of the light and dark periods of the cycle.

The statement announcing the fact and covering certain of the quantitative aspects of this situation was made a century ago by Talbot, and almost simultaneously by Plateau. Today we call it Talbot's law. It states that at a high rate of repetition, flashes lose their identity and the sensation is that of uniform illumination of a level equivalent to that produced if the total amount of light were equally distributed in time. For example, if the intervals of light and dark are equal (light-dark ratio, L-D-R = 1.0), the perceived intensity is one-half as great as it would be were the whole cycle filled with light. Though the outcome is simple enough, the mechanism underlying it is complex and obscure and has received a great deal of laborious investigation.

One of the most basic factors which controls the critical frequency is intensity. Though the dependence of the critical frequency on illumination was apparent over a century ago to Plateau and to later workers, it was scarcely fifty years ago that Ferry formulated what is now the Ferry-Porter law, *that the critical frequency is proportional to the logarithm of the illumination intensity.* The later data of Porter substantiated the statement and his work was borne out by workers who followed.

In the retina, central regions less than 2° in diameter contain only cones, while larger regions have rods as well. Correlating with this, Hecht and Smith find that the relation of critical flicker frequency to intensity is a single function for central regions below 2°, and a dual function for larger regions.

For a central 19° test field, the results of Hecht and Shlaer, using various parts of the spectrum, fall into a low intensity section commonly imputed to rod function, and a high intensity section imputed to cone function. The transition between the two sections is expressed by a sharp inflection point, except for radiations of 450 and 490 m$\mu$, where, though present, it is more or less rounded.

The curves picturing the rod data are similar for all areas of test-field, except for the values controlling the position of the curves on the coordinate axes. The cone curves, likewise, are similar for all areas.

The intensity range covered by the flicker function is shortest in the red, and increases progressively as the wave-length decreases. The increase is due to the extent of the low intensity rod section which is shortest in the red and longest in the violet. The high intensity cone section for all wave-lengths is in the same position on the intensity axis, and the single result of decreasing wave-length is to drop the rod section to lower intensities without changing its shape.

**Relation of light-time to darkness.** Several ways of studying the role of the light-dark ratio in the production of sensory fusion are possible. Intensity may be kept constant and various L-D-R's used to obtain c.f.f.'s, or various fixed c.f.f.'s, one at a time, may be used while intensity is manipulated. It is also possible to keep one or the other of the phases of the light-dark cycle constant and manipulate the other, but this is not usually done. A family of curves will result.

When the light-dark ratio is varied, definite shifts in the value of the c.f.f. occur. Early investigators found that with constant intensity in a flash, the c.f.f. passes through a maximum when the light and dark fractions are of equal length. Others found that as the light fraction was increased the c.f.f. rose. Still others using a "constant brightness at fusion" for the comparisons, found that c.f.f. declines as the light fraction is increased. Some of the differences are attributed by Crozier to the reflection from the black sectors when black and white discs were used, as in contrast to the cases in which transmitted light was employed. That this does not account for the major differences is shown by the findings of Bartley in which transmitted rather than reflected light was used. He found that for high intensities of flash, increasing the light fraction of the cycle reduced c.f.f. without any reversal, whereas at lower intensities increasing the light fraction raised the c.f.f. to a maximum at or near the 50-50 point, falling again as more and more of the cycle was occupied by the flash.

Bartley originally kept L-D-R constant for each set of trials and varied intensity. Thus the data were plotted with c.f.f. against intensity. This gave a family of curves as in Figure 30, and each curve exhibited a reversal, its position depending upon the L-D-R. Those with a large light fraction reached the reversal sooner as the intensity was increased. This information can be transformed into another family of curves which bears directly on the question. In these curves L-D-R is plotted against c.f.f., each curve representing a fixed intensity. It will then be found that an L-D-R near 1.0 is the condition for maximum c.f.f. in the low intensity curve, whereas at high intensities a low light-to-dark ratio gives the maximum c.f.f. There is a progressive shift of the maximum from low to high L-D-R's, as intensity is reduced, so that if intensity were made low enough the maximum c.f.f. might possibly be expected to lie not in the region of 1.0 but somewhere below. This tends to reconcile the discord in the results of various investigators by showing that the *effectiveness* of stimulation was probably a critical factor in the character of results obtained.

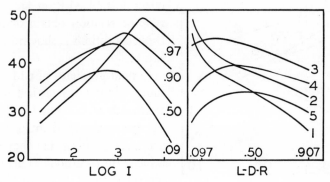

F IG . 30.—Critical-flicker-frequency curves. Each curve in the family to the left is for a separate light-dark ratio, the values indicating dark time. The family to the right was derived from the other curves. Each curve in this case is for a separate intensity. Curve 1 represents 4 log units; 2, 3.5; 3, 3.2; 4, 2; and 5 is about 1 log unit (c/ft.²). The ordinate for each set of curves represents critical flicker frequency. It is evident that at the lower intensities the curves exhibit a reversal, and that then the highest c.f.f.'s are obtained with equal light and dark times. (*Bartley—J. Exptl. Psych.*)

If the effect of the temporal course of the stimulus pattern alone on c.f.f. is to be determined, Talbot's law may be applied. For example, a cycle in which the light period is one-half as long as the dark (L-D-R = ½ or L/L + D = ⅓), may be changed to one in which the light period is twice the length of the dark. (L-D-R = 2; L/L + D = ⅔). The first arrangement delivers to the eye one-third of the total light incident on the disc, the second, two-thirds. In order that the average amount of light will be the same in the two cases, compensation may be made by making the light in the first case twice as intense as in the second. According to Talbot's law, the effect in the two cases will be identical above c.f.f. It can well be assumed that the equality of effect will extend beyond the appearance of brightness and color and include the adaptive state of the eye. It can be further supposed that the identity of adjustment of the eye in the two cases also holds true just below fusion as well as above it. This allows for experimental manipulation for finding c.f.f. Cobb took advantage of this technique in his study of the effect of the L-D-R on c.f.f. The type of relation obtained under these conditions is shown in Figure 31.

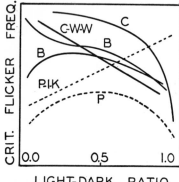

LIGHT-DARK RATIO

FIG. 31.—A composite of the findings of several investigators on the relation between c.f.f. and the light-dark ratio of the flicker cycle. All of the curves represent only the general relationships and not actual values. Curve C represents the findings of Cobb; curves B, Bartley; curves C-W-W, Crozier, Wolf and Zerrahn-Wolf; curve P-I-K, Porter, Ives and Kingsbury; and curve P, Pieron.

**Retinal gradients of c.f.f.** The radial gradient of critical flicker frequency of the retina is similar in type to the gradient of visual acuity, suggesting that they have a factor in common. This is interpreted to be the diminishing density of cone population as the retinal periphery is reached. Cone density has been assumed by Hecht to lie at the basis for visual acuity alterations with changing stimulus intensity. As fewer and fewer cones per unit area can be activated, the function in question becomes poorer.

This fits in with the fact that critical flicker frequency of monochromatic light drops differentially with progressive dark-adaptation. With the same initial c.f.f. at the outset of dark-adaptation, the c.f.f. falls the sharpest for blue, less for yellow and red and almost not at all for green stimuli.

**Range of flash frequencies producing flicker.** When intensities are very low, flashes as infrequent as three or four per second will give the impression of continuous illumination. The highest critical flicker frequency for the human eye, reported by Hecht,

Shlaer and Verrijp, is between 45 and 53. This may prove to be slightly too low, but an additional few flashes per second would not alter the conclusions to be drawn from results.

The bee will respond to flashes as high as 55 per second when illuminations are very high. Dragonfly larvae can respond to 60 or more flashes per second. High rates are reported for other arthropods, so that it may be taken for granted that they respond to rates slightly higher than do humans. It is plausible that this difference may have some significance for us after a little more investigation.

At present one of the main facts in connection with this relatively high critical flicker frequency for the bee is its comparatively poor vision for static situations as expressed in its visual acuity and intensity discrimination. Its visual acuity is about $\frac{1}{100}$ of ours and its brightness discrimination about $\frac{1}{25}$. From these two measurements we should not assume much form perception.

**Subjective flash rate in relation to critical flicker frequency.** The very simplest assumption that could be made relative to the apparent frequency of the last vestiges of flicker just before arriving at c.f.f. would be that it would approximate the c.f.f. That is, the subjective appearance of the flash rate would follow the physical rate. With slowly repeated flashes, they would appear slow, with rapidly repeated ones they would appear rapid. According to the photochemical formulations that now exist, their relationship should be one-to-one. Were this relationship to be otherwise, or at least were it to differ radically from this simple one, it would be good evidence that response to flicker is not controlled alone by the sense-cell. This would be a blow to the very common interpretation of photochemical theory. It would make the photochemical prediction of Talbot's law a mere coincidence.

As was stated above, the minimum c.f.f. lies in the neighborhood of 3 or 4 per second. On the assumption of a one-to-one relation between the subjective and the physical rates of flashes, the last remaining flicker just before satisfying the conditions for c.f.f. would appear to be very slow. Bartley found this not to be the case. The following example will serve to make the matter clearer.

With very dim illumination where the c.f.f. is about 4 per second, the last remnant of flicker appears to be a high-frequency "flutter." If the intensity of the test-object is now raised to

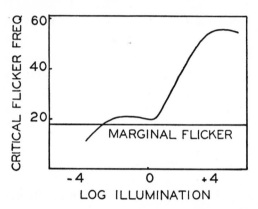

FIG. 32.—A diagram showing the discrepancy between the stimulus rate (critical flicker frequency) and the rate of the residual or marginal flicker seen by the observer. Note that as the illumination is raised, a faster flash rate is required to produce a subjectively steady illumination; but that regardless of this, the rate of the last seen flicker before perfect fusion occurs is about the same.

where the c.f.f. would by necessity be 20 or more per second, the flicker seen is of course vigorous but instead of having a high phenomenal rate it is slow. As nearly as can be told, it matches the physical rate. If the intensity is now increased to a level which requires a c.f.f. of 40 per second, on the one-to-one assumption, the last vestige of flicker should be very high. One cannot assume that a rate of 40 per second can be definitely counted, but at least the difference between 4 and 40 ought to be distinguishable. What actually happens is that the flicker as it gives place to fusion has about the same frequency appearance as that resulting from a flash rate of 4 per second. It has a high frequency but nowhere near 40 per second.

From this, Bartley suggests that the steady sensory state is brought about by the intrinsic properties of some mechanism other than the sense-cell which must follow the flashes in a one-to-one relation. This means that the properties of the visual pathway further along are responsible, and the determination of the c.f.f. is neural.

In light of the evidence already obtained from several diverse kinds of experimentation, certain suggestions as to how the nervous system controls c.f.f. can be made. They would involve the introduction of work that has not yet been discussed and for that reason they are reserved for a later chapter. It can be said here, however, that the present experiments along with the other just alluded to have an important bearing upon our understanding of visual response looked upon from the standpoint of Talbot's law.

**Terminal conditions for critical flicker frequency.** C.f.f. increases as intensity is increased but this does not hold true throughout the complete scale of usable intensities. For example, with weak spectral blue light, c.f.f. does not change with intensity. Ives used such conditions for studying the dependence of flicker upon the temporal pattern of stimulation.*

As the intensity of white light is increased, a point is reached at which further increments do not raise the c.f.f. In some cases the curve exhibits a plateau, in others, definite decline sets in. This general phenomenon is most marked when test-objects are used on a dark field. Figure 30 shows a family of curves all of which represent test-objects with dark surrounds.

Another important factor in the determination of the maximum c.f.f. is the L-D-R. The curves in the figure are for different L-D-R's and indicate that a very brief and very intense flash produces the highest maximum c.f.f. We might suppose that very intense stimulation tends to synchronize the activity in the elements involved. There would seem to be two factors in this ability. First, very intense stimulation activates all of the

---

* Since changing the L-D-R under most conditions alters c.f.f. through its manipulation of the average amount of light received by the eye, he was able to avoid this complication by using dim blue light, the c.f.f. for which did not change with intensity.

available elements, second, the frequency of discharge is more nearly alike for all elements than with lower stimulation where some are only slightly above threshold, while others are greatly above theirs.    These factors should contribute optimum synchrony and require that the flash rate be increased in order to produce fusion.    The shortness of the flashes contributes to synchrony and avoids stimulation not useful in the immediate production of response and in that way avoids retarding recovery between flashes.

**Interaction between retinal areas.**    A steady stimulus applied to one region of the retina modifies the c.f.f. of an intermittent stimulus in another.    As the intensity of the steady stimulus is increased from zero upward, the c.f.f. rises until a critical point is reached when it falls again.    This has been accounted for by Fry and Bartley, assuming that the steadily stimulated area depresses activity in the flickering area; below a critical intensity it depresses the weak phases of the flicker and raises the c.f.f.; above the critical intensity it depresses the strong phases also and thereby lowers the c.f.f.    That the reversal of the effect fails to occur when the distance between the two stimuli is large, is due to the fact that critical intensity increases with distance and when the distance is great the critical intensity lies beyond the range of intensities investigated.

**Area and critical flicker frequency.**    The larger the area of the test-object, the higher the maximum c.f.f.    It has been stated that the tendency for maximal frequency to increase with area is the expression merely of the value of a constant which determines the position of the data on the frequency axis.    What this would really mean in neurological terms is undetermined.    In this view, area does not influence the basic nature of the flicker relation but merely alters the extraneous constants of the relation. This statement is meant to imply that the essential dynamics of the situation lie in the photochemical process itself.    Though the mathematical formulation may hold for geometrically simple test-objects (discs) of ascending size, nevertheless the fact that the larger the test-objects the more likely their areas not to be homogeneous with reference to flicker complicates the matter. Residual flicker may occur in small portions while all of the remaining regions are decidedly stable. The shape of the test-object is also a factor in determining where the flicker is last seen. These facts indicate that the elevation of c.f.f. by increasing area is determined in part by the intrinsic properties of the neural organization of the retina. The greater the area the more easily the elements may be synchronized, raising the effective frequency of the pulsations in the constituent elements.

**Critical flicker curves for the lower animals.** A large part of the more recent information concerning reaction to intermittent light has been gained from sub-human species. The technique used in many of these experiments consists in testing the response of an animal to a moving pattern of black and white stripes. In the case of aquatic animals a swimming motion in the direction of the moving stripes is the response utilized. For example, in the technique used by Crozier and colleagues, the animal (fish) is kept in darkness for several hours before testing. The stripe mechanism is set into motion at a fixed speed and the light is turned on, though the diaphragm admitting it to the animal is still closed. The observer then opens the diaphragm very gradually while watching the animal. As soon as a little light strikes it a slight backward movement is elicited, after which it comes to rest. This first response is not due to the flicker which confronts the animal for it can be obtained with steady light just as well. The animal's response to the moving stripes consists in an abrupt motion of the body in the direction they are moving. At low flicker frequencies such as from 3 to 10 stripes per second passing in front of its eyes, the animal commonly pursues the stripes. It frequently stays in the middle of the tank and rotates like the needle of a compass, keeping one set of stripes in its field of vision. At velocities up to 15-20 flickers per second the fish follows the wall of the jar while pursuing the stripes. If the frequency is above 20 per second, the animal swims backward after a short forward thrust at a rate becoming faster as flicker increases. From this, it would appear as if the animal attempts to make flicker disappear by moving backward just fast enough to increase the relative motion of the stripes to the fusion point, creating for itself a uniform field. Despite the difference in type of reaction at the frequency ranges, thresholds of response can be determined quite accurately and seem to have a common meaning.

The moving striped pattern used on the lower animals has also been used by the same investigators on human observers. The result has been that the c.f.f. intensity curves have the same properties as those obtained under other conditions. They likewise have the same quantitative characteristics as the curves constructed from the motor reactions of the lower animals to the movement. The similarity also applies to the nature of the variability of the readings as well as to the shape of the mean curve itself, showing that the two sets of data are homologous.

For the sunfish *Lepomis* increasing the flicker frequency necessitates raising the intensity of illumination to elicit a marginal response. The curve representing critical illumination as a function of flicker frequency consists of two portions. For lower illuminations up to somewhere between $-2$ and $-1$ log ml., the slope of the curve is about .13. This portion covers a flicker range between 3 and 10 per second. The upper portion of the curve is much steeper having a slope of 16.8 until a frequency of about 43 per second is reached. Thence it tapers off to a plateau at about 50 flashes per second. The dual contour of the curve signifies a rod-cone visual system. The rods function up to intensities slightly above .04 ml., and cover flicker up to about 10 per second.

The c.f.f. curve for this species is quite comparable with that of the human eye except that its extent at low illumination is greater. The transition from rod to cone vision in the two occurs at about the same intensity and flicker frequency, and the upper extent of the curves in the two cases is about identical.

**Duplex flicker curves.** With reference to the duplex c.f.f. curve found in some animals as an expression of the activity of two groups of functioning sense-cell, it may be said that the upper portion can be described by a probability integral.  The lower portion can be dissected away.  When the lower portion is uncovered it exhibits a contour which rises to a maximum and then declines.  This suggests that as the photopic elements come into action the scotopic decline in their contribution.  The statistical concept required for the general analysis would have the curve

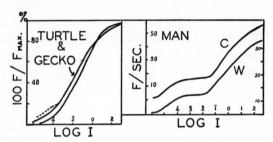

Fig. 33.—Two sets of curves showing the relation between critical flicker frequency and the logarithm of the intensity.  The left-hand graph contains two curves, one for the Gecko rod retina and the other for the turtle cone retina. Note that they are much more nearly similar in shape and in the range of intensity and flicker frequency involved than might be expected according to the more simple notions of the duplicity theory.  (*Crozier and Wolf.—J. Gen. Physiol.*)  The right-hand graph contains two curves representing the c.f.f. response in man.  In them the rod and cone portions are both evident. Intensity in millilamberts.  (*Crozier, Wolf and Zerrahn-Wolf.—J. Gen. Physiol.*)

picturing this group (scotopic) also form a probability integral.

Crozier and Wolf suggest several possible interpretations for the curve not following the statistical expectation.  The discrepancy might be an expression of the intrinsic scotopic or rod group-effect.  If the cone population could be eliminated, this could be directly tested.  In the case of the Gecko, this has in effect been accomplished since the animal has a pure rod retina. Strangely enough, however, the contour of its flicker recognition curve describes a probability integral and thus shows no dropping out of activity in the way the rod population does in the duplex retina.  Furthermore the range of response shows that the rods are not limited to low intensity functioning but instead are active over the range attributed to cones, and photopic vision.

Another possibility these investigators offer is that in the retina exhibiting a double critical flicker curve, the cone elements inhibit the rod elements. A possible though indirect test exists in the manner in which the two segments behave with reference to each other. The more abruptly the cone segment arises, the more quickly does the rod contribution fall.

This and other features of the analysis as a whole suggest rather clearly that if cone activity could be suppressed in the duplex eye, there would be no decline in the rod contribution. This is taken by Crozier and Wolf to mean that the quantitative features of visual response are not determined by retinal properties but the properties of central nervous activity. This need not be the case, however. The implied distinction in function need not have been drawn between retina and central nervous system, but between the mosaic of more or less isolated sense-cells and the unitary nervous system. The latter begins in the retina, and it is not certain what the essential distinctions in type between it and the later levels of the central nervous system are. It is preferable then to assume that the suppression of the rod or scotopic group occurs in the retina.

**The effect of shape of lens upon c.f.f.** Among the species tested by Crozier and colleagues were arthropods whose c.f.f. curves possessed a marked degree of asymmetry and did not yield to the statistical concepts which seemed amply to fit the results of testing other species.

The c.f.f. curves of all species were affected in the same way by changes in temperature, but such stimulus conditions as intensity and L-D-R differentially manipulated the results in the two classes of curves. Either raising intensity or increasing the L-D-R reduced the amount of distortion in the asymmetrical curves.

A difference in the curvature of the lens of the compound eyes of the various species was obvious and the attempt was made to attribute the c.f.f. curve asymmetry to it. It can easily be seen from geometry that eyes with lenses having high curvatures will suffer from a disadvantage from weak stimulation. The light falling upon the surface of the outlying (peripheral) ommatidia will be so oblique as to be ineffective until intensity is raised or its duration is prolonged considerably above threshold for the more central elements. This means that throughout a certain intensity range such eyes are at a disadvantage.

**The crayfish.** The c.f.f. curve of the crayfish *Cambarus bartoni* as predicted by Crozier and colleagues on account of the higher curvature of the optic receiving surface, is more asymmetrical than for the bee and dragonfly nymph under similar circumstances. This corroborates the theory that asymmetry is due to that source. The slope of the crayfish c.f.f. curve is lower than that of the bee and dragonfly, denoting a broader effective distribution of logarithmic intensity thresholds involved in recognition of flicker. This may be attributable to either the higher curvature of optic surface or to the placement of the eye upon a movable stock.

The artificially forced migration of retinal pigments of animals kept in the dark into positions typical for animals kept in the light, manipulates the features of the c.f.f. curve. In the latter condition the ommatidia are light-shielded from each other, whereas in the "dark" condition, the shielding formed by the pigment is absent due to the pigment's removal to another position.

When the pigment is present in the light-shielding position, the maximum c.f.f. is lowered, the whole curve showing light intensities needed for a given c.f.f. is raised, and the distribution of the log intensity thresholds for the cumulative sensory effects is narrowed, and furthermore the asymmetry of the c.f.f. curve is reduced. The outcome is in line with the idea that the asymmetry of the c.f.f. in dark adaptation is based on the relation between intensity and lens curvature.

**The isopod.** The c.f.f. curve for the isopod *Asellus* is a simple probability integral throughout its whole extent. Its eyes are smaller and more nearly flat than the eyes of other arthropods tested, hence an extreme curvature of lens does not have opportunity to determine any of the features of response. This lack of distortion in the isopod c.f.f. curve which was obtained with the bee, dragonfly nymph, and the crayfish, the eyes of which all possess high lens curvatures, corroborates the attribution of the asymmetry of the c.f.f. curve to the geometrical features of the eye surface.

**The frog c.f.f. curve.** The curve for the frog, in contrast to those of certain other animals for which there is evidence of the presence of but one class of sense-cells, shows the dual character typical of a great many vertebrates. The low intensity (scotopic) section is the smallest that has yet been found, and the cone section like that of all others examined can be described by a probability integral.

**The albino c.f.f. curve.** The c.f.f. curves for albino individuals of the genus of teleost fishes, *Xiphophorus helleri* are the same quantitatively as well as qualitatively as those constructed from the data of other individuals of the same stock. This fact is taken to mean that pigmentation of retina and iris has no effect upon the elements responsible for the essential nature visual response, and this is a result certainly not predicted but instead seemingly confusing to the type of photochemical theory that lays essential brightness discrimination to the sense-cells themselves.

**The meaning of variability of results.** Crozier, Wolf and Zerrahn-Wolf believe that the theory of the relations between illumination and the response to flicker must be based on something more than the usual c.f.f. curves or curves of critical intensity for fixed frequency. They declare that the simple averaging of the data to produce these curves masks the exhibition of a real property of the mechanism involved. This property is revealed by the index of dispersion of the individual trials as conditions are varied. Such indices are not measures of experimental error conditioned upon faulty technique or unavoidable lack of control, but instead are taken to be expressions of a property of the responding organism itself, and must be recognized.

The relationship of c.f.f. and intensity is to be looked upon as a band in which region there is a given probability that threshold recognition of flicker or the threshold for fusion will occur.

The position of these investigators is that the recognition response accrues from a comparison of two activated groups of nervous elements, either peripheral or central, at least not the sense-cells themselves. The comparison progresses on a statistical basis as if dependent upon the standard deviation of the effects induced in the two populations. Thus with intermittent light stimulation at the point of threshold recognition of flicker, the differentiation is based upon the result of the flashes and the effects occurring during the dark intervals. This is a new concept and falls in line with the other neurological ideas that are developing in the field of visual behavior.

As has been supposed by others, the effect produced by the light phase of the flicker cycle fluctuates. This has been described as a fluctuation in the concentration of a given activating substance in the sense-cells, the level of which drops during the dark phase and rises during the light phase. But the important feature of the theory of Crozier and colleagues is that this alone does not determine the point at which flicker becomes marginal or that fusion just occurs. The after-effect of the light also fluctuates, more or less as an independent process. Flicker recognition is a form of intensity discrimination.

**The effect of temperature.** Crozier, Wolf and Zerrahn-Wolf show that the descriptive adequacy of Hecht and colleagues' formulations which utilize only the fluctuation in the concentration of one product for such phenomena as Talbot's law are inadequate since the result upon flicker recognition of varying temperature turns out just the opposite of that predicted by the latter, whereas the result is predicted by the intensity discrimination theory of the former. According to Hecht, c.f.f. should be lower the higher the temperature, for a given illumination, since according to him the animal should be in a more dark adapted state the higher the temperature. The opposite happens to be true as was shown for anax larvae and for the sunfish.

Until maximum c.f.f. is approached the shifts in the curves caused by temperature are nearly proportional to the temperature difference. The data show that maximum c.f.f. where the curve reaches a plateau is independent of temperature. The c.f.f. reaches maximum at an intensity independent of temperature.

**Differences obtained with fixed flicker rate and fixed intensity.** Crozier and colleagues show also that empirical curves expressing critical illumination as a function of fixed flicker frequency and critical frequency as a function of fixed illumination are not identical, but differ in a way previously predicted. According to them these differences are of fundamental importance when such measurements are utilized for constructing an excitation theory. Their meaning brings up the propriety of the universal use of averages as measures of response.

They predict that the curve for critical flicker frequency as a function of intensity should lie above that for intensity as a function of fixed frequency. The contour of the two curves should not be identical and the difference between them should become maximum as intensity increases, and at the inflection of the curves showing critical flicker frequency as a function of the logarithm of intensity. The variation of intensity measured by its standard deviation should be directly proportional to the intensity found for fixed flicker frequency. The variation of flicker frequency determined at fixed illumination should pass through a definite maximum near the inflection point of the curve relating flicker frequency to the logarithm of the intensity.

The response curves constructed by plotting critical illumination against fixed flicker frequency depart from the probability integral type in arthropods with large convex eyes. Crozier and colleagues, using anax nymphs in which parts of the eye were masked, show that a particular shape of the critical flicker curve accrues from the mechanical disadvantage of the periphery of the eye in receiving light obviated by higher intensities.

**Effect of collateral stimulation on c.f.f.** The effect of stimulation in another sense department upon critical flicker frequency has been investigated by Kravkov. Two different types of stimulation were used, a sound and an odor. The former had a frequency of about 800 Hertz and an intensity of 85 decibels. The latter was oil of Bergamot saturating a cotton wad in a bottle held close to the nostrils.

A period of dark adaptation was begun and every 7 or 8 minutes during the first 30 minutes, c.f.f. measurements were made with two wave-lengths of monochromatic light, 520 m$\mu$ and 610 m$\mu$. The extraneous stimulation was begun at the end of 30 minutes and continued for 10 minutes, during which time a total of three readings were taken. Following this period, dark adaptation was continued for 20 to 25 minutes more, during which additional c.f.f. readings were taken.

The c.f.f. results gained under these conditions were compared with those on sensitivity to color taken under similar circumstances. Under the influence of sound, c.f.f. rises when the light used for flicker is intense, and declines when the light is weak. This holds true also for the influence of the odor. Furthermore there are differences in the outcome between cases of c.f.f. and of color sensitivity. When using green light (520 m$\mu$) for the flashes the odor reduced the c.f.f. while it enhanced color sensitivity. When using orange-red light (610 m$\mu$) the effect was the opposite, c.f.f. was enhanced, and color sensitivity was diminished.

This leads us to believe that increase in c.f.f. does not depend on an increase in the sensitivity of the eye, at least to color. It would have been better had experiments on the achromatic threshold been introduced along with those of color so that we could have come to some conclusions about quantitative brightness sensitivity. Nevertheless, since two colors were used and both the sensitivity to them and c.f.f.'s were compared, the results are suggestive. Looking at them from the standpoint of excitation, the discrepancy between the results on c.f.f. and color sensitivity disappears. If the extraneous stimulus such as an odor enhances excitation it may have an effect on both phases of the flicker cycle, the dark as well as the light. It may thus diminish the relative difference of the activities during the two and thus decrease the c.f.f. by that means, while it increases excitation and causes the observer to appreciate smaller amounts of color.

This effect would then be similar in principle to the effect of one retina area upon c.f.f. in another. Steady stimulation on one part of the retina may either enhance c.f.f. on an adjacent part or diminish it. Strong stimulation on the adjacent area diminishes the c.f.f., weak enhances it. Fry and Bartley explain this by suggesting that weak stimuli depress the dark phase of the flicker cycle, enhancing the difference between the two, and strong stimulation finally depresses both phases.

The determination of c.f.f., according to the view of the photochemist, is dependent upon the achievement of a pseudo-stationary state in the sense-cells from which follows uniform activity beyond them throughout the whole nervous pathway responsible for visual sensation. It would seem that if this were to be the case, the modifying effects we have just discussed could not occur, for neither the effects of one retinal area upon another nor those of extraneous stimulation on the c.f.f. can be transmitted through the sense-cells, but rather through the nervous system.

If sensory uniformity (fusion) were determined in the sense-cells, the influences we have described could not be brought to bear on the final sensory result, for it would have already been determined before later segments of the optic pathway would be involved and thus activity there could not change it. Hence these experiments are to be looked upon as examples which demonstrate that sense-cell behavior is not the controlling factor in determining the quantitative features of the various forms of brightness discrimination.

### STIMULATION BELOW FUSION

**Enhancement of brightness below fusion.** Even though it so happens that the critical flicker frequency is virtually the only measure used in studying intermittent stimulation, it is not the only one possible. Recently significant information has been obtained by using various critical transition points below the sensory fusion point. Not only does one not need to use flash rates which will produce a uniform sensation in order to study intermittent stimulation, but it will be shown later that it has been an unfortunate circumstance that attention has been focused almost exclusively on the c.f.f.

The intensity of the sensation produced at fusion, as was stated in referring to Talbot's law, is never as great as the sensation produced by continuous illumination. The level of this intensity is spoken of as the Talbot level and is immediately determined by noting the fraction of the cycle occupied by the flash as compared to the length of the cycle itself. With flash rates below c.f.f. estimates may be made of the level of illumination, despite the existence of flicker. To the observer, flicker seems to be superimposed upon a steady level. As flash rates are made lower and lower, judgments of the steady level become more difficult, but are still possible until the flash rate is only a small fraction of c.f.f. This is true more especially when the field observed is on an unilluminated background.

Bartley has reported that as measurements of the average levels are pursued with lower and lower flash rates, the brightness of the steady level begins to rise and not only reaches a value equal to that with steady illumination, but even transcends it, reaching a maximum when the flash rate is about 8 to 10 per second.

Many years ago Brücke pointed out a phenomenon which only now takes on real significance. He stated that the white areas of a rotating disc made up of black and white sectors became more brilliant at a certain rate of rotation than when stationary. This rate was about 17.6 per second, and was probably in the range at which Charpentier's bands are evident, which is to say, the situation in which the sectors seem more or less to stand still. Helmholz explained this added brilliance to his own satisfaction by attributing it to brightness contrast.

Bartley used transmitted light rather than black and white discs. Under such conditions the point at which maximum brightness is achieved occurs at a constant flash rate regardless of the L-D-R, though the absolute value of the general brightness level is varied by the L-D-R. It should be pointed out, however, that when the light fraction of the cycle falls below one-half that the phenomenon begins to become difficult to measure, and soon becomes prohibitive. Furthermore, a distinction is to be recognized between the Brücke and the Bartley effects. Brücke, it seems, was measuring the enhancement of the bright phase of the *fluctuating component* while Bartley was measuring the enhancement of the *steady component*. It turns out that the maximum

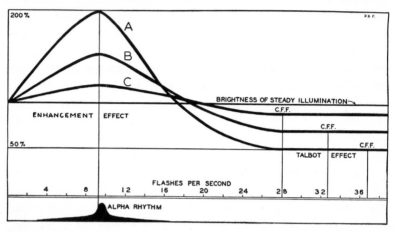

Fig. 34.—The relation between the Talbot and the brightness enhancement effects. The curves show the shift in the subjective brightness of a series of flashes as the rate is reduced from c.f.f. to a very few per second. Curve A is for flashes and dark intervals of equal length (L.D.R. 1/1); Curve B, L.D.R. 7/2; Curve C 8/1. (*Bartley—Psych. Rev.*)

of the latter effect is the reciprocal of the Talbot effect with reference to the level of brightness produced by a steady stimulus.

**Possible muscular origin of enhancement eliminated.** Halstead pointed out that one effect of intermittent photic stimulation could be to "drive" the pupillary and accommodative mechanisms of the eye. Their failure to "follow" flash rates might result in opening the eye to more light, or in changing the extent of its distribution on the retina, thereby enhancing brightness.

Bartley found the maximum brightness enhancement to occur at low flash frequencies near the range producing maximum ocular discomfort and intra-ocular muscular origin was made highly probable.

Halstead investigated this question by eliminating both the pupillary and accommodative reflexes by scopolamine. In which case brightness enhancement was clearly retained showing that it was not due to either of the intra-ocular muscle reflexes.

The discovery of the enhancement of the steady component and the elimination of a change in light flux due to muscle behavior, add another phenomenon to the list of those which seem contrary to photochemical predictions, for nothing that has yet been said about the sense-cell would have led to a critical repetitive rate for enhancement of brightness over the level produced by steady illumination. One of two things must occur. Either conceptions of sense-cell behavior must be radically reformulated, or else the phenomenon must be attributed to the neural part of the optic pathway. Inasmuch as we already have a coincidence between the rate necessary for the enhancement maximum and the alpha rhythm, and since the alpha rhythm represents a periodic fluctuation in excitability, we have every reason to believe the enhancement is of neural origin.

**Relative effects of flickering and "steady" light in other species.** The relative excitatory effects of flickering and steady light have been studied in a number of other ways. The investigation by Wolf and Zerrahn-Wolf of the phototropic reactions of young *Limuli* in flickering fields is an example. When two fields of equal area and intensity are presented to the animals, the number of individuals going to them is proportional to their flicker frequencies. The two fields can be equated in their stimulating effects by reduction of the area of the more rapidly flickering field. It turns out that for equal effect the areas must be inversely proportional to their flicker frequencies. From this it was concluded that the effects are dependent upon the number of elements activated per unit time.

Ewald, with *Daphnia,* found that light below the fusion point varied in its effectiveness depending upon the reflex used to test it. Dolley and Mast and Dolley also found that flickering light varied in its effectiveness according to rate. At a middle rate, the various insects tested were stimulated more than at either higher or lower ones. The flash range involved in these phenomena cover a range of 12 to 20 cycles per second.

**Other phenomena at sub-fusion flash rates.** The sequence of changes which occur as flash frequency is lowered from the sensory fusion point when the test-object subtends less than the total field and is surrounded by darkness, is as follows.

First, slight transient flicker which is so slight as to escape all but fixed observation appears in the test-object. In test-objects of larger visual angle, this flicker appears first in small patches. With a progressive rise in intensity or drop in flash rate, flicker becomes more noticeable and its apparent rate finally somewhat lower. The fluctuations begin to cover the whole object, although if the test-object be large uniformity is lacking. While flicker is still weak enough for its fluctuations to be secondary to the constant component of the brightness of the test-object, it retains its original features. But as the flash rate is further reduced, the fluctuations become more and more vigorous and the object through a limited flash range assumes a mottled appearance. Soon definite flicker can be seen immediately surrounding the test-object itself. As flash rate is still further lowered, this flicker spreads over the whole field surrounding the test-object. The transitions from no field flicker to field flicker adjacent to the test-object and from this to flicker over the whole field are relatively abrupt. From here on, with lower and lower flash rates, the fluctuations become more vigorous, the brightness of the flashes surpassing that of continuous light of the same physical intensity. At very low rates, the alternations of light and dark produce a feeling of ocular tension, as if the eye muscles were trying to contract and relax concurrent with them. The maximum of this ocular discomfort is reached just before the dark phase of the cycle emerges as a definite shadow. From here on, the dark phase becomes progressively more pronounced until it is seen as a full-fledged dark interval separating two flashes.

Throughout the whole range, but especially at the lower end, the light-dark ratio determines the nature and emerging place of the phenomena described. Nine phases have been mentioned.

They are shown in Figure 35. (1) A steady field, (2) slight flicker on a relatively steady field, (3) mottled field and coarsening of flicker, (4) flicker surrounding the test-object, (5) flicker

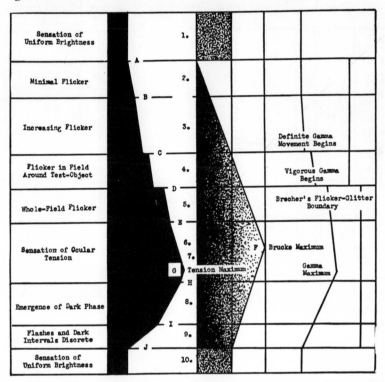

FIG. 35.—A diagram to show the more salient sensory stages which emerge as the flash rate is lowered from the fusion point (at top) to a place where the individual flashes are perfectly discrete (at bottom). (*Bartley—J. Exptl. Psych.*)

over the whole field, and the beginning of gamma movement, (6) the region of the Bartley maximum, (7) rise of ocular tension, (8) emergence of the dark phase, and (9) the emergence of flashes and dark phases as discrete entities.*

* The foregoing stages imply boundaries between each of them, the first distinct one being between stages 3 and 4 or boundary (c). The second between 4 and 5, or (d). Boundary (e), the beginning of ocular tension. Boundary (f) the Bartley maximum; (g) point of maximum ocular discomfort; (h) first emergence of the dark phase; (i) the beginning of discreteness in flashes and dark intervals.

**Stages when flickering object is surrounded by an illuminated field.** The sequence of phenomena observable when the test-object is surrounded by an illuminated field is somewhat more complicated. The test-object has more than one important as-

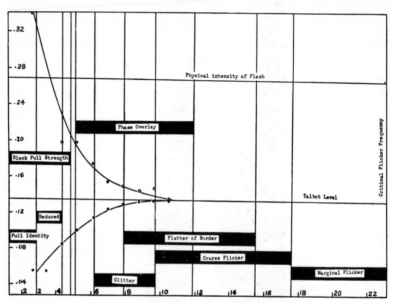

Fig. 36.—A diagram involving the same principle as Fig. 35, but in which the flickering field is surrounded by an illuminated annulus. In comparing this diagram with the previous one, it will be noted that more complications enter in the present case. The abscissa represents flashes per second, while the ordinate for the curves represents intensity of flashes in c/ft.². The black bars represent the stages that occur as flash rate is set at various values. (*Bartley—J. Exptl. Psych.*)

pect, each of which may be followed separately. It turns out that there is more or less overlapping of these aspects on the flash-frequency scale.

Owing to these circumstances, several sequences have been enumerated with less detail for each than was given for the test-object surrounded by darkness. See Figure 36.

As to flicker, the following stages are noticeable: (1) marginal flicker, (2) coarse flicker, (3) glitter, (4) after further reduction in flash frequency, the black of the dark interval shows up as a shadowy entity, (5) it then appears as a fully discrete phase.

Other aspects which are very noticeable are the following: (1) border flutter, which overlaps coarse flicker to quite an extent. It does not appear so soon as the latter when flash rate is reduced, but persists after it has vanished. (2) Phase overlay, the phenomenon of the dark and light phases appearing simultaneously, or at least the end of one lagging behind the beginning of the next. This stage begins at the flash rate representing the middle of the border-flutter phase and lasts approximately until the black of the dark phase takes on its full-fledged depth. It is during the middle range of this phase that glitter occurs.

These details are mentioned in order to show that below critical flicker frequency there are numerous definite qualitative phenomena each of which has a more or less fixed place in the range, and is as real a phenomenon as c.f.f. itself. The flash rate, light-dark ratio and various other conditions necessary for the production of each of them can be measured. Each has a significant set of neurological correlates which may be sought and when discovered will throw further light on the relation of nerve physiology to sensory psychology. Study in this field would seem to promise a way to help complete the picture. Already certain facts which have been obtained by using flash frequencies below c.f.f. have been very helpful.

**Flicker and contour.** It is known that the intensity of the area surrounding a test-object helps to determine the critical flicker frequency, but below c.f.f. the relative intensity of the surrounding area in conjunction with flash rate, determines the degree of prominence of the light and dark phases. Concomitant with manipulations of this phase dominance are those of contour. Predominance of a phase has correlated with it *definite* contour, whereas subordination of phase and *lack* of definite contour are associated.

The following experiment is an example. If a disc-annulus arrangement is chosen, in which the disc is made to flicker by alternating from complete darkness to light, at each of several slow rates, the intensity of the annulus will determine whether the two phases are subjectively equal (in brightness and definition of contour, etc.) or whether one or the other is extremely predominant, even though they be actually of the same duration. So extreme is this manipulation that either phase may be subordinated to the role of a mere shadow, while the other seems

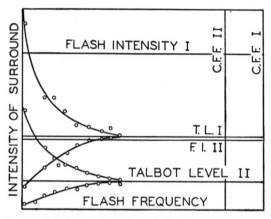

Fig. 37.—Curves showing the relation of the brightness of the surrounding annulus to the flash frequency of the test-object for producing a subjective predominance of either of the two equal-length phases of the flicker cycle. The upper curve in each case is for the predominance of the dark phase, the lower for the bright phase. Intensity is given in c/ft.² and flash frequency in flashes per second. (Relative scale as in Fig. 36.) (*Bartley—J. Exptl. Psych.*)

to occupy most of the cycle and possess sharp contour. Figure 37 shows the levels of the surround necessary for the dominance of either of the two phases.

It will be seen that in order to subordinate the bright phase and make the dark phase dominant, the intensity of the surround (with very low flash frequencies) must exceed not only the Talbot level of the test-object but the physical intensity of the flashes themselves. Increasing the flash rate reduces this level till it reaches the Talbot brightness of the test-object. The flashes grow less bright as c.f.f. is reached although the Talbot brightness of the test-object is reached somewhat below c.f.f.

On the other hand, in order for the bright phase to predominate to the extent of appearing as a contoured disc intermittently disappearing by virtue of the sweep of a shadow across it, the level of the surround must be reduced to less than one-half of the Talbot level, when the flash rate is very low. This level rises to the Talbot brightness at about 10 flashes per second under the conditions illustrated in the figure.

With low flash rates, the level of the surround must be as much above the physical intensity of the flashes for the dark phase to predominate as the surround level must be below the Talbot level for the bright phase to predominate.

## REFERENCES

Bartley, S. Howard. The basis of the flicker in the visual field surrounding the test-object. *J. Exptl. Psych.*, 1936, 19:342-350.

Bartley, S. Howard. The relation of retinal illumination to the experience of movement. *J. Exptl. Psych.*, 1936, 19:475-485.

Bogoslovski, A. I. Fusion of flickers of light induced by electric stimulation of the eye. *Bul. de Biol. et de Med. Exp.*, 1937, 3:303-306.

Bogoslovski, A. I. Changements de la fréquence critique des papillotements lumineux à caractère de réflexe conditionné. *Arch. d'ophth.*, 1938, 2:219-227.

Cobb, Percy W. The dependence of flicker on the dark-light ratio of the stimulus cycle. *J. Opt. Soc. Am.*, 1934, 24:107-113.

Cobb, Percy W. Some comments on the Ives theory of flicker. *J. Opt. Soc. Am.*, 1934, 24:91-98.

Crozier, W. J. On the sensory discrimination of intensities. *Proc. Nat. Acad. Sci.*, 1936, 22:412-416.

Crozier, W. J. The theory of the visual threshold. *Science*, 1939, 90: p. 405.

Crozier, W. J. Temperature and the critical intensity for response to visual flicker. II. *Proc. Nat. Acad. Sci.*, 1939, 25:78-82.

Crozier, W. J., and A. H. Holway. On the law for minimal discrimination of intensities. I. *Proc. Nat. Acad. Sci.*, 1937, 23:23-28.

Crozier, W. J., and A. H. Holway. On the law for minimal discrimination of intensities. III. *Proc. Nat. Acad. Sci.*, 1938, 24:130-135.

Crozier, W. J., and Ernst Wolf. The flicker response contour for the crayfish. I. *J. Gen. Physiol.*, 1939, 24:1-10.

Crozier, W. J., and Ernst Wolf. The flicker response contour for the crayfish. II. Retinal pigment and the theory of the asymmetry of the curve. *Biol. Bul.*, 1939, 77:126-134.

Crozier, W. J., and Ernst Wolf. The flicker response contour for the frog. *J. Gen. Physiol.*, 1939, 23:229-237.

Crozier, W. J., and Ernst Wolf. The flicker response contour for the Gecko (rod retina). *J. Gen. Physiol.*, 1939, 22:555-566.

Crozier, W. J., and Ernst Wolf. The flicker response contour for genetically related fishes. II. *J. Gen. Physiol.*, 1939, 22:463-485.

Crozier, W. J., and Ernst Wolf. Temperature and critical illumination for reaction to flickering light. III. Sunfish. *J. Gen. Physiol.*, 1939, 22: 487-499. IV. Anax Nymphs. *J. Gen. Physiol.*, 1939, 22:795-818. V. Xiphophorus, Platypoecilius, and their hybrids. *J. Gen. Physiol.*, 1939, 23:143-163.

Crozier, W. J., and E. Wolf. On the duplexity theory of visual response in vertebrates. II. *Proc. Nat. Acad. Sci.*, 1938, 24:538-541.

Crozier, W. J., and Ernst Wolf. Temperature and the critical intensity for response to visual flicker. III. On the theory of the visual response contour, and the nature of visual duplexity. *Proc. Nat. Acad. Sci.*, 1939, 25:171-175.

Crozier, W. J., and Ernst Wolf. Specific constants for visual excitation. III. *Proc. Nat. Acad. Sci.*, 1938, 24:542-545. IV. On the nature of genetic differences. *Proc. Nat. Acad. Sci.*, 1939, 25:176-179.

Crozier, W. J., Ernst Wolf, and Gertrud Zerrahn-Wolf. On critical frequency and critical illumination for response to flickered light. *J. Gen. Physiol.*, 1936, 20:211-228.

Crozier, W. J., Ernst Wolf, and Gertrud Zerrahn-Wolf. Critical illumination and critical frequency for response to flickered light, in dragonfly larvae. *J. Gen. Physiol.*, 1937, 20:363-392.

Crozier, W. J., Ernst Wolf, and Gertrud Zerrahn-Wolf. Temperature and critical illumination for reaction to flickering light. I. Anax Larvae. II. Sunfish. *J. Gen. Physiol.*, 1937, 20:393-431.

Crozier, W. J., Ernst Wolf, and Gertrud Zerrahn-Wolf. Critical illumination and flicker frequency in related fishes. *J. Gen. Physiol.*, 1937, 21:17-56.

Crozier, W. J., Ernst Wolf, and Gertrud Zerrahn-Wolf. Intensity and critical frequency for visual flicker. *J. Gen. Physiol.*, 1937, 21:203-221.

Crozier, W. J., Ernst Wolf, and Gertrud Zerrahn-Wolf. Critical illumination for response to flickered light, and dragonfly larvae (anax), in relation to area of eye. *J. Gen. Physiol.*, 1937, 21:223-247.

Crozier, W. J., Ernst Wolf, and Gertrud Zerrahn-Wolf. Specific constants for visual excitation. *Proc. Nat. Acad. Sci.,* 1937, 23:516-520. II. 24:221-224.

Crozier, W. J., Ernst Wolf, and Gertrud Zerrahn-Wolf. Critical illumination and flicker frequency, as a function of flash duration: for the sunfish. *J. Gen. Physiol.,* 1938, 21:313-334.

Crozier, W. J., Ernst Wolf, and Gertrud Zerrahn-Wolf. Critical intensity and flash duration for response to flicker: with anax larvae. *J. Gen. Physiol.,* 1938, 21:463-474.

Crozier, W. J., Ernst Wolf, and Gertrud Zerrahn-Wolf. On the duplexity theory of visual response in vertebrates. *Proc. Nat. Acad. Sci.,* 1938, 24:125-130.

Crozier, W. J., Ernst Wolf, and Gertrud Zerrahn-Wolf. The flicker response function for the turtle *Pseudemys. J. Gen. Physiol.,* 1939, 22:311-340. The flicker response contour for the isopod *Asellus. J. Gen. Physiol.,* 1939, 22:451-462.

Crozier, W. J., Ernst Wolf, and Gertrud Zerrahn-Wolf. Temperature and the critical intensity for response to visual flicker. *Proc. Nat. Acad. Sci.,* 1939, 25:216-221.

Ferree, C. E., and M. G. Rand. An experimental study of the fusion of colored and colorless light sensation: The locus of the action. *J. Philo. Psych., and Scient. Meth.,* 1911, 7:294-297.

Ferree, C. E., and M. G. Rand. Flicker photometry. I. The theory of flicker photometry. *Trans. Illum. Eng. Soc.,* 1923, 151-207.

Fry, Glenn A., and S. Howard Bartley. The effect of steady stimulation on one part of the retina upon the critical flicker frequency in another. *J. Exptl. Psych.,* 1936, 19:351-356.

Halstead, Ward C. A note on the Bartley effect in the estimation of equivalent brightness. *J. Exptl. Psych.* (in press).

Hecht, Selig, and Simon Shlaer. Intermittent stimulation by light. V. The relation between intensity and critical frequency for different parts of the spectrum. *J. Gen. Physiol.,* 1936, 19:965-977.

Hecht, Selig, and Emil L. Smith. Intermittent stimulation by light. VI. Area and the relation between critical frequency and intensity. *J. Gen. Physiol.,* 1936, 19:979-989.

Hecht, Selig, and Ernst Wolf. Intermittent stimulation by light. I. The validity of Talbot's law for Mya. *J. Gen. Physiol.,* 1932, 15:369-389.

Holway, A. H., and W. J. Crozier. On the law for minimal discrimination of intensities. II. *Proc. Nat. Acad. Sci.,* 1937, 23:509-515.

Kravkov, S. V. Critical frequency of flicker and indirect stimuli. *Comptes Rendus,* 1939, 22:64-66.

Ross, Robert T. A comparison of the regional gradients of fusion frequency and visual acuity. *Psych. Mono.,* 1936, 47:306-310.

Ross, Robert T.  The fusion frequency in different areas of the visual field: I. The foveal fusion frequency. *J. Gen. Psych.,* 1936, 15:133-147. II. The regional gradient of fusion frequency. *J. Gen. Psych.,* 1936, 15:161-170. III. Foveal fusion frequency and the light-dark ratio for constant retinal illumination at fusion. *J. Gen. Psych.,* 1938, 18:111-122.

Wolf, Ernst, and Gertrud Zerrahn-Wolf.  Flicker and the reactions of bees to flowers. *J. Gen. Physiol.,* 1937, 20:511-518.

Wolf, Ernst, and Gertrud Zerrahn-Wolf.  Reactions of *Limulus* to illuminated fields of different area and flicker frequency. *J. Gen. Physiol.,* 1937, 20:767-776.

Wolf, Ernst, and Gertrud Zerrahn-Wolf.  Threshold intensity of illumination and flicker frequency for the eye of the sunfish. *J. Gen. Physiol..* 1936, 19:495-502.

# VII

# PERCEPTION OF MOVEMENT

## REAL MOVEMENT

**Significance of the experience.** In the last chapter we were concerned with stimulation delivered repeatedly to the same retinal area, and thus with what happens when the same sense-cells are intermittently stimulated. This stimulation gave rise to the general phenomenon of flicker in its many forms. Interest now turns to another form of stimulation which in a sense may also be thought of as repeated. The stimulus impact is made upon successive retinal elements, giving rise to the experience of movement. To achieve this succession, stimuli themselves need not move to produce an image traversing the retina. Under proper conditions this is achieved with stationary light sources, the result being called apparent movement. Some of the conditions providing for apparent movement give rise to results which are indistinguishable from real movement.

It might be said that Exner, one of the early sense physiologists, was the first to see that the problem of seen movement holds important implications for psychological theory. He was interested in the distinction between sensation and perception, a distinction drawn rather definitely in psychology, up until very recently.

Naturally Exner was eager to discover whether the seeing of movement was a matter of sensation or perception. Providing there are these two categories, the step he chose would have been the first one to make. He concluded that the experience of movement is a sensation, and it is interesting to note his criteria. They are the following. The experience of movement has a limen just as any sensation has. The minimal interval for seeing it is less than for seeing two separate lights in succession. In peripheral vision, movement can be observed between two points which cannot be resolved in visual acuity experiments. Movement also has a negative after-image.

Nowadays, though we find it sometimes convenient to use the idea of immediacy implied in the term sensation, we realize that sensation as an experience wholly dependent upon the sense organs does not exist in fact. Today sensation and perception are to a degree synonymous and both are reserved to label experiences, many of whose determinants can be traced quite directly to the stimulus situation, and whose qualitative and quantitative properties can be fairly well controlled. The fact that not all situations impinging upon the higher sense organs are equally compelling in outcome, no longer leads to the division of the outcome into essentially different categories.

In dealing with the experience of movement there is no reason for a different form of treatment than is considered adequate for brightness discrimination and visual acuity.

**Visual perception of velocity.** It has long been known that the subjective velocity of a moving object varies under different conditions. Czermak in 1857 observed that motion in the periphery of the visual field is phenomenally slower than the same movement observed in the center. Fleischel noted that an object seen while fixating a stationary point moves subjectively faster than when followed by the eye. Aubert calculated the threshold for movement in homogeneous fields both when seen centrally and peripherally. He also measured the difference in phenomenal velocity as conditioned upon the mode of observing, as did Fleischel. Since then the phenomenon has been called the Aubert-Fleischel paradox. Bourdon in 1902 observed that the threshold for movement with large objects is higher than with small, the difference only roughly approximated Weber's law. Wertheimer pointed out that phenomenal velocity in apparent movement varies greatly. Filhene, in studying the Aubert-Fleischel paradox, concluded that when movement is perceived with pursuit eye movements an apparent movement of the background in the opposite direction brought about the subjective difference involved. Metzger observed that the subjective speed of a continuous succession of figures moving past the resting eye is greater than when only three figures are involved, although the physical velocity is the same. He found that broad figures seemed to move faster than narrow ones. Granit found that apparent velocities showed little correspondence with the velocities of the images traversing the retina, and from this he assumed a transformation of subjective velocity directly from the apparent constancy of visual size. Dembitz also demonstrated that there is little correlation between subjective velocities and velocities of images across the retina. He also found a high constancy of apparent visual velocity that is not based on the apparent constancy of visual size.

**Factors determining velocity.** Within the past decade, the study of velocity has been renewed. Brown's investigations have covered a variety of the possible aspects of the subject, reducing each question to quantitative measurement. To do this, he used two sets of moving stimulus-objects, a standard and a variable. Each set consisted in a series of figures moving past an aperture, on an endless belt.

The linear dimensions which were involved in the experiments were: Distance (s) from the moving object to the observer; the length (d), and width (w) of the aperture which defines the illuminated field; the size (h) of the object; and the spacing (i) of the objects on the belt. Physical velocity will henceforth be known as V, and subject velocity as v.

Six factors were investigated: (1) *The distance of the moving object from the observer.* It was found that as this distance increases, for example, from 1 to 20 meters (m), the phenomenal velocity decreases so that to retain a constant effect, physical velocity must be varied only 1:1.56. The relative stability of subjective velocity as the rate of movement of the image across the retina changes is spoken of as the apparent constancy of visual velocity, and is reminiscent of the well known phenomenon of apparent constancy of visual size.

(2) *The size of the visual field within which motion occurs.* If movement takes place in a homogeneous field, a change of all of the linear dimensions involved requires a corresponding change in the physical velocity to retain the same phenomenal velocity. If the homogeneity of the surrounding field is decreased, the ratio $V/v$ for change in size is decreased.

(3) *The structure of the surrounding field.* If it is heterogeneous the phenomenal velocity is faster than it would be for the same physical velocity in a homogeneous field.

(4) *The dimensions of the moving field.* Decrease in the width of the field increases apparent velocity as does also the decrease in the length of the field.

(5) *Size of the moving object.* Increase in its size decreases its apparent velocity.

(6) *Orientation of the object with reference to direction of motion.* Objects oriented in line with motion appear to move faster than if the orientation is otherwise.

**The differential limen for visual velocity.** Using the same apparatus that Brown had previously employed for the study of visually perceived velocity, Brown and Mize measured the difference limen (D.L.) for velocity. Thus two moving objects were seen by the subject who was asked to judge directly which was moving the faster. Bourdon had previously investigated the difference threshold and through the limitation of his conditions had concluded that it followed Weber's law. Brown and Mize's results, however, showed that this is, by no means, the case.

Their experiments indicated the following: (1) That differential sensitivity for visual velocity is maximum at 10 cm./sec. and declines both above and below this point independently of the particular subjective velocity obtaining during the measurements; (2) that the structure of the visual field in which the motion occurs influences differential sensitivity so that the subjectively faster has a higher difference limen at similar physical velocities; (3) that this effect is unpredictable from the effect of field structure on suprathreshold subjective values.

**Subjective perseveration of movement.** If certain objects are observed while in motion, their motion continues subjectively for a very appreciable time after the objects come to rest. This impression is sometimes spoken of as a movement after-image. It in one form is the familiar illusion, James' "waterfall."

One of the best known facts about this perseveration is that its duration is a function of the velocity of the moving stimulus. The duration of perseveration at first increases rapidly with increase of the velocity of the previous stimulus, but quickly reaches a maximum from which it gradually diminishes with further increase in stimulus speed.

Granit suggested that the movement perseveration might be a function of subjective velocity.* He showed that subjective velocity is a direct function of neither retinal nor stimulus velocity, and that the impression of duration from watching moving objects and the thresholds for movement depend upon subjective rather than physical velocity. This led Brown and Mize to investigate whether length of perseveration is best to be expressed as a function of phenomenal velocity. They found that it is a function of the structures of the visual field in which motion occurs and is influenced in a predictable way based on the effect of the particular structurization on subjective velocity.

## SUBJECTIVE MOVEMENT FROM STATIONARY OBJECTS

**Apparent movement.** It is well known that external objects need not have moved in order to create the impression of motion. For example, it has just been stated that under certain conditions movement subjectively continues after the moving object stops. A temporal sequence of stationary events will also give the impression very well. In the laboratory, the study of visually perceived movement as dependent upon stationary stimuli is simpli-

---

* In this connection, it must be pointed out that when it is stated that the value of some factor is a function of phenomenal (subjective) velocity, that the latter is not to be taken as a *cause*. Field structure determines subjective velocity and all the other phenomena in a manner that when knowing its effect on subjective velocity one may foretell the occurrence of the other events by using subjective velocity as an index.

fied by simply using two patches of light whose intensity, spatial separation from each other, and sequence in appearance can be controlled. The impression of motion so created is called *apparent movement*. Actual and apparent movements under the limited conditions become indistinguishable; the classification between them is capable of being made only on the basis of stimulus conditions. Among stationary objects, there is a variety of situations which produce apparent movement. Most if not all of them have been classified, and they will be presented according to the existing classification.

If a limited area of a completely dark visual field is suddenly illuminated, or the illumination of a dim field suddenly increased, the observer will experience the impression of illumination expanding from the area in question to fill the whole visual field, even though after the movement is completed the visual field outside the test-area is considered to be unilluminated. Anyone can observe some aspects of this for himself by looking directly at the ceiling light in a room and alternately turning it on and off. The whole room becomes quickly lighted as the switch is turned on. The light, however, originates in the light bulb and expands from there to all other parts of the room instead of appearing simultaneously everywhere. At the cessation of the movement the light source is definitely brighter than the remaining visual field. Under suitable laboratory conditions, the field outside the test-object will be totally dark. When the light is turned off a centripetal movement takes place, the illumination disappearing last in the light bulb rather than everywhere concurrently. This expansion and contraction effect is known as *gamma* movement. It plays a role in many visual experiences and forms a component of situations classified as examples of other kinds of apparent movement. Neither gamma movement nor the others which are about to be mentioned require that bright test-objects appear on dark fields as when they are their own sources of light. The fields may also be illuminated. Or the reverse conditions may be used, namely, dark objects may be made to appear on bright fields. White cards with black solid or outline figures may be employed tachistoscopically. Gamma movement is the subjective transition from a uniform field, either illuminated or totally dark, to a final stationary differentiation or pattern, or the reverse.

The following examples in which sidewise or unilateral movement occurs are classified as forms of *beta* movement. Two or more areas illuminated in succession give rise to a certain amount of symmetrical gamma movement but the main phenomenon is their separate movements (jumps or jerks) in the direction of the succession. This is called *part* movement. If the patches are limited to two, it is *dual* part movement, if more patches are included it is *serial* movement. If the time intervals between their appearance is too small they seem to emerge simultaneously, the sidewise jerk is reduced to zero and the only apparent movement is the simple gamma type. This is an example of *stationary simultaneity* according to customary terminology. If the time intervals between the appearance of the succeeding patches is made very long, their gamma movement is the only apparent movement discernible. This is an example of *stationary succession.*

The timing may be adjusted so that the individual patches lose their identity and instead a single patch is seen to move from the neighborhood of the actual place of the first patch to somewhere in the neighborhood of the second patch. This is a case of *optimal* movement. When the patches are not limited to two, this single "apparent" patch moves continuously and smoothly along a course in the field where otherwise the actual patches would be seen.

If the physical sizes of the members in the series are unequal the unitary moving object waxes and wanes in keeping with their inequality. This is a special case of beta movement. But if the subjective sizes of the physically equal members of the pair or series vary, the single object seen in unbroken movement will also vary in size. This has been called *alpha* movement, and is demonstrated by using the two halves of the Müller-Lyer illusion in succession.

If the second member of a pair of objects happens to be much brighter than the first there may be a backward movement from the bright to the dim and this is *delta* movement.

Apparent movement is usually seen in the plane occupied by the members of the series but at other times the third dimension is involved. Gamma-movement situations sometimes include motion toward and away from the observer. The existence of such movement is presumably determined by the rate of increase or reduction of the illumination in the test-area; the angle subtended by it; and the level of illumination of the area surrounding it. Under some conditions, beta movement, like gamma, will leave the plane occupied by the stimulus. When beta movement does this it will swing out into space toward the observer. This has been called *bow* movement.

The ways in which some of the factors involved in the production of beta movement compensate for one another have been worked into a set of "laws" by Korte. The factors are those of intensity (I) including stimulus size; spatial separation ($s$); and temporal interval ($t$) between the presentation of the members of the series. If optimal beta movement exists, the manipulation of one factor, such as the lessening of the stimulus intensity, can be compensated for within limits by the alteration of one of the other factors. If I is reduced, $s$ must be decreased or $t$ must be increased. If $s$ is reduced, with I constant, $t$ must also be reduced.

A paradoxical characteristic of the perception of movement is the fact that under some conditions, the observer experiences movement without being able to say just what it is that moves. The object or "something" which moves has lost most all of its object or thing-like character, and the aspect of motion has become predominant. This is the *phi phenomenon* and is the opposite extreme from the situation in which an object is experienced in detail and clarity but without movement. Obviously all sorts of intervening situations may exist.

**Gamma movement.** The simple case already described, in which alternately lighting and darkening a room produced gamma movement, served as an initial illustration but did not provide for an analysis of the essential traits of this kind of movement.

The conditions for producing the phenomenon must be controlled and manipulated. Very often devices employ an episcotister (a revolving disc with an open sector) to control the rate of onset and decay of illumination. When the edge of a solid sector of the disc passes in front of the light, its travel is observable in one way or another depending upon the particular optical arrangements used. To avoid this and thus provide for fields whose every part is illuminated simultaneously, the light passed by the disc must fall upon some intermediary surface such as that of a lens or an opal glass diffuser. Whereupon the passage of the sector's edge in front of the light varies only the intensity and does not cause the exposure or withdrawal of the light in one part of the field before another. Gamma movement is definitely seen even when this factor is controlled and all parts of the test-object are illuminated together.

The rate of onset of illumination (development to full intensity) in the test-object is another factor that has been controlled. For this, a disc with a wedge-like sector was used, so that the pencil of light passed by the disc gradually grew from a point to a broad beam, thereby gradually increasing the brightness of the test-object. Newman, one of the most recent investigators to make a study of gamma movement, used a wedge providing a developmental period of as much as 1.8 seconds.

Long developmental or transition periods have revealed three stages in gamma movement. There is, first, the coming on of the light. Something bright is seen. The second is the growth stage, during which the light spreads to the full size of the final object. And the third is the motion of the object toward the observer. This is the depth movement. Increasing the brightness of the object enhances depth movement. Prolonging the transition time favors depth movement, the optimal range being from 200-800 ms. That a number of studies failed entirely to report this type of movement seems to be a consequence of using very short transition times.

With a rapid onset, the depth effect is slight or absent due either to the fact that the rate of stimulation of the retina external to the image is wrong or that the effect cannot be separated out from the other aspects of movement. With increasingly gradual onsets the depth effect finally emerges. With rapid onsets, the object and the field both expand, while with increasingly slow onsets the time arrives when the object expands very little, if any, as it grows in intensity.

**Test-object vs. total field in gamma movement.** Most investigators center their attention upon what happens to the test-object when exposed, instead of including the whole visual field. Though this may be legitimate for answering specific questions, it seems to have circumvented the arrival at the significance of the gamma phenomenon from the stimulation standpoint. Figure 38 shows typical patterns of the physical stimulus, those of retinal illumination, and the direction of the subjective movement created. It is obvious from this that the stimulation of the retina external to the image of the test-object cannot be ignored. It is responsible for the movement seen in the field in general when the transition rate is not too low for changes in weak intensity to be significant.

This is brought out clearly in the protocols of Newman's subjects who report that the quicker transitions created movement further out into the field. They said that the quicker onsets provided for better spread. There is, nevertheless, an optimal range and a maximum for this. Some of Newman's observers also reported the existence of a shadow at slower transition speeds. All of this evidently was reference to field movement without the full recognition of it.

From the stimulation patterns given in Figure 38 and from what is known about *flicker* in relation to rate, it would be expected that field movement would suffer more from changes in transition time than the test-object proper.

Different absolute values hold true for the sequence of stages characterizing the field around the test-object. With rapid onsets, field movement is marked. As was said, expansion extends farther into the field than with slow onsets. By the time that the onset or transition covers 300 ms. the test-object fails to expand appreciably. With 200 ms. transitions, depth movement

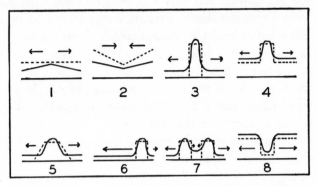

Fig. 38.—Eight typical cases of light distribution. The dotted lines represent the gradients in the stimuli and the solid lines those upon the retina. It is evident that the distribution of the light in the stimulus object and in the retinal image are not identical. Case 1 indicates that with a uniform visual field confronting the eye the intensity of light on the retina is likely greater at the fovea. Case 2; when the stimulus is less bright at the center than at the periphery of the visual field. Case 3; when a bright spot is seen on a dark background. It will be noted that there is some illumination over the entire retina, even though the visual field is dark except for the small spot. Case 4; when a bright spot is seen on an illuminated field. Case 5; when a bright spot with much blurred border is seen on a dark background. Case 6; when a bright spot appears in the periphery of the visual field instead of at the fixation point. Case 7; when two bright objects lie equidistant, but on opposite sides from the fixation point. Case 8; when a black test-object appears on an illuminated ground. The arrows indicate the direction of gamma movement as the patterns of illumination are instituted. This is due in part to the relative amounts of light on the different parts of the retina and to the fact that the center of the retina behaves differently than the periphery (probably more rapidly). (*Bartley—J. Exptl. Psych.*)

has emerged and is determined in part by what is happening to the retina outside the image of the test-object.

The expansion movement induced by the appearance of the test-object and the contraction movement at its disappearance are not fully opposite. The former seems to be slightly more impressive. With very short exposures, the best contraction effects were obtained, signifying some connection between the two. It is very probable this is dependent upon the fact that less residual activity is left by a disappearing short stimulus. When the expansion and contraction were separated by more time, as when using long exposures, the contraction was found to be appreciably the weaker and the less extensive. This applies both to the field and the shift in contour of the object itself.

There is a phenomenal difference in the *rate* at which the two processes of expansion and contraction take place. With objectively equal times used for the onset and decay of the light, the expansion movement seems to take longer. In some cases when the onset is made objectively one-half as long as the decay, they seem phenomenally equal.

Newman feels that the results here are not what would be expected from our knowledge of physiology. In this he refers to the classical fact that the *Anklingen* time is shorter than the *Abklingen*. Since the results seem to be directly opposed to this, he feels that physiological processes within the eye are ruled out.

In this connection, it may be said that we do know that in certain elements the onset of their activity following stimulation is quite abrupt. With cessation of stimulation their activity decays only gradually. But when we deal with vision, we are confronted with a situation which is much more complicated. There are processes in the eye which are instituted only at the cessation of stimulation (off-responses) and we have to take into account the possible sensory effects they may produce.

A special case of gamma movement is that of Harrower's *Lochversuch,* an experiment in which a black object is made to appear or disappear upon a white ground (see Case 8, Figure 38). When it appears it expands. When it disappears it withdraws within itself. The whole situation is similar to that described for gamma movement with a bright object on a dark ground. Since it is a black object which expands the fact was taken by Harrower to prove the dependence of gamma movement upon the appearance and disappearance of a figure rather than upon the nature of stimulation changes in the retina. The *Lochversuch* and certain other related experiments were taken by her to show that expansive movement in a given portion of the visual field could occur regardless of any intensity change in that area and consequently did not critically depend on retinal processes. In no case yet cited is it true that movement occurs despite lack of illumination shifts on the retina. The view expressed by Harrower is an example of the common failure of investigators to determine the actual distribution of light on the retina and thus to consider gamma movement in light of what happens physiologically when unequal amounts of stimulation are presented or withdrawn from two regions, as is the case in the *Lochversuch*. The diagram illustrating this experiment makes it obvious that at the center of what is to be the final image of the black object, more light is withdrawn as the dark object looms into existence than at its edges. The center becomes blacker first and the blackness expands toward its borders and even beyond.

Differential removal of light from several areas causes subjective visual movement to originate at the point where most light is removed and progress to regions from which less has been removed. This phenomenon follows from the fact that the latency of the *off*-response depends upon the amount of light that has been withdrawn. All of the factors which were employed in the treatment of gamma movement when the test-object is brighter than the ground hold good here also. These together provide a physiological account of what the sensory message to the brain is like in order that gamma movement may be seen.

Another special case providing for gamma movement was used by Newman, and later by Bartley. It consists in two bright rectangles separated by an interspace equal to the width of one of them. Naturally the movement that occurs when these two bright patches emerge upon a dark field is complicated. There is a broad and extended movement from the fixation point which lies midway between the patches. Included within the extensive expansion are two lesser ones extending radially from the lighted areas. A complete report must include both of them. The failure to differentiate them signifies an incompetency to see the major details of what is happening. If the dark area between the patches is seen as a figure (a black rectangle) the observer can see the area expand as it comes into existence. This was reported by some of Newman's observers.

· At first thought it would seem to indicate that the occurrence of movement and its actual direction were dependent simply upon one's mode of perception. It is to be taken for granted that the attitude or mode of perception does give character to what is seen. But the point at issue is the question of whether the perceptional mode itself originates movement in a unique way.

To answer this we must examine what actually happens when the two bright squares on a black field, separated by a distance equal to the width of one of them, are suddenly presented to the eye. The space between them can be seen as a square. This area, as the lighted squares come into existence, also comes into existence, and in so doing its borders are illuminated before its center. In other words, its edges are the parts finally illuminated the most by the spread from the bright squares on either side. The point to be recognized is that even in this "black" square, the illumination level is shifted as the stimulus objects are presented and withdrawn, just as in the *Lochversuch* or any other situation producing gamma movement.

According to the usual rule, this black area would tend to *shrink* when the two bright squares on either side emerge. It generally does this rather than expand, even when it happens to be seen as a square in its own right. But on the other hand, it is possible to see it expand as its periphery lights up and finally reaches equilibrium. The essential condition for movement, as was stated before, is the passage across the retina of an illumination gradient. The individual fixes on something in connection with the gradient, some part of it, etc., and if it shifts, movement is seen. The movement seen may be either centrifugal or centripetal within the figure. The retinal conditions set the stage for movement itself, while in complex stimulus patterns the choice of which of the two directions it will be, is effected elsewhere. The point to be made is that centrifugal movement is not a by-product of figure formation but has a retinal basis. Unless one wishes to insist that the individual imagines movement and thereby movement is experienced without the employment of retinal gradients, it is necessary to recognize the origin of movement which has been stressed here.

**Gamma movement of the test-object's contour.** The visual field confronting the observer may be considered a figure-ground construct, and the properties of the test-object as a figure be given especial consideration. Among them is its *contour*. Some investigators have declared that gamma movement is conditioned upon the emergence of a "figure," and that movement of its contour is one of the developmental properties of a figure as such. But this in connection with the assertion that movement may be seen in the field where there is no diminution or enhancement of light intensity, leads to the erroneous conclusion that it is not the pattern of retinal stimulation that primarily conditions the existence and character of apparent movement, but that it is certain configurational processes higher in the nervous system.

It has already been shown that such a theory is untenable in light of the facts pertaining to retinal stimulation. A further test of this notion consists in comparing the results obtained by using a series of bright discs which cover a range in visual angle from about 3 degrees to 48 degrees. The contours of the smallest one are therefore not far removed from the fixation point. The circumference of a middle-sized disc ($10° 40'$) lies appreciably further away, while the borders of the largest disc lie quite far out toward the periphery of clear vision.

When once pointed out, it should be clear that, with small test-objects, gamma movement is not confined within them but extends over large portions of the field, tapering off toward the periphery (certain time and intensity factors of stimulation setting the limits).

On the other hand, large discs may extend far enough that their boundaries lie in regions characterized under ordinary circumstances by little definite movement. Whether contours emerging and disappearing in such parts of the visual field are more nearly free from gamma movement constitutes one large aspect of the general problem.

Bartley's experiments (unpublished) make it clear that the range of conditions represented by the above discs produce six kinds of movement; (1) movement within the confines of the

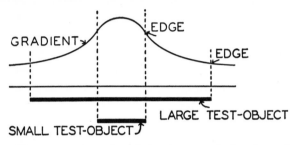

Fig. 39.—Diagram to show the relation between the locations of the edges of large and small retinal images (when their centers are in the fovea) and the center-to-periphery retinal gradient. Note that the edge of the small test-object when centered on the retina falls on a steeper part of the gradient. Since the edges of large images fall in regions having only a very slight gradient there is little cause for the apparent movement of the edges, whereas the opposite is true with small images whose edges fall within or just outside of the fovea.

discs themselves, starting from the fixation point and filling out the area to the fixed circumference; (2) movement in the dark field beyond the borders of the discs; (3) unified movement, of the disc, in which the contour is moving centrifugally as it comes into existence; (4) depth movement which puts in its appearance under conditions much like those for the type just mentioned. When it appears, it is an integral part of the vigorous expansion movement of the whole disc; (5) wabble of the whole disc up and down or laterally, thus involving a displacement of contour but not the usual expansion and contraction; and (6) movement which looks as if the disc were revolving on a vertical axis running through its diameter.

The main difference in the behavior of the largest disc and

the smaller ones, for present purposes, concerns the first kind of movement. All of the discs regardless of size exhibited this kind under the proper intensity conditions. The large disc covered so much of the visual field that considerable action could take place within its borders, leaving greater opportunity for movement of type 1. Only conditions conducive to the most vigorous movement tended to involve the contour. The smaller discs, though covering smaller fields and thus less of the center to periphery gradient of the retina, were located on a steeper portion of it and thus gamma movement of type 3 was more easily induced.*

It can thus be concluded that the contours of an object behave in keeping with the intensity of stimulation used, and their location on center to periphery gradient of the retina. *Gamma movement of contours is not of a fixed kind, and does not appear under identical circumstances for all objects, and may not occur at all, so that it would not seem to be a necessary property of an emerging figure.* Figures were shown in these experiments to emerge without any gamma movement whatsoever and in cases in which a whole visual field is intermittently illuminated and darkened gamma movement occurs without the emergence of any well-defined figure. Gamma movement is only incidental in figure-ground formation and may be understood and controlled by taking into account merely the nature of stimulation and the nature of the retina.

**Special cases of beta movement.** Movement appears in a number of cases in which the outcome is not phenomenologically so simple as was first described for optimal beta movement. It may be said that optimal movement occurs in some of these cases although two stationary test-objects do not give rise to the appearance of a *single* subjective moving object. The essence of the term optimal movement, if we are to use it in any of the cases

---

* The total amount of light flux reaching the retina was a large factor in determining the vigor of movement. This light could be in the form of a bright small image with its attendant entoptic scatter or in the form of a much less bright large image, such as produced by the largest disc. To reach fair conclusions this factor had to be equated.

whose description follows, is that the movement seen is of an apparent object traversing the whole interspace between the positions of separate objects seen under poorer movement conditions. Movement varies in extent from this down to part movement, and to vague field movement which is ordinarily labeled the *phi* phenomenon.

Two lighted discs appearing concurrently in a dark field may be relatively so different in brightness that the one masks the other. If the brighter one is extinguished, the weak one emerges. Higginson says that this situation may give rise to optimal movement, movement from the disappearing disc to the remaining one. He labels this situation as one in which there is physical sequence without a temporal interval. Hence it demonstrates that a temporal interval between the existence of two stationary objects is not necessary for optimal movement.

A second special case is that in which an object is presented, and following its emergence, another object is added. The time interval here is totally indifferent. The first object may subjectively remain fixed and the second disengage itself from it and move to its final position. At other times the first object may appear to divide, one part moving alongside, both composing the members of a final figure. It is to be noted that the first member does not move from its position, only the second carries the movement. It is reported that the relative intensities of the two objects are of little consequence. Naturally the ratio must reach a critical limit somewhere. A third case is as follows. Let the illumination of one of two bright test-objects, the proper distance apart, be extinguished. Instead of the cessation of illumination simply causing the ordinary gamma movement by the object withdrawing within itself, it disappears by way of the remaining object. Results may be modified by withdrawing all of the light from one object and a large part from the other. That is to say, the one object remains but is much dimmer than it was. It is not claimed that optimal movement will occur under such conditions, though very definite *phi* does. The case does show, nevertheless, that movement starts from the region from which the more light is withdrawn and progresses from there to other areas. It thus is in line with the results in the *Lochversuch*.

Movement may be seen to pass over the same area in two directions concurrently, the essential condition being that the first and second members of each of two pairs of objects have a common region lying between them. For this, Higginson presented in alternate succession the members of one pair of horizontal parallel bars while presenting in a similar manner a pair of parallel vertical bars. The movement resulting is optimal in the original sense. The subjective result is one bar moving up and down and another moving back and forth over the same area. The same investigator has used a more complicated example involving the same principle. The first member to be presented is the black outline of a square at whose center is a small circle in outline. The second member is the outline of a circle with a diameter equal to the square. Within the circle is the outline of a parallelogram whose corners touch the circumference, the one dimension being over three times as great as the other. When the two members are alternately presented in proper timing to the eye, the circle expands and shrinks, and the square changes to the parallelogram and back again.

A good example of beta movement which does not involve the existence of an interspace to begin with is in the following. Let the two members of the arrangement be black lines on a white background. Instead of being parallel let them diverge from a common point. When presented in alternate succession without any geometrical additions, the subjective result will be that of a single line waving up and down from the axis formed by the point of divergence. If an additional line is injected into the pattern to form an extension of one of the original ones, but not continuous with it, the added line will give rise to apparent movement. It will move at right angles to its length instead of having the sweeping movement of the line of which it is an extension. It, as it were, moves up and down while its companion rocks. Further complications may be added but they only show the same principle.

The same two diverging lines which at times appear as a single rocking line may be seen simultaneously and moving as if parts of a rigid unit. Higginson calls this *dual* movement. The first shift that takes place under these conditions is in the same direction as the motion when a single line is seen, and

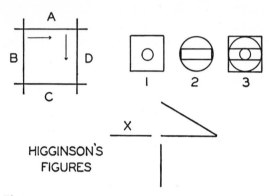

HIGGINSON'S
FIGURES

Fig. 40.—Figures to show that apparent movement may traverse the same area in two directions simultaneously. If A and B in the left-hand figure are presented to be followed by C and D, movement is produced in line with the arrows. In the right-hand figure if pattern 1, and then pattern 2, is presented, the small circle swells to the size of the large one and the square shrinks to the dimensions of the rectangle. In the bottom pattern the two parts of the angular pattern are presented in succession at such a rate that a single line is seen swinging about the axis of convergence. If an additional line (X) is included, it moves up and down at right angles to its length in time with the first-mentioned movement. (*Higginson—J. Exptl. Psych.*)

this is followed by the opposite shift both of which we may more descriptively call jerks. With alteration in the temporal factors, various other phenomenal complications result.

**The stroboscope.** The apparent movement of objects may be accomplished by use of the stroboscope. This device consists in a pattern of stripes moving either in a linear direction, as when on a belt, or radially, as when on a revolving disc. In either case they are intermittently illuminated, and thus are seen only during each flash. During the dark phase of the intermittency they move unobserved to a new position. As a consequence the stripes will be seen to move, or will subjectively stand still, depending upon several factors, one of which is the amount they move during each dark interval relative to their own spacing. If they seem to move, it is not necessarily their real motion which is seen, but the outcome of the amount of spatial displacement during each dark interval. The flash frequency used to illuminate the stripes may be so high that the illumination appears to be constant, but the principle producing movement may operate nevertheless.

The apparent movement is either one of two kinds, smooth or jumpy. That is to say, the stripes may be seen to float smoothly or they may flutter or jump from position to position.

The relationship between the flash rate and the actual movement of the stripes determines not only which of these two kinds of movement will be seen, but also the direction which it will take. If during the dark interval, each of the black stripes moves into the exact position that its predecessor occupied during the last light flash, no movement will be seen. If, instead, each stripe moves less than half way toward the position held by its predecessor, the new flash will reveal it in that position and thus movement will be perceived. If the stripes move more than half way to the position held by their predecessors, the next flash will reveal them in that position, but the observer's impression will be that the predecessor stripes have moved backward, rather than the successors have moved forward.

With a fixed flash frequency, the rotation rate of a striped disc may be determined if the number of stripes are known. For example, if 60 flashes per second are provided as with the usual 60-cycle house illumination, a disc possessing 10 black stripes may be making 6 revolutions per second if the stripes appear to be standing still. In other words, each stripe will move up to the position of its predecessor in each $\frac{1}{60}$ of a second. Since there are 10 stripes this distance will be $\frac{1}{10}$ of the circumference, thus the disc will move $\frac{1}{10}$ of a revolution each $\frac{1}{60}$ of a second, a whole revolution requiring $\frac{10}{60}$ or $\frac{1}{6}$ of a second. It also happens that the stripes will appear to stand still if the disc moves at certain other speeds. If, instead of moving to the position of its predecessor, during each interval, each stripe moves up to the position of the second one ahead of it, the appearance to the observer will be the same. That means that the stripes will stand still if it is revolving at 12 per second. This will likewise hold true for other multiples of the original speed of 6 per second.

By using a disc upon which are placed concentric rings of dots, each ring having a different but known number, the rate of revolution of the disc can be ascertained by picking out the ring whose dots stand still. A number of useful devices such as set-ups for ultra highspeed photography employ this visual principle. Discs for timing phonograph turn-tables employ the stroboscopic principle.

**Apparent movement by other devices.** Apparent movement may also be accomplished in several other ways. If the finger, for example, is interposed between the eyes and a more distant object, the finger will move back and forth as the two eyes are alternately used. Similar but greatly reduced movement of a fixated (preferably near) object will occur when the eyes are alternately used. Such cases employ the successive use of cortical points representing different points in space, brought about by the appropriate successive use of the two eyes.

**The stereoscopic pendulum.** Pulfrich's stereoscopic pendulum is another example of a set of conditions which will induce the perception of movement of a kind not corresponding with the real movement of a physical object.

The conditions are provided by an ordinary suspended bob swinging at right angles to the line of regard and viewed binocularly. In front of one eye is a filter reducing the intensity of the light entering it. When the gaze is fixated in a plane passing through the center of the arc made by the swinging bob, its excursion is not linear as might be expected, but appears to traverse a course somewhat elliptic in shape. Since the "apparent" component of the movement or the distortion is in the line of regard, it is a depth or third-dimensional effect. For that reason it is called stereoscopic. Since the path of movement does not follow the known physical path, it is a form of apparent movement.

The explanation of the depth effect is as follows. There is a time interval (latent period) between the light reaching the eye from the pendulum bob and the sensation aroused. This being the case the bob is not where it is seen to be but somewhere further along its swing. This discrepancy is greater the faster the swing, hence it is maximum at the midpoint and zero at the ends of the swing where the pendulum stops for an instant. If a neutral filter or simply a piece of smoked glass is placed in front of one eye the impression of the bob is dimmer. That is to say, stimulation is weaker and the response is slower in developing. Thus the impressions in the two eyes will differ and bring about the stereoscopic effect. The difference in the latency of the impressions produced on account of the difference in brightness is transferred into a difference in depth between the moving bob and the fixation point.

A colored filter may be used instead of the neutral one, in which case the stereoscopic effect will be the same. This is, however, due to the fact that the colored glass also reduces the amount of light received by the one eye. Such a device provides, theoretically, a means whereby the brightness of a colored light and that of a neutral gray may be compared. This means of heterochromatic photometry has not found very much use so far, due probably to two disadvantages: need for training in stereoscopic observation, and the requirement of a large field of view which by its size involves an intense light source to exclude the phenomena of peripheral and twilight vision.

**The autokinetic sensation.** There are still other conditions for seeing movement. The conditions about to be described include stimulus movement in no part of the visual field. The most usual circumstances for autokinetic movement are a darkened room and a single dim small spot of light which is fixated. One or both eyes may be used for the observation, though a single eye is preferable. In a few seconds following fixation, the spot will appear to float off in some direction or other at a rate of 2° to 15° per second. One typical course is that of a figure eight, the fixation point being its center.

Guilford and Dallenbach have been among the most recent investigators of the phenomenon, though it has been occasionally studied since the days of Charpentier and Aubert. Guilford and Dallenbach photographed the eye movements occurring during the phenomenon, and found them to be too slight and of the wrong character to account for it. Instead, they believed that the streaming phenomena, possibly such as described by Ferree and by Edridge-Green would account for the movement. Their findings terminated the eye-movement theory originated over sixty years ago.

Guilford followed this investigation by a further examination of the conditions for the appearance of autokinesis. As a result he came to conclusions which may be summarized as follows:

(1) Entoptic streaming is a crucial factor responsible for the autokinetic sensation.

(2) The streams concern all parts of the retina concurrently and are not those of Edridge-Green or Ferree.

(3) A number of spots will always move together in any part of the field within 30° of the center.

(4) The direction inward or outward in which a spot moves is a matter of chance within a 30° area.

(5) Motion is in the direction of certain types of eye pressures.

(6) Prediction is possible on the basis of the existing direction of eye pressures and streaming.

(7) By institution of eye pressures the observer can control spot motion.

(8) A change in eye pressures thus can be made to alter direction of spot motion.

(9) Differences in fatigue and recovery of the external eye muscles were not thought possible as determiners of the direction of motion.

The phenomenon is to be thought of as what might be expected when the visual field is characterized by sufficient differentiation for fixation but too little for other anchorage points. Though the visual field is dark and the spot light, the reverse conditions have been reported, this, with other things such as absence of gross eye movements, indicating that it is minimal differentiation rather than minimal stimulation that is essential for such factors as the streaming process to become effective.

**Apparent vs. real movement.** Apparent and real movements were compared by De Silva under the same set of conditions. His apparatus was so constructed that the perception of apparent movement arising from successive presentation of two stationary parallel bars could be compared with the outcome from using the same two bars when the spatio-temporal interval was filled with a real moving bar. The distance between the bars was set at each of three visual angles, about 35 minutes, 1.4°, and 3.16°. Their width was roughly 14 minutes, and their length about 1.7°.

When the speed of the real movement was in the vicinity of 3° p.s. distinction between real and apparent movement was always possible regardless of which of the three traversal distances were used. When the angular velocity was about 10° p.s. it was definitely more difficult to distinguish between the two kinds of movement using the two shorter traversals. In most cases the difference was still obvious with the longer distance.

When the angular velocity was increased to the vicinity of 20°/sec., accurate judgment was not possible between the two kinds of movement for the small and medium distances. Identification was possible but very difficult when the greater distance was employed. When the velocity was pushed beyond 21°/sec. it again became more easy to identify the two movements more accurately.

De Silva also determined the influence of exposure time and light intensity on the quality of apparent movement. He found that when exposure was made very short (10 ms.) the moving line was less bright and more jerky than with longer exposures. When the exposure time was very long (200 to 500 ms.) what he calls intramembral movement was absent. When the bars were made as bright as they could be with the apparatus used, with exposures of 200-500 ms., they appeared flashy and spread beyond their sharp original boundaries, and the interspace was somewhat luminous. Under these conditions, the movement was more compulsory. Extreme decrease in intensity resulted in more marked intramembral movement, without improvement in the seeing of the bar definitely during the middle stage of its movement from the one position to the other. This is called "carry-over" and is the opposite of the case where part of the movement is inferred.

When the intensity of the bars used for real movement was made higher than for apparent movement, distinction between them was improved. When the illumination conditions were changed in the opposite direction, the distinction between the two kinds of movement was reduced below the usual accuracy prevailing when the intensities were equal.

Prolonging the exposure of the first bar is more effective in reducing the "carry-over" of the movement than the lengthening of the exposure of the second bar, though little effect upon accuracy of judgment was made by either alteration.

**Velocity, apparent movement, and fusion.** Experiments may be so arranged as to give rise to a variety of phenomena, such as real movement, apparent movement, and fusion such as occurs in flicker experiments, by the simple manipulation of a single stimulus factor, the linear velocity of a series of objects in a limited field. That is to say, the subjective qualities of a body in actual motion vary considerably as velocity is varied. As a consequence, there are several relatively distinct stages which can be segregated. Movement of an object may be so slow that its existence is only deduced from successive observations of its position relative to other objects in the field. If physical velocity is increased, suddenly the object can be directly apprehended as moving. As physical velocity is greatly increased, this stage is succeeded by one in which the object is still recognized, though its appearance is markedly changed. This stage is followed by terminal conditions producing only a streak in the visual field.

The following illustration will serve to make clear what is to be expected as physical velocity is increased. The apparatus consists in an aperture 15 cm. long and 5 cm. wide, exposing black squares 1.6 cm. spaced at 20 cm. intervals on a moving band of white paper which is lighted from behind. Since the room itself is dark, the 15 x 5 cm. rectangle is the total illuminated field. A black thread with a central knot horizontally bisects the rectangle, the knot being the fixation point for the observer 2 meters away. When the velocity of the objects is varied from zero to 200 cm/sec., the following stages can be noted:

(1) No subjective movement. Movement is deduced from successive observations of position of the square within the rectangular field.

(2) Square seen in motion when in certain parts of the field but not in others.

(3) Slow movement when in all parts of the field.

(4) Subjective velocity increases as physical velocity is increased up to a certain limit.

(5) Subjectively the object moves up and down between the top and bottom edges of the aperture defining the field.

(6) Two squares replace the one square subjectively and move up and down as in (5).

(7) A streak with intermittent darker sections begins to replace the last phenomenon.

(8) The final stage, consisting in a smooth gray line.

The onsets of stages 3, 5, 6, and 7 represent thresholds which have been measured by Brown, the results comparing favorably with the calculations based on the working hypothesis that those factors which influence subjective velocity also affect the thresholds for motion similarly and to the same extent. *Stages 5 and 6 represent apparent movement.*

It is concluded that each of the movement thresholds is absolute in the subjective scale, though all vary greatly in the physical scale. Experiment also indicates the differential threshold for velocity is dependent upon phenomenal rather than physical velocities.

Brown points out that when a physiological theory of seen movement appears it must explain both real and apparent movement, phenomenal velocity, the lower threshold for movement, the subjective increase in the number of moving objects, the threshold for fusion, and the impression of duration produced by watching objects in motion. This means that a really satisfactory theory of any one of these phenomena will account for the others.

De Silva, in measurements of angular velocities of real movement, reports the following. In the neighborhood of $3°$/sec. the object has distinct contour, by the time $10°$/sec. are reached, the outlines become slightly blurry. In the range from $14\text{-}21°$/sec., the object acquires a luminous tail or after-glow. As velocity is increased from $21\text{-}58°$/sec., the tail becomes a sheet of light, unrolling at the beginning of the object's excursion and rolling up at its termination. When velocity is increased from $58\text{-}116°$/sec. the sheet fills the whole excursion. It is somewhat vibratory and its surface gives the impression of moving in the direction the actual stimulus moves. Above $116°$/sec. the sheet becomes stationary in all respects.

It is interesting to note that the velocity range in which actual and apparent movements are most difficult to distinguish is the one in which the moving object possesses the tail or after-glow. That is to say, when actual movement is rapid enough to begin to leave definite retinal after-effects it is more nearly similar to apparent movement where separated retinal stimuli are seen as a unitary succession. The temporal conditions for connecting separate areas have reached their best. When actual movement is made faster than this it can either be distinguished by rate alone or on account of the fact that tendency toward stationary simultaneity arises in apparent movement.

**Eye movements.** There has been a tendency on the part of many to utilize eye movements as a partial or sufficient explanation for many visual phenomena. Apparent movement has been placed in this category by some. As early as 1886, Fischer proposed an eye-movement theory for stroboscopic movement. Lately eye movements were used again to account for many of the observed phenomena appearing in apparent movement experiments.

A number of reasons were given to support the eye-movement theory among which are that the observers report ocular movement; that there is dual movement such as we have already described; that intermediate members subjectively appear between the two commonly observed terminal ones; and that in some cases there is movement decidedly beyond the second of two members. Still other reasons have been advanced, the applicability of which is difficult to make obvious.

Guilford and Helson, in order to put an end to needless speculation and error, investigated the possible connection between eye movements and the perception of apparent movement. This they did by photographing the eye when confronted with conditions producing apparent movement. *They found no correlation whatsoever between the two.* In fact, their conclusions went even beyond this; namely, that *eye movements interfere with good subjective movement from successive stationary stimulation.* On the basis of the implications involved in the study of the role of the retinal illumination, this would be expected. Many of the more common forms of apparent movement are dependent upon the illumination reaching the eye from stationary objects having such timing as to cause moving gradients of light across the retina. If eye movements happen to be injected into such situations they are more than likely to interfere with the proper sequence of events.

**Retinal factors in apparent movement.** This section is intended to picture in a simple manner the retinal factors in the apprehension of at least some forms of apparent movement. Not all forms are similarly dependent, but it is profitable to consider what retinal factors there may be. In light of the prevalent disregard of entoptic stray light in visual investigation, its role cannot easily be overemphasized in apparent movement studies. It is to be admitted that most of the neural details of retinal function are as yet obscure, but it is at the same time true that we have not made the easier steps we might have, namely, in determining just how retinal illumination behaves in apparent movement situations. (See Figure 38.)

The understanding of apparent movement must begin with the realization that many critical factors in the production of most of its forms are retinal. We have already indicated in some cases that retinal areas must be stimulated in sequence to produce it. The required succession is dependent upon four factors. The most obvious one is the serial presentation of stationary stimuli in different parts of the visual field. The next factor is the differential in the reaction speeds of various areas of the eye. The cones, or cone pathways, are credited with being faster than the rods and their connections, thus the latency of most of the elements at or near the fovea is shorter than those lying toward the periphery. The third factor is that elements strongly stimulated react sooner than those weakly stimulated. Thus if it happens that more intense light falls on one part of the retina than another, sensation dependent upon it would tend to result first. The fourth factor is scattered light in the eye which produces a broad differential in retinal illumination.

The last three factors provide the basis for gamma movement occurring under a wide variety of conditions. If a bright spot is suddenly presented on a dark field these factors operate to cause a centrifugal movement in the visual field. If the spot happens to be fixated, the movement is roughly equal in all directions. If it appears toward the periphery of the field the movement is not symmetrical. The expansive movement tends to be accented in a peripheral direction, which indicates that the center-periphery latency gradient is dominant over the gradient formed by the illumination of the spot and its surround.

If two bright spots equally distant from the fixation point suddenly appear on a dark background the gamma movement will, as in other cases, progress outward from the brightest illumination. In this situation, however, the center-periphery gradient tends to become dominant, so that the fixation point is the center from which field expansive movements originate. Only a slight movement can be detected as originating from the two spots and progressing to the fixation point.

Since in most cases the center-periphery gradient is dominant and the gamma movement in the field progresses outward from the fixation point, it might be thought that gamma movement in that direction is compulsory. Gamma movement progresses in this direction even when the whole visual field is suddenly uniformly illuminated. Nevertheless, a simple experiment will show that gamma movement can be reversed so as to progress from the periphery toward the fixation point when the field is suddenly illuminated. The necessary conditions for this is a field whose periphery is more intensely illuminated than its center. A light source providing a large field, such as an opal glass screen covered by a filter which has been made more nearly opaque at the center, produces the desired result and demonstrates that the usual outward direction of gamma movement is a function of the illumination gradient of the retina. A stimulus area which covers most of the visual field must be used, or else the pattern will simply form the center of outward movement from it to the field's periphery.

How the retina behaves in optimal beta movement is reserved for the chapter on contour for questions concerning contours are paramount.

**The path of visual movement as a function of the vector-field.** Thus far the discussion of movement has confined itself to presentation of experimental details gained under the simple attempt to correlate stimulus conditions and sensory outcome, and to point out that the actual though unrecognized illumination patterns of the retina in conjunction with other retinal factors are the original basis for seeing movement.

This section introduces an entirely different concept in the study of perception. As a predictive concept it undoubtedly has value. As one which is connected with any neural or other physiological details it is as yet negative. The possibility of translating its terms into physiology may nevertheless be inherent in it, thus it deserves serious attention. The question arises as to whether in the future, physiology will become modified to fit into some sort of a dynamic scheme such as the present exemplifies, or whether it will become translatable into the details of nerve physiology of the current type. Herein lies one of the major considerations in all the study of behavior.

Brown and Voth recently set up a vector-field hypothesis regarding the path of seen movement which they were able to verify experimentally. They began by regarding the visual field as a spatial construct within which visual experience may be

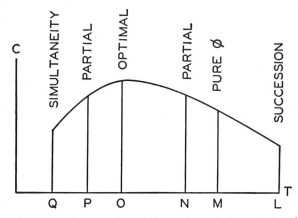

FIG. 41.—Diagram showing the relative values of the cohesive field-forces for different values of T, when intensity and spatial separation are held constant. The ordinate indicates the cohesive field-force values while the abscissa indicates time. (*Brown and Voth.—Am. J. Psych.* 49:545. 1937.)

ordered. They recognized that values within its structure have direction as well as magnitude, hence are vectors. They assumed field forces which they divided into two classes, cohesive forces and restraining forces. The former tend to make all the objects in the visual field come together, but since objects show stability there must also be restraining forces which oppose the cohesive forces. Both of them are functions of distributions of time, space, and intensity in the visual field, and consequently can be manipulated by altering these factors.

Brown and Voth in developing their theory further utilize the work of Wertheimer in which he gives reason to believe that the cohesive vectors between objects increase as the time-interval between their presentations is shortened to the stage of optimal movement where they become maximum. With further shortening of the time-interval the value of the cohesive forces decreases, becoming equal to the restraining forces when the objects are seen simultaneously.

For their experimental set-up, they chose four points of light arranged as the corners of a square and presented successively. The spacing and timing of the points could be so arranged that they were not only seen as individual points but at other times as a single point moving in a circle. With other time-and-space values, they could be seen as moving part way along the sides of a square, or they could be seen as one point moving completely around a square. That is, they gave optimal movement along the sides of a square, optimal movement with some circularity, as well as good circularity. At other times all of the points could be seen simultaneously and stationary.

That their theory predicted these paths can be seen from the following. Let the four points be labeled A, B, C, and D, and the cohesive vectors between them be AB, AC, AD, BC, BA, BD, etc., the directions of which are from the first to the second letters in each case. When all of the points are presented simultaneously there is no movement and the restraining forces

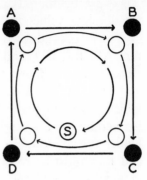

Fig. 42.—A diagram to represent the behavior of four discs of light forming the corners of a square and being presented serially from A to D. When the time intervals between the separate discs are long, the discs are seen as stationary objects appearing one after the other. If the time intervals are shortened there is movement of A toward B and B toward C, etc., in straight lines. As the intervals are further shortened the lines become curved and the location of each disc is moved inward as illustrated by the open circles in the diagram. Under optimal conditions the observer sees a single moving spot describing a circle as is shown by S and the arrows.

are equal and opposite to the cohesive, but this may be changed by presenting the points in succession. The cohesive values will then depend upon the time-intervals between the presentations of the successive individual points, $T_{ab}$, $T_{bc}$, etc., and likewise the intervals between the presentation of the first and third points, and between the first and fourth points, $T_{ac}$ and $T_{ac}$. Thus $T_{ad}$ is greater than $T_{ac}$, and $T_{ac}$ is greater than $T_{ab}$ regardless of the absolute values.

When $T_{ab}$ is adjusted for optimal apparent movement, the vectors AB, BC, CD, and DA will be great as compared to AC, BD, CA, and DB, and even greater as compared to AD, BA, CB, and DC. If $T_{ab}$ is sufficiently decreased, a point is reached at which AB will equal AC due to the fact that the cohesive forces for certain very short intervals are equal to certain long ones. Under such conditions, AC, BD, etc., can no longer be ignored, and they must be considered at the same time as AB, BC, etc., in terms of a resultant. For a succession of instants, $t_1$, $t_2$, $t_3$, etc., the integration of the path of movement will be a circle for at successive temporal instants the vector complex at subsequent points of the field must be considered.

Detailed consideration of the theory would show that it predicts that progressive decrease in the time-intervals between the appearance of the points which first mark the corners of a square will produce the perception of movement along the sides of the square, first in straight lines, then in curves, and finally in continuous movement in the form of a circle. In the last case it will follow a path of minimal length.

Brown and Voth's experiments verified their predictions in every way. In them, they were able to transpose the size-relations and the velocity-relations in keeping with the previous findings of Brown, which we have already discussed, and retain the movement paths once set up.

These investigators suggest that the cohesive forces are largely centrally conditioned and that the restraining forces are largely the role of the retina. This is possible, but such an assumption supposes that the retina is unable to act differentially on the basis of temporal differences in stimulation. It implies that regardless of the values of $T_{ab}$, etc., the retinal points stimulated are the same, and the retinal output must be the same with respect to the spatial attributes it conveys.  This need not be the case at all, and we have no reason to believe that this fluid type of organization is reserved for the brain.  No one is yet in position to deny to the retina any basic kind of activity attributed to the brain.

## REFERENCES

Bartley, S. Howard.  Relation of entoptic stray light to flicker and the perception of movement. *Proc. Soc. Exptl. Biol. & Med.,* 1935, 32:1180-1181.

Bartley, S. Howard.  The relation of retinal illumination to the experience of movement. *J. Exptl. Psych.,* 1936, 19:475-485.

Brown, J. F.  The visual perception of velocity. *Psych. Forsch.,* 1931, 14:199-232.

Brown, J. F.  On time perception in visual movement fields. *Psych. Forsch.,* 1931, 14:233-268.

Brown, J. F.  The dynamics of visual speed, time, and space: A reply to Cartwright, Koehler, Wallach. *J. Psych.,* 1939, 8:237-246.

Brown, J. F., and Robert H. Mize.  On the effect of field structure on the duration of the movement after-image. *Psych. Forsch.,* 1932, 16:171-175.

Brown, J. F., and Robert H. Mize.  On the effect of field structure on differential sensitivity. *Psych. Forsch.,* 1932, 16:355-372.

Brown, J. F., and A. C. Voth.  The path of seen movement as a function of the vector-field. *Am. J. Psych.,* 1937, 49:543-563.

De Silva, Harry R.  An experimental investigation of the determinants of apparent visual movement. *Am. J. Psych.,* 1926, 37:469-501.

De Silva, H. R.  Kinematographic movement of parallel lines. *J. Gen. Psych.,* 1928, 1:550-577.

De Silva, H. R.  An analysis of the visual perception of movement. *Brit. J. Psych.,* 1929, 19:268-305.

Guilford, J. P.  Ocular movements and the perception of time. *J. Exptl. Psych.,* 1929, 12:259-266.

Guilford, J. P.  Autokinesis and the streaming phenomenon. *Am. J. Psych.,* 1928, 40:401-417.

Guilford, J. P., and K. M. Dallenbach.  A study of the autokinetic sensation. *Am. J. Psych.,* 1928, 40:83-91.

Guilford, J. P., and Harry Helson.  Eye-movement and the phi-phenomenon. *Am. J. Psych.,* 1929, 51:595-606.

Higginson, Glenn D.  Apparent visual movement and the Gestalt.  I. Nine observations which stand against Wertheimer's cortical theory. *J. Exptl. Psych.*, 1926, 9:228-252.

Kennedy, John L.  The nature and physiological basis of visual movement discrimination in animals. *Psych. Rev.*, 1936, 43:494-521.

Neff, Walter S.  A critical investigation of the visual apprehension of movement. *Am. J. Psych.*, 1936, 48:1-42.

# VIII

# ADAPTATION PHENOMENA

## GENERAL STUDIES

**Vision under extreme ranges in illumination.** The eye functions under such a wide range of intensities that long ago a special mechanism of adaptation was attributed to it. The process which adjusts the eye for seeing in low illuminations is dark adaptation. Such vision is called scotopic. The opposite process is light adaptation, providing for photopic vision. The intensity of sunlight is in the neighborhood of four or five million times as bright as that of moonlight. Nevertheless under dark adaptation the eye is sensitive enough to distinguish the contours of objects in moonlight. Sunlight and moonlight, however, represent extremes and not the conditions under which the most efficient vision occurs. A moderate illumination of about 100 foot-candles, which is only about one-thousandth as intense as bright summer sunlight, is best.

The mechanism of adjustment to illumination consists not only in the "adaptation" about to be described, but also in the regulation of the size of the pupil, so that under the dimmer illuminations its diameter is about four times as great as under intense illumination. The maximum dilation allows the passage of sixteen times as much energy as the maximum constriction, a factor small compared to the great range of intensities to which the eye is subjected. The change of pupil size, however, accomplishes other ends.

Visual adaptation means one of two things, the improvement in ability to see, following shifts in general illumination, or the reduction in the ability to see during prolonged fixation. An

example of the latter is the supposed reduction in the saturation
of a color after steady fixation, or other uniform conditions.

Cases of the former type of adaptation most commonly encountered are recovery from glare of facing automobile head-
lights, and the progressive ability to see in semi-darkness, as when
entering a motion picture theater from the outdoor sunlight.
Appreciable amounts of time are required for these adjustments
to progress even to a practical degree. But when their entire
course is measured they are found to necessitate many minutes
or even several hours. These are examples of dark adaptation.
Light adaptation also occurs when the shift in the illumination
is in the opposite direction. It, however, is much more rapid.

According to the broad definition, adaptation is the *improvement* in vision consequent upon shifts in illumination levels.
Adaptation may be also considered from the standpoint of *levels,*
or states as well as a progression. In this respect it can be measured by excellence of function at any given illumination level.
Adaptation so considered is only light or dark adaptation on the
basis of the illumination level used.

Dark adaptation was first definitely described by Aubert in
1865, and first measured by Piper in 1903. Nowadays we have a
fairly good idea of its rate and extent. The most remarkable
thing about it is its extent, since it covers a sensitivity range of
100,000 to 1. Perhaps no other sense adjustment is able anywhere
nearly to approach that figure.

**The common means of measurement.** The usual procedure in
measuring dark adaptation is to put the eye into total darkness
following exposure to a given level of illumination. Hecht and
Mandelbaum suggest for general purposes a field of about 35
degrees visual angle having a brightness of about 1,500 ml. and
viewed for 3 minutes. The test-object best covers a visual angle
of about 3 degrees in order that it be located on a relatively uniform part of the retina and still be not too small to be readily
seen by the average observer.

Adaptation is generally thought of in terms of the eye-as-a-
whole and in the common tests the maximum homogeneity of

field is used. Notwithstanding, it will be found that certain local differences in adaptation do occur throughout the retina.

The chapter on the retina has already shown that the human retina is not by any means a homogeneously acting surface. It

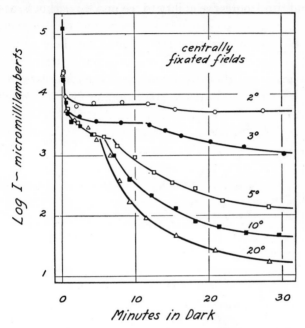

FIG. 43.—Curves showing the threshold during the course of dark adaptation for test-objects of various sizes whose centers were fixated. The early and late portions of the curves are separated by a short gap, since it is unknown whether the transition from one to the other is abrupt or rounded; the investigators think it is probably rounded. (*Hecht, Haig and Wald.—J. Gen. Physiol.*)

is populated with reciprocal densities of two kinds of sense-cells from center to periphery and their neural interconnections also vary along a gradient in the same direction. Differences in adaptation are manifest in terms of this histological differentiation.

Dark adaptation, or the lowered threshold shown by the eye kept in darkness, progresses in two stages. The first is rapid, short and relatively slight. The second is slow, prolonged and large.  The first period, expressed by the first section of the curve, covers 6 to 11 minutes.

In central visual fields, the two stages of adaptation change differently with area.  With small foveal areas, the first stage dominates and only traces of the second appear.  As the area

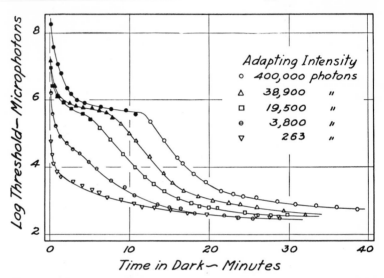

F<small>IG</small>. 44.—Dark adaptation determined with violet light following preadaptation to various levels of light. The solid symbols represent the fact that the observer saw the violet color at the threshold, whereas the outlined symbols indicate a colorless threshold. (*Hecht, Haig and Chase—J. Gen. Physiol.*)

increases the first stage changes a little, while the second extends over an increasing range of intensities and appears sooner in time.

Hecht, Haig and Wald state that measurements with an annulus test-object involving only the circumference of a 20° circle show most of the properties of a 20° whole circle centrally located.  Likewise a 2° field placed at different distances from the center manifests dark adaptation properties essentially like those of large centrally located fields whose edges correspond to the same position on the retina.

Dark adaptation of centrally located fields of different size is determined for the most part not by area as such but by the fact that the retina progressively changes in sensitivity from center to periphery, and consequently the larger the field, the farther it reaches into peripheral regions of greater sensitivity.

In the human eye, Hecht, Haig and Chase find the course of dark adaptation varies with the intensity of the light used for preadaptation. Preadaptation to intensities below 200 photons is followed only by rod adaptation, whereas preadaptation to 4000 photons or more is followed first by cone and thereafter by rod adaptation.

With increasing levels of preadaptation, cone dark adaptation remains essentially the same in form, but covers an extending range. The highest preadaptation sets the stage for more than 3 log units of threshold intensities.

Rod dark adaptation is of two types, a rapid and a delayed. The rapid rod dark adaptation appears after preadaptations to intensities within the range of rod function. The delayed rod dark adaptation appears only after preadaptation to intensities hundreds of times higher than those producing the greatest rod function in such situations as flicker and intensity discrimination, and in visual resolution. Such adaptation remains essentially· constant in shape after different intensities of preadaptation, though its manifestation is delayed accordingly, and after the highest intensity emerges only after 12 or 13 min. of darkness.

**Study of adaptation by the flicker method.** The work of Lythgoe and Tansley in which they studied c.f.f. in connection with different states of adaptation and different parts of the retina can equally well be examined from the standpoint of adaptation, critical flicker frequency, or of retinal gradients.

We have chosen the first alternative. If c.f.f. is thought of as expressing retinal excitation it can be used as an index by which to judge adaptation. These investigators felt it satisfied the needs of the case better than any of the other measures which have been commonly used. In justifying it, they listed the qualities necessary for a suitable method.

It should be accurate as judged by its reproducibility, alterations in adaptation should induce large changes in the observations made, the method should be usable on both the central and peripheral retina, and it should be sensitive to changes in the illumination of the test-patch itself. They believe that tests of visual acuity satisfy none of these criteria, and that the discrimination of contour is only a little better due to the fact that it is more nearly reproducible. Measures of the absolute threshold are variable and at the same time give information only at the level of the general illumination itself. Differential thresholds of brightness are poor in the more peripheral parts of the retina and the influence of the brightness of the field surrounding the test-object on them is not large. The study of adaptation by the flicker method seems to have none of the disadvantages to so great a degree.

For their study they chose a preadapting illumination of 7.2 footcandles (f.c.) cast upon the walls of a cubicle within which the observer sat. At the end of 15 min. the light was withdrawn and dark adaptation was begun. Four different retinal locations were studied in this way, 0°, 10°, 50°, and 90° during the course of 60 minutes, by rotating the readings of c.f.f. of a test-patch illuminated at a level of 6.8 f.c. The foveal c.f.f. fell from 36 to 31.5 flashes per second; the 10° region from 39 to 25; the 50° region, from 35.6 to 21.5; and the 90° region, from 26.5 to 20.5. It is evident that the peripheral c.f.f.'s, excepting that of the 90° region, fell much more rapidly and much farther during the course of dark adaptation.

When the test-patch was illuminated by only 0.25 f.c. the results were somewhat different. The foveal region fell more rapidly at first than it did under higher illuminations. The c.f.f. to begin with was about 25.6 flashes per second, and in 10 minutes was down to about 21.6, at the end of the hour to 21. The c.f.f. curves for the 10° and 50° regions also behaved differently than they did with higher illuminations. They first fell very rapidly to a minimum at about 7 or 8 minutes from which they rose again to a value almost half way to the original. The curve for the 90° region remained on a level for the first few moments and then rose rather steadily during the whole hour.

A still more feebly illuminated test-patch was used, in which case the curve for the fovea changed very little during the hour, the main shift being in the downward direction. Both the 10°

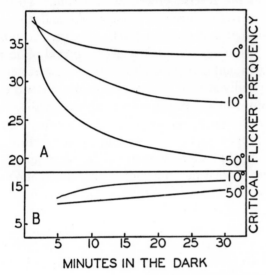

FIG. 45.—Two sets of curves showing critical flicker frequency in relation to degree of dark adaptation for various distances from the fovea, after a preadaptation period under moderate illumination. The curves show the approximate, though not the literal, results obtained by Lythgoe and Tansley. The upper curves represent the outcome with a moderately bright test-object while the lower ones are for a test-object illumination below the cone level.

and the 50° curves rose. Finally a fourth illumination of the test-patch which was too feeble for foveal use induced a rise in all three of the peripheral c.f.f. curves. This ended the samplings for c.f.f. during the course of dark adaptation.

For the completely dark adapted eye, the curves for the fovea and the 10° and 50° regions all show a positive relation with the intensity of the test-patch. The minimum c.f.f. for each is about the same; namely, about 7 or 7.5 flashes per second. The curve for the fovea does not begin until the test-patch reaches a value of .001 f.c. It ascends more rapidly than the other two and crosses them, reaching about 36 flashes per second as compared to about 21 for the 50° region.

After obtaining the c.f.f. for each of the conditions during the course of dark adaptation and with complete dark adaptation, readings on the reverse process were begun. To do this, the observer was rested in the dark for 5 min. and then the cubicle was illuminated at a constant level of 7.2 f.c. and the test-patch at 6.8 f.c. Readings were taken over a period of 12 to 15 min. For the fovea and each of the three peripheral regions, the c.f.f. rose very rapidly at first. For the fovea the rise was complete in about 4 min. whereas it was only completed at the end of about 6 or 7 min. in the periphery. The curves either remained at a level or dropped slightly, depending upon whether a rest was taken during the latter moments of the experiment.

They also studied the influence of the illumination of the surrounding field on the c.f.f. of the test-patch. Such readings taken alone might be considered to indicate the effects of brightness contrast or what is often called spatial induction, but the experiments taken as a whole show the effects of the general level of illumination on the activity of a given region and thus are indications of the influence of adaptation upon such activity.

The procedure consisted in resting the eye in complete darkness for 5 to 25 min. and then illuminating the cubicle for 5 min. at the level to be used for the observation. The lowest level was used first and was followed by the progressively higher levels of the cubicle intensities. Readings were taken for the fovea and the three peripheral regions in rotation. The surrounds were never illuminated at a higher intensity than the test-patch.

For the fovea, the highest c.f.f. was always obtained when the test-patch and the surrounds were equally bright and the c.f.f. became progressively lower as the surrounds were made dimmer and dimmer. This was not true for the three peripheral regions. In each of them when the test-patch illumination was low, the curves representing the c.f.f's for the different intensities of surround crossed each other. Though, in the fovea, the uppermost curve was the one representing equal brightness of the test-patch and surround, and the curves for the lower surround brightnesses branched off from it along its course, some of the curves representing these same intensities for peripheral regions crossed this curve. That is to say, the curves representing the dimmer surround illuminations lay above it when representing the three peripheral regions. Nevertheless the curves for the peripheral regions were quite like those for the fovea when they represented surround illuminations more nearly approaching the level of the test-patch. The shift of the peripheral curves from similarity to those of the fovea was progressively greater as the distance from the fovea was increased.

Lythgoe and Tansley drew attention to several features in connection with the fall in c.f.f. at the fovea, aside from the absence of rods, which indicate that the dark adaptation manifested there is that of cones. Similar results are obtained with a red test-patch in both the fovea and periphery and the peripheral readings are quite different than those obtained with white light. Neither the magnitude nor the rate of fall of c.f.f. is great the first 10 min. in the dark. And finally the changes in c.f.f. at the fovea are never like the reactions obtained in the periphery at low illuminations where we expect the responses to be those of the rods.

In contrast to this, when using low illumination and a peripheral test-patch the longer the dark adaptation or the less the light adaptation the greater is the c.f.f. This must be a rod response for it is obtained only at low illuminations of the test-patch and is absent with red light and at the fovea. It becomes more and more marked in its characteristics as the extreme periphery is reached. Moreover, c.f.f. continues to rise for a very long time when a weak test-patch illumination is used.

The fact that c.f.f. is sometimes higher in the periphery than at the fovea brings up the question of whether the result is due to the rods or cones. The strongest reason for believing that these high c.f.f.'s are brought about by cone function is that they occur at high illuminations; and under such conditions, the same general responses are found at the fovea. For example, with bright surrounds a decline in the level of the test-patch reduces c.f.f. about the same amount everywhere in the eye. Raising the level of the surround increases c.f.f. for all regions. The same result is also obtained when using red light of relatively low intensity which is considered incapable of stimulating rods. Lythgoe and Tansley also point out that the spectral luminosity curve for the light-adapted retina has the same contour for all parts of the eye and for high intensities is undisturbed by the Purkinje effect, a rod phenomenon.

They believe that to explain a number of the complications found in their adaptation curves, the idea that the eye as a whole manifests the higher of two concurrent responses, those of the rods or cones, is the simplest of the various possibilities, notwithstanding the precise explanation is probably much more intricate since for a given retinal region in which the rods have one c.f.f. and the cones a much higher one, the resulting c.f.f. might either exceed or fall below it.

They also present reasons against the idea that the eye as a whole responds in terms of the maximum c.f.f. of its individual elements. In cases utilizing higher illumination and constant intensities of test-patch, the decline of c.f.f. with decreasing light adaptation is more rapid farther and farther from the fovea, at least up to 50°. When the intensity of the surround and the test-patch are equal, the decline of c.f.f. with decreasing illuminations is also faster at 50°. They believe that to explain such an outcome one must either suppose that the cones become "more cone-like" towards the periphery or else that as it is approached, the rods play a more active role in lowering the c.f.f. which would result from the cones alone. Also when the test-patch is red, the decline in c.f.f. with decreasing light adaptation is less rapid than for white light making it seem as if the rods when activated can reduce the cone reaction in the periphery.

The general summary of Lythgoe and Tansley's findings is as follows. *The c.f.f. of the cones declines during dark adaptation and with progressively lower levels of light adaptation. It is greatest when the test-patch and its surrounds are equally bright. Certain reactions make it seem as though the peripheral and foveal cones are not functionally the same. The level of the surrounds is the strongest factor determining whether the c.f.f. is of the rod or cone type. At moderate illumination of the test-patch and surrounds, c.f.f. seems to be due to both rods and cones.*

**Local adaptation.** Granit and von Ammon assuming c.f.f. to be an index of subjective brightness also used the flicker method to study adaptation. In their experiments they used a test-patch of 2° for the foveal region, and a 2.5° patch at various points toward the periphery. Their criterion of adaptation was the fall of c.f.f. during the first 6 seconds.

With the test-patches in the fovea, little or no local adaptation is evidenced during the period used, but in passing toward the periphery the effect begins to materialize. Beyond 4°, there is a relatively large drop in c.f.f. during the first 3 sec. and the rate of drop is greater the higher the intensity.

It was deduced that the rate of local adaptation is mainly a function of the activity per receptor-unit, rather than of total activity enhanced by the process of summation in the retinal synapses. The conclusion was based on the following. The total activity in the synaptic layers increases with the number of elements activated through the existence of the greater number of interconnections, making the curve relating log intensity to c.f.f. assume a steeper slope for large areas than for small.

In one case, both a large (4°) and a small (1°) area were used, and the drop in c.f.f. plotted for three conditions, the large area (A) and the small area (B) at a high intensity (94 m.c.) and the large area at a low intensity (C) which gave the same original c.f.f. as the small area at high intensity. It resulted that the c.f.f. of A dropped more than that of C during the test period, signifying that the stronger stimulus gives the greater adaptation. Granit and von Ammon showed that the patch with the larger amount of total energy did not adapt faster than the other one. That is, the drop in the c.f.f. of A was not greater than B, but happened to be even smaller. Consequently there was no spatial compensation in terms of adaptation for the lack of intensity C. As adaptation was not accelerated by an increase in total activity as propagated along interaction paths in the synaptic layers beyond the sense-cells, it must have been determined by the sense-cell itself.

### STUDIES REVEALING NEUROLOGICAL ADAPTATION

**Neural factors in adaptation now recognized.** Except for the last one, the studies which have just been described, while outlining the more outstanding features, do not indicate the source of adaptation. They merely show that the rods and cones act differently. Thus most of the results do not distinguish whether the photochemistry or the synaptic layers of the retina are at bottom. The following studies, however, make it certain that all visual adaptation is not photochemical, as has for sometime been taken for granted. In clearly revealing this misconception, they are very important and initiate a new stage in our view of visual adaptation. But on the other hand, it is to be recognized that these changes which have to do with the organizational factor in nerve physiology may later be given some other name.

**Monocular vs. binocular adaptation.** The effect of binocular preadaptation upon monocular vision is more prolonged than it is upon binocular vision and less prolonged than the effect of monocular preadaptation upon monocular vision. This, like any other function which differs when two eyes are used instead of one, may be said to depend in part for its critical determination upon the central nervous system beyond the chiasm. This experiment is therefore one of the several which demonstrate that light and dark adaptations are not wholly determined by the eye and therefore cannot be exclusively matters of photo-chemistry of the sense-cells as has been commonly supposed. Elsberg and Spotnitz show that the findings can be accounted for if it is assumed that, in monocular vision, the visual centers of the brain require a greater contribution from the single eye than from either of the two eyes when used together.

To give more detail to the principle, the relations are illustrated by use of hypothetical values. Let the requirement upon the retina for a threshold test-object seen by the one eye be a value of 5 units, exposed for 1 sec., and likewise the requirement upon each retina in binocular vision be 3 units for 0.6 sec. If the effect of the preadaptation of one eye to a bright light be given a value of 15 units and the effect of the exposure of each of two eyes to 9 units, and if it be supposed that recovery after both monocular and binocular preadaptation occurs at a constant rate of 4 units per sec., the following will be the outcome.

In monocular vision after monocular preadaptation, 3.75 ($^{15}\!/_4$) sec. will elapse before the restoration of equilibrium. In addition to this, the predicated 5 units of function, or 1 sec. of time, must elapse before the test-object can be seen. In other words, it will require 4.75 sec.

For monocular vision after binocular preadaptation, 2.5 sec. will be required for restored equilibrium with an additional second for reaching threshold. That is, 3.5 sec. will be required.

For binocular vision after binocular preadaptation 2.5 sec. will be required to restore equilibrium and 0.6 sec. to reach threshold. In this case the total will be 3.1 sec. during which the test-object will be invisible. These are only hypothetical values, but they follow the results of Elsberg and Spotnitz's actual experiments.

**Sources of influence modifying adaptation of retinal areas.** Adaptation as it has been discussed thus far has, with one exception, either concerned the eye-as-a-whole, or else local portions as affected by conditions existing in those regions. This being the case there was no actual study of how one part of the retina might affect the other. We turn now to investigating adaptation in limited parts of the retina, the fovea, for example, in which case the possibility of other parts of the retina influencing it will be taken into consideration. Six sources of possible modification have been pointed out by Schouten and Ornstein. They are presented in rearranged order, as follows: (1) Illumination of the whole fundus by the image of a glare source such as is used in certain experiments yet to be described; (2) illumination of the fundus by light passing through the sclerotic coat of the eye; (3) change in the sensitivity of the part of the eye which is being investigated (fovea) by the part of the retina containing a glare source. This would presumably be some sort of a neural effect, such as transmitted by the lateral cells; (4) change in the sensitivity of the part being studied by the part of the retina through which the sclerotic light is passing. The nature of effect would presumably be the same as (3); (5) diffraction and scattering in the entoptic media. This would include reflection from the image of the test-object, the light modifying other parts of the retina which in turn might have the influence as suggested in (3) and (4); (6) change in the sensitivity of the part studied by the stray light within the eye which happens to fall directly on it.

This provides for two possible kinds of adaptation, *direct* and *indirect,* the distinction being on the basis of whether the change is produced by light falling on the region tested or falling elsewhere. Source 6 would produce direct adaptation; 1, 2, and 5 would produce direct and possibly a slight amount of indirect; and sources 3 and 4 would produce indirect adaptation.

**Indirect adaptation.** Indirect adaptation may be measured by an arrangement in which two identical test-objects (discs of light) against a dark background are so screened that each of them is seen by one eye alone. An experimentally produced difference in sensitivity of the two eyes will be manifested by a difference in their subjective brightness. By manipulating the physical intensity of one of them, a subjective match in brightness can be achieved. The difference in the physical intensity of the two will be a quantitative measure of the sensitivity difference. When the difference produced is a matter of adaptation then the method is a quantitative way of investigating adaptation itself.

Schouten and Ornstein used this technique for matching two test-objects when one of them was altered in subjective brightness by the existence of a glare source in the peripheral field, which made it appear much darker than the comparison field. Following the termination of short exposures, the brightness quickly returned to its original state of equality with the comparison field. With longer exposures to the glare source, recovery took longer. With more than 5 min. exposure, a final maximally slow recovery requiring 5 min. occurred.

Let $I_1$ be the physical intensity of the test-object before, and $I_2$ during the exposure. We can then call $S = I_1/I_2$ the *relative sensitivity* of the exposed eye. For some purposes the changes produced may be more conveniently expressed by the relative increase necessary for the two equatings. This quantity R will be called the *glare index*. ($R = (I_2 - I_1)/I_1$ or $1/S - 1$). While S shifts from 1 to .04, R varies from 0 to 24.

S was found to be independent of intensity. This was also stated in von Kries' law of coefficients. Schouten and Ornstein found S to behave the same both for direct and indirect adaptation, and also to be independent of the size of the field used. Aside from a gradual fall (not more than 30% of S), no difference was found when S was ascertained at instants ranging from 4 to 600 sec. after onset of exposure, but the rate of recovery was found to be greatly dependent upon exposure time. The constancy of sensitivity during indirect adaptation is called the law of *constant level*.

**Alpha and beta adaptation.** Schouten and Ornstein distinguished two processes occurring under the influence of the glare source. These they named alpha adaptation and beta adaptation. The former reaches a fixed value within a fraction of a second, appearing as a sudden fall in the sensitivity of the entire retina upon the exposure of a small region, and likewise a quick return of former sensitivity after termination of brief exposures. On the other hand, the beta process reaches a fixed value only after 3 to 5 min. It appears as a progressive decline in the rate of recovery following longer exposure times, but does not become manifest in the sensitivity during exposure of the glare source.

**Nature of alpha adaptation.** In searching for a possible mechanism of this quick drop in sensitivity to a fixed level, two possibilities are confronted, one a transmission across the retina to the fovea of an effect produced at the glare source, the other a veil of light produced by the glare source and cast onto the fovea where it produces its effect directly.

A method of choosing between these alternatives has arisen out of a modification of the method used a few years ago by Schouten in which he employed light sent through the eyeball, comparing the result with diffuse illumination produced by light admitted through the pupil.

If light is thrown on the temporal part of the sclerotic the whole field of view with the exception of the shadows of the blood vessels is seen homogeneously illuminated. If light is thrown alternately on a point of the sclerotic and on diffusing glass immediately in front of the eye the two brightnesses which result may be matched by a photometric wedge.

In such experiments the brightness of the diascleral reillumination definitely drops during the first .1 sec., while the brightness of the other source does not. On this account a different match is obtained for the succession of glass to sclerotic than from sclerotic to glass. That is to say, comparisons require a different physical intensity for the diascleral illumination if judgments are made rapidly or after a little longer exposure, on account of the fall in the brightness of the diascleral source. The equatings could be made by shifting either from the direct to the diascleral light, or vice versa, the difference in the intensities needed for an equation in the two directions being a measure of adaptation.

The experiment was modified so as to proceed further with the distinction between the two possibilities as originally stated. This is made possible by the fact that not all of the light passing through the scleral walls of the eye pass through the retina. The retina ends at a point corresponding to a ring 8 mm. outward from the iris. Light falling on the sclera farther away from the iris than this will pass through it without passing through retinal tissue, and its effect can be compared with that of diasclerotic illumination passing through the retina. Measurements of the subjective results under these two conditions by matching with diffuse light entering through the lens show that the drop in subjective brightness is dependent upon retinal function and not upon some special adaptive effect of oblique illumination.

A control experiment in which the subjective effect of the two types of diascleral illumination were compared, led to the same conclusion. Again the transition from the first to the second type of illumination differed from the reverse transition, substantiating the idea that the lowered sensitivity originates in a part of the peripheral retina and travels toward the fovea.

So far only the influence of the rest of the eye on the fovea has been examined. Fixation elsewhere was also tried and by this method a system of glare indices was constructed, showing the value at each of a number of points in various directions from the fovea. It was found that all points equally distant from the fovea do not have the same glare index, and that the fovea is affected more by the surrounding retina than other regions are by the fovea. Areas remote from the fovea have more influence on each other than areas in or near it. Since the angle of incident illumination of the test-object is unchanged under various fixations, the situation provides another disproof of alpha adaptation being an expression of a special influence of oblique illumination.

**Measurement of adaptation during exposure.** As was already stated, the drop in sensitivity due to a glare source is too rapid to measure without some method of precise control. Such a method was used by Schouten and Ornstein. It consisted of a revolving disc having two open sectors unequally distant from the axis and separately adjustable. One of the openings exposed the glare source for durations ranging from 20 to 200 ms. and the other exposed the test-objects for 10 ms. following the glare. An interval between the cessation of glare to the one eye, and the exposure of the test-objects, precluded summation effects. The results showed that the sensitivity by the end of the first .1 sec. is as low as it ever will be. In fact it is slightly lower than it is at the end of 3 or 4 sec.

The different and simpler dependence of alpha adaptation on time in contrast to that of brightness perception would seem to show that the latter is not the determiner of the influence upon one area by its surrounds, but that such influence is determined prior to reaching that stage or by processes following an entirely different course.

**Velocity and pattern of adaptation.** For measuring the velocity of transmission of the alpha process across the retina, the two slits on the revolving disc were set at 10 ms. By varying the separation of the two slits on the disc, the time elapsing after the glare flash was controlled. By this the sensitivity of the fovea as a function of elapsed time was measured. The angular separation between test-object and the glare source was $10°$. This was compared with the results using a very strong flash on the sclerotic, so that any appreciable difference in time of transmission would appear as a temporal lag between the two curves obtained. It happened, however, that no difference was manifested between the curves. They both showed sensitivity to be minimum at about 50 ms. and back to its original level at the end of 150 ms. Transmission time is somewhere within the relative error made in obtaining the data for the two curves, which is about 20 ms.

Sensitivity was also measured as a function of the angle between test-object and glare source for various levels of test-object illumination. This was done by using the continuous method, since for longer exposures the time factor is immaterial. A family of curves, each for a separate illumination in which sensitivity drop is plotted against the glare angle, shows that the sensitivity drop decreases with increase in glare angle and increases with elevation of illumination.

The results suggested that the illumination of a region produces a depression of sensitivity close around it, rather than a uniform drop over the whole retina, the absolute level depending upon how far from the fovea it originated. The confirmation of their supposition was obtained by fixating the glare source and employing various glare angles, since the dependence of S on the glare angle was found. The glare index R is a simple function of illumination of the test-object and the glare angle.

For direct adaptation Wright found that the sensitivity is inversely proportional to the intensity of the glare source. The linear relations between R and I in the present experiments can be looked upon as a generalization of Wright's relations.

As it happens, his rule holds well for values of S below 0.2. It cannot hold for much higher values, however. Schouten and Ornstein show that when I becomes 0, S must equal 1, whereas Wright's rule would imply ∞. The formula they give for their glare index R clears the matter up by showing that for low values of S, the glare index R becomes virtually inversely proportional to S.

**Measurement of recovery after exposure.**  Schouten and Ornstein's recovery curves in which sensitivity level S is plotted against recovery time, after an exposure of 60 ms. (each curve for a different intensity), run quite parallel, confirming Wright's results with direct adaptation. But when exposure time is varied, the slope of the curves shows a great deal of dependence upon it. Different rates of recovery can exist for any sensitivity level. This leads to the deduction that recovery and the state of adaptation depend upon a minimum of two independent parameters.

**Photochemical adaptation and alpha process.**  There is a characteristic difference between the manner of action of the illuminated and non-illuminated parts of the retina. In the former, the sensitivity falls rapidly during the first second of exposure, and then falls gradually during the next few minutes. In the non-illuminated regions the sensitivity immediately falls to a constant level.

Processes concerned in local adaptation seem to be restricted to the stimulated area whereas the alpha process is transmitted across the retina and affects the state of other regions. Local adaptation is more or less independent of adaptation elsewhere and of the brightness of the surrounding field. These facts seem to show that it is different in kind than the alpha process.

That the alpha process cannot be photochemical is attested by the fact that it is a reversible process which can be set up within .1 sec. over virtually the entire retina. To attribute it to a photochemical basis, the occurrence of lateral diffusion of photo-products would have to be supposed. This would require a rapidity of such action beyond the rate that could be well supposed. The electrophysiology of the eye offers a more plausible and promising vehicle for operation.

The adaptation that has been commonly described by photochemical theories is the *beta* process, though Schouten and Ornstein believe that the strong connection of it with the *alpha* process indicates rather that it is also due to electrical processes in the retina. They have even suggested that it represents a later stage in the sequence of visual processes. Placing the beta process in the electro-physiological category does not seem justifiable merely for the reason they give.

**Crozier's view of adaptation.** Crozier asserts that the dynamics of dark adaptation, as revealed in threshold as a function of time in the dark, represents the statistics of the recovery of excitability in the neural elements involved in the effect produced by activated units having variable thresholds. In opposition to the attitude held by certain other investigators, he believes the form of the dark adaptation curve does not reveal the physiochemical characteristics of the processes involved in receptor excitation. It is rather a probability integral in which the reciprocal of the threshold is the ordinate and the log of the time in the dark is the other axis. This would mean that although the photochemistry of the sense-cell is surely involved as a factor in sensory adaptation, the actual nature of the data does not reveal it as the critical determiner of the end result. To support his contention, Crozier asserts that the parameters of the integral act in accord with it. He points out that the photochemical hypothesis of the threshold assumes, (1) that its quantitative features are determined by the sense-cell, being the manifestation of the kinetics of a system in balance with its disintegration products, (2) that the reciprocal of the stimulus intensity or of its logarithm is an index of the ultimate sensory effect, and (3) that both the absolute and the differential limens are correlated with constant amounts of sensory and photochemical effects.

Crozier's statistical hypothesis does not make these assumptions. In fact, he has shown that in addition to finding no reason for making the assumptions, the data contradict the third one. His hypothesis also accounts for the similarity in form of adaptation curves for animals as diverse in visual receptor systems as insects and man.

**Adaptation as stimulus failure.** It will be recalled that the term *adaptation* has been applied to the results in testing the sense-cell responses in several different kinds of physiological preparations. In such preparations investigators have correlated stimulation and the afferent nerve discharge, the essential outcome being that supposedly constant stimulation evokes a discharge whose frequency suffers considerable diminution with time. This decrementation is commonly attributed to the end-organ or sense-cell, and thus adaptation is assigned a neural origin. This concept of the situation is by no means as safe as it appears to be. First of all it has never been determined until recently just what the stimulus used in the physiological experiments referred to consists in. It was supposed that a constant load such as the pressure of a fixed mass to produce skin deformation or a constant load on a muscle to produce stretch constituted constant stimulation. Reasoning from this, it was simple to suppose that it was the sense-organ which gradually adapted.

Nafe and Wagoner have recently shown in a careful and intensive study, that weights applied to the skin adapt in accordance with their rate of sinking into it. By sensitive instrumentation they measured the amount and rate of cutaneous depression caused by cylinders of different areas and masses and found that these objects sink into the skin at first very rapidly and then more slowly until the rate reaches a critical minimum. When such a point is reached, the subject reports he no longer feels the pressure. The curve for the cutaneous depression with time is the same as the adaptation curve. The conclusion to be drawn from these facts is that stimulation consists in the *changing* deformation of the skin rather than the mere contact with it or a resulting constant deformation. When the rate of deformation reaches a certain minimum, stimulation ceases and the subject reports complete adaptation. *Adaptation then is a matter of stimulation failure* rather than a fatigue or other similar process in the end-organ.

Nafe and Wagoner point out five considerations bearing on this problem, some of which have appeared elsewhere.

(1) Fatigue is greater or more rapid the greater the stimulation (work): whereas adaptation requires a greater length of time, the greater the stimulation.

(2) Though there is evidence for fatigue in nerve due to the accumulation of waste products, fatigue as failure of excitation from overwork is not known, and the sense organ is not known to be different than nerve fibers in this respect.

(3) They, as well as Bronk and Matthews, found that increase in the stimulus load following complete adaptation elicits a response. This is contrary to what would be expected were it fatigue instead of adaptation.

(4) Release of the load following adaptation elicits a response, this too being contrary to expectations with fatigue.

(5) Best and Taylor point out that the results attributed to adaptation occur to the same degree with both slow and rapid rates of nerve discharge, while fatigue effects ought to be greater with rapid discharge (more work).

Nafe and Wagoner point out that full adaptation does not necessarily mean a full cessation of nervous excitation or a return to the previous equilibrium frequency of discharge, but may mean the institution of a new resting frequency which will not be altered till conditions change. This view of the matter would characterize the *mediator* in the skin as similar to the mechanism (visual purple and other substances) which determines the level of adaptation in vision, where a shift in illumination causes an adjustment to occur in the visual mechanism but even after general equilibrium is reached, action (vision) still persists. There is, however, one difference between the two senses. Whereas the observer reports he no longer feels the weight on his skin when adaptation is considered complete, he is able to *see* when visual adaptation is complete. The range of stimulus intensities involved in vision is much greater than that in touch, so the outstanding adaptation in vision happens to be the adjustment to the gross level of stimulation. Having arrived at such a level, minute differences within the spatial or temporal pattern are still responded to.

Regardless of the difference, it seems quite sure that the adaptation assigned to the sense-cell is a stimulation failure. *The energy external to the organism which we conventionally call the stimulus is not always equally effective for it must act on some sort of a mediator.* When the energy of the external stimulus and the mediator reach an equilibrium, stimulation *ceases* or *reaches a steady level.*

Part of the chapter demonstrated that certain adjustment processes were electro-physiological, that is to say, most likely neural, and others were most certainly neural. These may still be included under the term adaptation, if the consensus of opinion prefers, or they may be given a different name. To say the least, their separate existence must be recognized.

It will be fortunate when the processes of change in the individual units (cells and axons) of the nervous system are well enough understood for them and the adaptive processes just discussed to take their proper positions in a unified picture.

## REFERENCES

Bogoslovsky, A. I. Changes in the electrical sensitivity of the eye during visual activity. *Bul. de Biol. et de Med. Exp.,* 1937, 3:130-133.

Brown, Robert H., and Howard E. Page. Pupil dilatation and dark adaptation. *J. Exptl. Psych.,* 1939, 25:347-360.

Crozier, W. J. The theory of the visual threshold. II. The kinetics of adaptation. *Proc. Nat. Acad. Sci.,* 1940, 26:334-339.

Elsberg, Charles A., and H. Spotnitz. Factors which influence dark adaptation. *Am. J. Physiol.,* 1937, 120:689-695.

Elsberg, Chas. A., and H. Spotnitz. Is cerebral activity a physicochemical process: Studies based on the physicochemical equivalent of a formula for dark adaptation. *J. Gen. Psych.,* 1938, 19:263-276.

Elsberg, Charles A., and H. Spotnitz. The neural components of light and dark adaptation and their significance for the duration of the foveal dark adaptation process. *Bul. Neurol. Inst. N. Y.,* 1938, 7:148-159.

Elsberg, Charles A., and H. Spotnitz. A theory of retino-cerebral function with formulas for threshold vision and light and dark adaptation of the fovea. *Am. J. Physiol.,* 1938, 121:454-464.

Hecht, Selig. The instantaneous visual threshold after light adaptation. *Nat. Acad. Sci.,* 1937, 23:227-233.

Hecht, Selig. Intensity discrimination and its relation to the adaptation of the eye. *J. Physiol.,* 1936, 86:15-21.

Hecht, Selig, Charles Haig, and Aurin M. Chase. The influence of light adaptation on subsequent dark adaptation of the eye. *J. Gen. Physiol.,* 1937, 20:831-850.

Hecht, Selig, Charles Haig, and George Wald. The dark adaptation of retinal fields of different size and location. *J. Gen. Physiol.,* 1935, 19:321-337.

Hecht, Selig, and Joseph Mandelbaum. The relation between vitamin A and dark adaptation. *J. Am. Med. Assoc.,* 1939, 112:1910-1916.

Hecht, Selig, and Joseph Mandelbaum. Rod-cone adaptation and vitamin A. *Science,* 1938, 88:219-221.

Hecht, Selig, and Simon Shlaer. An adaptometer for measuring human dark adaptation. *J. Opt. Soc. Am.,* 1938, 28:269-275.

Helson, Harry, and Deane B. Judd. A study in photopic adaptation. *J. Exptl. Psych.,* 1932, 15:380-398.

Kravkov, S. V. The influence of the dark adaptation on the critical frequency of flicker for monochromatic lights. *Acta. Ophthal.,* 1938, 16: 375-384.

Lythgoe, R. J. The mechanism of dark adaptation. *Brit. J. Ophthal.,* 1940, 24:21-43.

Nafe, J. P., and K. Wagoner. (An article on adaptation.) *J. Gen. Psych.* (In press.)

Riggs, L. A. Dark adaptation in the frog eye as determined by the electrical response of the retina. *J. Cell. & Comp. Physiol.,* 1937, 9:491-510.

Schouten, J. F., and L. S. Ornstein. Measurements on direct and indirect adaptation by means of a binocular method. *J. Opt. Soc. Am.,* 1939, 29:168-182.

Travis, Roland C. The effect upon dark adaptation and visual periodicity of atropin and homatropin. *J. Exptl. Psych.,* 1926, 9:348-357.

Wald, George, and Anna-Betty Clark. Visual adaptation and chemistry of the rods. *J. Gen. Physiol.,* 1937, 21:93-105.

Wolf, Ernst, and Gertrud Zerrahn-Wolf. The dark adaptation of the eye of the honey bee. *J. Gen. Physiol.,* 1935, 19:229-237.

# IX

# NEURAL INTERACTION

**Conceivable kinds of interaction.** The principle of interaction includes so much of neurophysiology that no chapter can do it justice. It is our purpose here only to outline the possible results of interaction, following some of them with examples found in retinal function.

*There are at least four general results from interaction.* These may possibly be thought of also as being *kinds* of interaction. The first is summation, of which there are three degrees or varieties. It is nowadays taken for granted that no nerve cell can be activated by a single impulse from an incoming fiber. In *simple summation* it is possible for the impulses of several axons to converge upon a cell within the proper time interval for their accumulated influences to activate it. It is also conceivable that a number of impulses from a single axon might arrive within the proper time limit to produce an effect similar to the arrival of approximately the same number arriving over a group of axons.

Another degree or kind of summative interaction is *occlusion*. It arises when the overlapping or converging excitatory paths find the neurons already active. In such cases it is sometimes said that the neurons are saturated, and the additional impulses produce little or no appreciable enhancement of the end-effect, even though anatomically the stage is well set. Occlusion, then, is partial summation.

The last degree or kind of summative interaction is *facilitation*. As defined by some, it is the greatly exaggerated result which sometimes accrues from the convergence of additional impulses upon a neuron field. It is quantitatively much more than simple summation, and is supposed to arise from the fact that the "fringe" or the common part of the overlapping fields of two

groups of axons previously only subliminally excited become activated, due to the convergence of impulses from both groups of
axons. This is better understood if we envisage a group of
incoming fibers supplying a neuron field. The endings of the
fibers well within the group will interlace and the sum total of
impulses involved will excite certain cells. The endings of fibers
lying in the periphery of this bundle will become more and more
sparse the further away from the core of the bundle they are.
Cells in such regions will receive insufficient excitation to be
activated. The number of impulses impinging upon them on
this account will be subliminal. This subliminal effect, however,
is a real excitation and may be added to, within the short time
before its effect decays.

Facilitation results when the fields from two such bundles as
we have just described overlap. It is conceivable that the total
number of neurons involved in the overlap may be many times
greater than the cells involved in the cores of the two bundles.
When impulses arrive over both bundles the regions included in
the overlap or fringe receive double the number of impulses and
excitation is brought up to the supraliminal level. The consequent activity of the great number of cells in the fringe is added
to that of the cells on the core, with the result that the end-effect
may be tremendously enhanced.

The second result from or type of interaction is *inhibition*.
This effect is the cessation of something that is already occurring.
It is more difficult to explain than summation. The prevention
of an effect that has not yet begun but which otherwise would
have occurred is quite hypothetical and will not be considered
here. Whether there are fibers specifically given over to inhibition
is not certain. Since most of the views of inhibition employ
some form of timing to account for the effects, the existence of
specific inhibitory fibers may simply rest upon the time relations
their activity bears to certain others. On the other hand, it may
depend upon citoarchitectural considerations. It is not at all
likely that the fibers responsible for inhibition are qualitatively
different than those which are summative. One form of inhibi-

tion which has recently received some attention is the type that is dependent upon the functioning of closed chains of neural elements, or reverberating circuits. In such a mechanism, inhibition would result from the impinging of extraneous impulses upon the circuit in such ways as to effectively break the continuity of the activity in it, obliterating any end-effect dependent upon the perpetuity of the activity. This idea of inhibition rests, as it should, both upon morphology and timing.

*The third conceivable result from, or kind of interaction is one bringing about* synchrony *in the activity of a large number of elements.* It is known that some groups beat in synchrony and others do not. Various conditions may be supplied to change these groups from one state to the other. To say the least we would not lay the shift to mere matters of chance. Synchrony involves two factors, first, the existence of similar rates of activity in the elements involved, second, the matter of bringing the elements into like phase. It is thinkable that the two factors are not dependent upon the same mechanism. For example, the first factor (similarity of rate) in the case of discharging sense-cells might, as Adrian thinks, be accomplished when the stimulating intensity is high enough for all of them to have reached their maximum discharge frequency which is presumed to be the same for all. This says nothing, however, about how individual cells are all brought into the same phase. The explanation for that is a different matter.

We at least know that many cells which beat in unison at one time may not at another. Synchrony apparently then does not depend upon some structural linkage alone. A functional factor must be sought. By this we are saying that a particular kind of interaction is required.

*The fourth result from or kind of interaction is that posited to account for the seeing of contours and borders in the visual field.* It is known that borders are seen when the pattern of illumination on the retina is by no means as sharp as would be expected for their direct production. We shall not go into detail in this chapter concerning this type of interaction. The following chapter on Contour will be devoted entirely to it.

Since it is known that the optic pathway provides for vision which, instead of having the traits of a mosaic, is unitary, all parts of the visual field being able to affect each other, or at least assume membership in the field as-a-whole, an analysis of the details of nervous interaction is called for. The experimental evidence gives reason for believing a great portion of such interaction occurs in the eye itself.

**Experiments on the excised eye.** The interaction between non-adjacent areas of the retina has been investigated in the sub-human vertebrate eye. One of the studies of this sort is that of Adrian and Matthews. They demonstrated by means of the eel's eye that the illumination of four points (discs) forming the corners of a square results in a shorter latency of the optic nerve discharge than when one alone is illuminated. The application of strychnine, even though it prolongs latencies in general, increases the area of the retina over which this effect can be distinguished. Since the conditions were such as to rule out a functional amount of stray light, there seems to be no doubt but what the experiment demonstrates interaction. And it is significant that such a phenomenon is found in the retina itself.

In keeping with this, the failure of stimulation of added area to reduce latency of response in an eye which lacks interconnecting pathways was demonstrated by Graham in the *Limulus* eye. Such an eye is composed only of sense-cells, and the optic nerve is made up of their long afferent processes. It was shown that it did not matter whether few or many sense-cells were activated. The latency of the nerve response was the same, and was determined simply by the latency of the fastest fibers in it. The absence of neural summation in a system of this sort is according to expectations.

**Interaction in the human eye.** Granit applied the same stimulus arrangement to the investigation of interaction in the human eye. Here he could not determine the latency of the optic nerve discharge. As a substitute, he had to devise some other approach which would not involve a visual comparison field. Critical flicker frequency was chosen inasmuch as c.f.f. is a function of stimulus intensity. A rise in c.f.f. was taken as an expression of increased effect, which in terms of the experimental situation would be evidence of interaction.

The discs, arranged as the corners of a square, were 1° in diameter and separated so that the distance between their inner edges and the center of the square was 1°. He used also a second pattern composed of similar discs one-half as far apart. In order that these patterns fall one time at the fovea and another farther toward the retinal periphery, two fixation points were used. The first fixation point was the center of the square and the second one was 10° horizontal to the center. Two different illumination intensities of the test-objects were used, 94 and 0.94 m.c. The background illumination was about ½₀₀₀ as bright as the discs. Granit found that in peripheral vision the c.f.f. of the discs as a group was on the average about 2.5 flashes per sec. higher than for any one of them alone. A square which just inclosed the discs required a still higher rate. The c.f.f. of the discs when close together was higher than when forming the corners of the larger square. When the image of the test pattern fell at the fovea there was but little, if any, increase in c.f.f. when the four discs were used instead of one.

It can be concluded from these experiments that there is a physiological interaction between remote retinal points, its existence and amount depending upon distance, intensity of stimulation, and upon the region of the retina involved. Interaction becomes less and less as distance is increased, and as intensity of stimulation is decreased. It is absent in the fovea with very weak stimulation and only slight with higher intensities, while it is very noticeable in the periphery.

The differences between fovea and periphery are quite well correlated with the differences in the richness of interconnections in the two regions. The peripheral regions of the human retina are quite similar in interconnections to the eye of the eel. In line with this the results in the two investigations turn out about alike.

**Relation between area and intensity.** Granit and Harper continued the work that has just been described. One of the things they did was to determine the effect of increasing area on the c.f.f. for test-objects at different intensities. From their data they produced two families of curves, one for the periphery and the other for the center of the retina. For all intensities in which the brightness of the test-object was above that of the background there was a linear relation between c.f.f. and the logarithm of the area. The increase in c.f.f. was greater with high intensities and in the retinal periphery. That is to say, the slope of the curves picturing the relation was greater for higher intensities and in the periphery than for the center of the retina. The increase in c.f.f. with intensity was also greater the larger the area of the test-object.

The maximum c.f.f. is reached at different intensities with test-objects of different areas, the smaller areas reaching maximum first. Maximum c.f.f. is also reached first in the periphery of the retina. Since both parts of the retina conform to the same equation, it is concluded that the essential functional difference in the two portions is quantitative rather than qualitative.

This inference brings up the question of the relation between summation and visual acuity. It would appear that resolving ability and the ability of the various parts of the retina to interact are quite opposing mechanisms. But it is known that the resolving power of the fovea increases as illumination is raised, and this very same factor increases interaction. As yet this question has not been answered, and the fact that it has not is more than likely due to an entirely wrong way of viewing these two processes. A view must be sought which will not regard them as irreconcilably opposing one another.

**Visual acuity and interaction as measured by c.f.f.** One method of obtaining some indication of the relation between summation and visual acuity was devised by Granit and Harper. They used two halves of a disc whose distance apart could be varied. This test-object was viewed both at the fovea and 10° toward the periphery. By this set-up they wished to determine whether or not c.f.f. would suddenly rise when the two halves of the disc were brought close enough to make the disc appear undivided. The two possibilities were that the c.f.f. would rise gradually as the two halves became closer and closer together, or that there would be the sudden shift in c.f.f. when they came too close for the space between them to be resolved by the eye.

They found a gradual rise in the c.f.f. for both the fovea and the periphery, as the two halves were brought close together, though they had to be somewhat closer in the center to show the same degree of interaction. Furthermore the center of the eye did not show the same maximum of interaction as the periphery, the difference in the two ranges being greater for low intensities.

These results show that interaction in the center of the eye does not interfere with its resolving power. With a retinal interspace of 30 $\mu$ the full amount of interaction was reached in both parts of the eye, though to the observers a definite line about a millimeter and a half wide separating the two semi-discs remained. Granit and Harper offer two suggestions. Either the interaction between stimulated areas is expressed by some process invoking little or no discharge in the interjacent elements or else there is definite inhibition at the edges of the areas stimulated. They also mention the old view that the mechanism of contrast compensates for the irradiation of effects from one area to another. These suggestions, as they stand, though they well reflect common ways of thinking on such subjects, are not satisfactory.

**Evidence for occlusion and facilitation.** Summation has been the only interaction pointed out thus far. The retina also gives sign of a certain amount of occlusion and facilitation. Occlusion, for example, is demonstrated in the comparison of the c.f.f's of one and four discs. Critical flicker frequency is higher for the group than for the single disc and increasing the intensity of stimulation raises the c.f.f. more for the four discs than for the single one. Nevertheless, as intensity is made very great this is reversed. The advantage of the group over the one disc dwindles until finally the group and the one halt at the same maximal c.f.f.

To begin with the group had the advantage over the lone disc on account of activation of long lateral paths between the members of the group as well as the short lateral paths within the areas of the discs and the direct vertical paths down through the retina. As intensity was raised, more and more of the long lateral paths were excited above threshold and the group gained more and more advantage over the single disc. Since this ascendence over the latter was finally lost and the two patterns finally reached the same c.f.f., the result may be looked upon as a case of occlusion. The input to the cells receiving the greatest number of impulses is now being occluded. The additional impulses which are supplied yield less and less effect. The loss of effect of adding more input to these particular cells compensate the ability of the long lateral paths to add to the final result. Since the final outcome is the same for the group and the single disc, it suggests that the rise in c.f.f. stops when the final neurons which supply the optic nerve output are saturated.

Whether or not the retina gives evidence of facilitation in the sense of augmented summation, seems to rest on a comparison of the slopes of the curves of c.f.f. for area and intensity. There is a greater variation in c.f.f. as area is increased in the retinal periphery than at the center. The slope of the log area curves is much steeper than that of the log intensity curve for the greatest area. These two facts would seem to show that the area effect is dependent upon the richness in lateral connections and that area can be more effective than intensity in raising c.f.f., since we have shown that area and intensity produce their effects in the same way; namely, by the regulation of the number of impulses reaching certain cells or synapses in a given time. Thus the greater effect of area would be due to its production of a greater number of impulses, and presumably by the method described as facilitation. It is to be noted, nevertheless, that the facilitation here is not nearly as great as is found elsewhere in the nervous system.

**Spatial summation of subthreshold stimuli.** Beitel investigated the summation of subliminal stimuli. The test-objects he used

were semi-discs, one-half degree in radius, whose separations
varied from 0 to 150 min. of visual angle, their images falling on
the peripheral retina 15° from the fovea. A slit in a heavy
pendulum which passed through a narrow pencil of light furnished the timing of the stimulation. Wedges provided the necessary intensity control. Forty to fifty-five minutes dark adaptation
was allowed before beginning observations. The method of
limits was used and the range of uncertainty was obtained for
the readings at all intensity settings.

It was found that spatial summation does occur in the periphery.
It first decreases rapidly for about the first 20 min. of angular
separation and then maintains a slow drop which might be called
a plateau. At about 70 or 80 min. the decline again becomes
steeper and all summation ends at about 150 min. or 2.5° of
visual angle where it is found that the semi-discs are not seen at
lower intensities than is one. When the two semi-discs are
adjacent making a solid disc, the average intensity at which it is
seen by Beitel's observers was .000050 ml. With 2.5° interspace
between the discs, the intensity was .000089 ml. The ratio was
scarcely 1 to 2, making care in obtaining readings necessary.
The range of uncertainty (interval covered between definite perception of test-objects, and failure to see them) was, however, in
every case so small as to avoid overlapping anywhere in the
experiments.

The same procedure was applied to the fovea, except that the
test-patches were squares subtending visual angles of only 5 min.,
the results there showing that the intensity necessary for seeing
the two patches was lower than for one, over a separation range
of 10 min. Thus there is in the fovea also, a demonstrable
amount of spatial summation. The average absolute intensity
values required were much higher, being at zero separation for
the two patches, .088 ml., for the single patches about .169 and
.159, right and left respectively. It is obvious that the intensity
range in the fovea is about the same (1 to 2) as in the periphery,
though the distance over which summation occurs is only about
1/15 as great.

Beitel points out that convergence of retinal paths is of three kinds: the convergence of a number of sense-cells on one bipolar cell, the convergence of bipolars on ganglion cells, and the convergence of lateral neurons on the common foci. The curve describing spatial summation in the periphery is complex and hence may express the effects of several kinds of summation. Summation occurring with wide separations up to 2.5° can be accounted for only by the lateral internuncial elements. In this connection, it is significant to note that this distance is of the same order as found by Ramon y Cajal for the limits of extension of individual lateral interconnections in the eye.

Beitel attributes summation over lesser distances, the range of the first sharp drop in the curve, to the convergence of bipolars on ganglion cells. The curve representing spatial summation at the fovea plotted against separation distance of the test-patches is not the same shape as that for the periphery. Whereas the peripheral curve was complex, thereby suggesting several factors at work, the foveal curve can be considered simple. This, along with the much smaller limiting separation for summation, indicates the lack of such factors as lateral internuncial elements at work, and is, of course, in line with the anatomical descriptions given from time to time of foveal sensations. The complete agreement of the findings with expectations from retinal anatomy as well as with experiments on excised eyes and decerebrate animals reenforces the belief, already grounded on other considerations, that the phenomena are of retinal origin.

**Temporal summation of subthreshold stimulation.** It was pointed out to start with that summation possesses certain temporal as well as spatial aspects. In some physiological preparations, the period of *latent addition* which is an index of the time interval that might be expected to be involved in summation, has been found to be in the neighborhood of 1 to 2 ms. This would seem to mean that the excitatory after-effects of the first impulse last only a very short time.

For more complex pathways, if not for simple ones involving only one synaptic juncture, it is conceivable that summation might become effective over longer periods of time than was just indicated.

Granit and Davis set out to discover the temporal character-istics of summation in the retina. They modified the method of successive subliminal stimuli used by Eccles and Sherrington. The method consisted in producing a threshold response by add-ing the effect of a second subthreshold flash to the possible after-effect of a first subliminal one. The time interval between the two and the strength of the second was varied in order that the response would be just threshold. Since at threshold, time and intensity are reciprocal, the strength of the second flash was manipulated by either factor. As it was more convenient to vary time, this procedure was used after a preliminary test with varying intensities. The fully dark adapted retinal periphery was chosen for this work for it was thought to be the most stable. Nevertheless, its stability was far from perfect and repeated con-trols using the first flash alone had to be employed. As the interval between the two flashes was lengthened the second flash had to be made stronger and stronger in order to elicit a liminal response. A series of measurements taken at various times after the delivery of the first flash provided data from which the time course of the subthreshold excitatory after-effect was plotted.

The specific results may be summarized by stating that when a just subthreshold flash lasting 11.3 ms. is followed by a still shorter subthreshold shock, the two will elicit a visible effect over an interval of 130 ms. The shorter the interval between the flashes, the less the quantity necessary in the second to raise the after-effect to liminal value. If the abscissa of the curve plotting the results expresses the interval between the two flashes, and the ordinate (reading from top to bottom) represents the pro-gressively increasing strength of the second flash in percentage of the first; the contour of the curve so plotted is complex, exhibit-ing an initial rapid fall to a plateau which in turn ends in a further but gradual fall. It is perhaps significant that the break in the curve appears at a time corresponding to the upper limit of the interval within which intensity and duration are reciprocal, while the initial fast part of the drop occurs mostly within the short time range in which Bloch's rule does not hold.

It appears then that temporal summation is as basic a retinal property as spatial summation. It is admissible that part of the phenomenon might be photochemical, but it cannot be assumed that such processes will account either for the complexity or the full duration of the curves representing after-effects lasting 130 ms.

The summation that is demonstrated here, since it must represent neural activity, is of a vastly different order than that which must occur within the *period of latent addition* found by some investigators for certain synapses elsewhere in the nervous system. This situation brings up the question of whether prolonged effects which might come under the heading of summation are due to the persistence of an effect at a single locus or whether the "persistence" is accomplished only by a temporal sequence of phenomena involving a chain of elements, the period involved in each element being of the order represented by the usual period of latent addition. Suitable closed circuits, or circular pathways, seem to be an anatomical fact, at least.

The next step attempted in the analysis of temporal summation was to ascertain whether subthreshold excitation at the synapses spreads laterally in a manner comparable to excitation causing an actual end-response. For this Granit and Davis employed two semi-discs, each having a radius of 1° and separated by an interspace of 10 to 30 min. of visual angle. The semi-discs at a subthreshold level were presented in succession. Thus a constant subliminal flash was applied to one region and a second variable subliminal one was applied later to a second region.

The experiment was found to be extremely difficult and hence the results were not very reliable. After much painstaking effort, it became evident that successive adjacent subthreshold stimuli do sum, at least in the retinal periphery. It made little difference whether the two stimuli were concurrent or successive as long as the interval did not exceed a few milliseconds.

*This was taken as evidence that subliminal excitation spreads laterally, a result which the investigators point out would account for the summation brought about by area in reducing the limen.*

**Inhibition of suprathreshold stimuli.** Graham and Granit following the foundation laid down by the previous studies made by Granit and colleagues attempted to elucidate the matter of inhibition. It was difficult to see how visual acuity could improve as stimulus intensity was increased, when such a change in conditions increased summation. This suggested to them that when excitation on adjacent areas reach markedly different levels, new conditions arise so that the net result is not summation.

To study the outcome when two adjacent retinal areas are excited at different levels, they chose two flickering semi-discs unequal in brightness. To begin with they chose an intensity range within which changes in intensity altered the c.f.f. very little or none. Doubling or halving the intensity changed c.f.f. about 2%. The simultaneous presentation of both semi-discs raised the c.f.f. about 8.6% above the c.f.f. of the one alone. Thus the two patches summed spatially in spite of the fact that intensity changes had little effect.

Following this, the two areas were illuminated at different levels, the one 50% of the other. Under these circumstances, the c.f.f. of the less bright area diminished slightly, while that of the brighter increased. The drop of the one was about 1.5%, and the rise of the other was 5.4%. This is to say, that when the excitation of two adjacent retinal areas are different, some process exaggerates this in the sensory outcome, making the bright brighter and the dim dimmer. This as a phenomenon is none other than a case of brightness contrast, if we wish to call it that, only that it is demonstrated in a different set of phenomenological terms.

The investigators classify the phenomenon as one of inhibition since the more intensely excited area does not act upon the less intensely excited area to increase its c.f.f. They look upon the result as one of total removal of this otherwise expected summative effect. If the two half-discs were placed at the level of the darker, they would have given a c.f.f. from 5.4 to 8.5% higher than one alone. The lack of such an effect when the two areas are at different levels is taken to be due to inhibition.

It was pointed out at the beginning of the chapter that inhibition is the disappearance of some existing effect. The disappearance of the enhanced c.f.f. can be regarded in that light and called inhibition providing we also disregard the possible manner in which the disappearance of the initial result is accomplished. If, however, the two-level intensity arrangement is considered in a sense to be unique, it is not so clear that the results obtained with it must be regarded as due to inhibition, by virtue of the mere failure of the effect obtained in the single intensity arrangement of the patches to appear. Determination of the mechanism involved will await further details concerning the behavior of the two-level pattern.

Most of the further experiments took on the form of holding one semi-disc constant, and flickering the other. Manipulations of intensity were tried for both the fovea and periphery with notably different results. At the fovea with one area intermittently illuminated and the other steady, the two gave a summation of 4.6%. When the flickering patch was reduced to ⅔ of its original intensity, its c.f.f. when used alone also fell slightly, and when used with the steady adjacent patch it fell still more in some cases, and in others the so-called inhibition just canceled the expected summation and the c.f.f. remained as when used alone.

In the retinal periphery, the same type of procedure resulted in summation. That is, the c.f.f. of the patch when used with its steady neighbor was higher than when used alone, regardless of whether its intensity level was reduced as much as ⅓ below the steady patch.

As a final experiment, the intensity difference between the intermittent and steady fields with central fixation was reduced by little more than a threshold amount. Using both patches and reducing the intensity of the intermittent patch 2%, the summation is only 2.2%; with intensity increased 2% summation is still 5.3%, nearly the same (5.8%) as when the two patches were the same intensity.

Graham and Granit take it then that inhibition is primarily a foveal property at high intensities if not throughout the whole range. In this connection it is to be remembered that visual acuity and the finer degrees of brightness discrimination are also foveal properties, and may depend in some way on inhibition.

No detailed picture of how inhibition operates was offered by Graham and Granit, except to postulate specific fibers for it. Inhibition was supposed to operate in both directions, that is, the less highly excited area tends to inhibit the more strongly excited area and in turn the more strongly excited area inhibits it. Inhibition in the latter direction is conceived to be greater than in the other. Furthermore the specific elements were conceived to be the amacrine cells since they must have a special function and are much more highly developed in the fovea where the phenomena attributed to inhibition occur.

**Depression.** Fry and Bartley envisaged the mechanism involved in the enhancement and depression of c.f.f. by a steadily illuminated surrounding or adjacent field, in a different manner than Graham and Granit. The former thought of it in terms of some factor affecting the phases of the flicker cycle differentially, whereas the latter see it as the presence or absence of inhibition, the opposition of the summative effect, whereby summation is either diminished, eliminated, or an opposite effect appears in the end-result.

The work of Crozier, Wolf, and Zerrahn-Wolf has indicated flicker recognition is a process of brightness discrimination, the discrimination between the effects from the bright and dark periods. *The nature of the results indicate that flicker recognition is dependent upon two populations of excited elements between the activities of which there must be a sufficient average difference.* These elements are neural and may be located either in the eye or further inward along the pathway. Be that as it may, it will be sufficient for the present to remember that intermittent stimulation consists in two phases, the bright and the dark. The one is a definite stimulation period, the other is also a period occupied by excitation, though of a declining level marking a recovery, or partial return to rest.

For the c.f.f. to rise, a greater *difference* must be produced in the excitation or activity in the two phases than prevailing previously. Thus, though c.f.f. is a measure of the intensity of stimulation, alterations of c.f.f. are not always to be considered evidence of changes similar in *detail* to those brought about by changes in intensity. It is only that such alterations in conditions must produce the proper *differences* in physiological activity representing the two periods of the stimulation cycle, in order that flicker be recognized.

In the cases in which the c.f.f. is reduced, it is not necessary to postulate a summation which in turn is inhibited. Nor in cases in which c.f.f. is raised is it always necessary to suppose summation is at bottom. This is not to discard the idea of summation, but rather to reserve it for the situation in which it is more clearly necessary.

Fry and Bartley made a study which bears on this problem. The tests they made were a modification and an extension of the previous experiments of Geldard which he had conceived as isolating facilitation and depression.

Geldard found, when he placed both stimuli (semi-discs) in the fovea, the one steady and the other for obtaining the c.f.f. and separated by only a narrow line, that c.f.f. increased with the intensity of the steady patch up to a point beyond the Talbot brightness of the other patch, and then declined. When a region 5° from the fovea was illuminated, the c.f.f. of the fovea rose without reversal, with the intensity of the illumination. Geldard assigned the reversal of c.f.f. when the steady patch was in the fovea and its absence with the peripheral patch, to the activation of a depression mechanism in the fovea in addition to the one for facilitation already operating, and stated that no such depression mechanism exists in the periphery.

Fry and Bartley's experiments about to be described will show that the point of reversal of c.f.f. varies with the distance of the steady patch from the intermittent one, and consequently whether it occurs at all or not (with the intensities used) *depends upon the distances used and not upon a fovea-peripheral difference.* They used three different test-patterns each in the form of a disc with a surrounding annulus. In the first the annulus was contiguous with the disc, in the second they were separated by ⅛ inch and in the third by ⁵⁄₁₆ inch. Fixation was monocular from a distance of 33.5 inches, and an artificial pupil was used.

As the distance between the disc and annulus increased the reversal of the curve occurred higher in the intensity scale and failed to appear at all within the range of intensities used with the widest separation. The reversal failed to appear in Geldard's experiment when the object had a brightness of 369 c/ft.[2] so that at a distance of 5° it is problematical whether the object could ever be made bright enough.

Without commitment as to details, Fry and Bartley supposed some sort of depression was at work, so that with weak stimulation surrounding the test-object the dark phase of the flicker cycle is depressed, thereby raising c.f.f. and with stronger adjacent stimulation, the bright phase also is depressed, reducing the differential between the two phases and diminishing c.f.f.

In one of Graham and Granit's experiments, c.f.f. was raised either by adding to the area of the intermittent stimulus or by adding area in the form of steady illumination, but the former was more effective.

When two 1° intermittent semi-discs require a c.f.f. 5.9% over that of either alone when directly fixated, and 13.7% when in the periphery (10°), they increase c.f.f. only 2.9% and 6%, respectively, when one is intermittent and the other steady at the Talbot level.

The investigators concluded that true spatial summation was responsible in both cases for the enhancement of the c.f.f. It is likely, however, that the mechanism that has just been described is responsible for the elevation of c.f.f. by a steady adjacent field and summation in the other case. In the latter, impulses set up would be mainly in the bright phase of the flicker cycle, and no complications would arise. Whereas in the other case a *steady stream* of impulses would tend to pass from the continuously lighted area to the intermittent area. Under such complications, we do not yet know what happens. The farthest we have gone is to suggest a depressive influence, for the reasons involved in the descriptions of what happens when the intensity relations between steady and intermittent regions are varied.

**Inhibition of threshold stimulation.** Beitel performed some experiments the results of which were interpreted as due to inhibition. In essence these experiments consisted in determining threshold for a test-patch when presented alone and then when accompanied by another patch at one of several different distances from it. In the latter cases the threshold was found to be raised.

Four separations between stimuli were used at the fovea, which varied from 3.5′ to 17.2′ of visual angle, and two separations in the periphery, 50′ and 130′. Separations less than 50′ were too small to yield dependable results. Both monocular and binocular determinations were used.

Three different results were obtained depending upon relative intensities of and separations between the two stimuli.

In the fovea, under monocular fixation, if the second test-patch is of the same value as the threshold for the single patch, the threshold of the latter is decreased, the amount depending upon the spatial separation.

If the intensity of the second patch is increased tenfold over the previous value, the threshold of the first patch is unaltered. If the intensity increase is raised to an hundredfold, then the threshold of the first patch is raised, the amount depending upon the separation between the two.

In the periphery under monocular fixation, summation is demonstrable when the second patch is of the same order as the threshold value of the first. This effect is demonstrable over an interspace of 130′ of arc. When the intensity of the second patch is raised an hundredfold above the former level, the threshold intensity of the first patch is unchanged, but when the increase

reaches a thousandfold, the threshold of the first patch is raised.
The increase is larger the smaller the separations, and continues
with still higher intensities.

When the image of the test-patch was made to fall in one eye
and the image of the second in the other eye, no demonstrable
difference in threshold was observable regardless of its intensity
or the apparent distance of separation of the two patches.

These experiments are interpreted as showing interaction between threshold excitations, and that summation does occur between regions somewhat separated from each other, in both
fovea and in the periphery. But it must be recognized that the
disappearance of such summation and the substitution of a higher
threshold when the intensity of the second patch is greatly ele-
vated is not to be taken as absolute proof that summation is
substituted by inhibition. This caution is made pertinent by the
fact that bright images reflect a functional amount of stray light
over the retina. The effect of any possible stray light in this
case would be to cast a veil over the test-patch and thereby necessitate its intensity to be raised to reach threshold.

The spatial separations examined for summation and inhibition
in the periphery were much greater than those at the fovea. It
will be noted that the intensity differences between the test-
patches were also much greater. This is in keeping with the
expected outcome were stray light to be at the bottom of the
effect. It is also recognized that with liminal stimulation, the
test-objects do not have definite contours to set up a brightness-
contrast situation which was the concomitant of the alleged process of inhibition in supraliminal stimulation.

The conclusion, summarizing the findings as a whole, would
be that *summation and inhibition do exist in the retina.* They
can be clearly demonstrated in very simple cases. *Nevertheless,
so many of the functions of the retina call for processes which
would not be predicted by simple summation or inhibition that
a view providing for such phenomena as brightness contrast and
contour formation must be found.* It is conceded that in a concept of that kind there might be part-effects in the picture as a

whole that could still be spoken of as addition and subtraction, or summation and inhibition, but the picture must be a dynamic one and provide a reason for the phenomena as we know them. It must tell when and where to expect these algebraic effects.

## REFERENCES

Beitel, Robert J., Jr. Inhibition of threshold excitation in the human eye. *J. Gen. Psych.*, 1936, 14:31-61.

Beitel, Robert J., Jr. Spatial summation of subliminal stimuli in the retina of the human eye. *J. Gen. Psych.*, 1934, 10:311-327.

Fry, Glenn A. Depression of the activity aroused by a flash of light by applying a second flash immediately afterwards to adjacent areas of the retina. *Am. J. Physiol.*, 1934, 108:701-707.

Graham, C. H., and Ragnar Granit. Comparative studies on the peripheral and central retina. VI. Inhibition, Summation, and Synchronization of impulses in the retina. *Am. J. Physiol.*, 1931, 98:664-673.

Granit, Ragnar. Comparative studies on the peripheral and central retina. I. On interaction between distant areas in the human eye. *Am. J. Physiol.*, 1930, 94:41-50.

Granit, Ragnar, and William A. Davis. Comparative studies on the peripheral and central retina. IV. Temporal summation of subliminal visual stimuli and the time course of the excitatory after-effect. *Am. J. Physiol.*, 1931, 98:644-653.

Granit, Ragnar, and Edward L. Hammond. Comparative studies on the peripheral and central retina. V. The sensation-time curve and the time course of the fusion frequency of intermittent stimulation. *Am. J. Physiol.*, 1931, 98:654-663.

Granit, Ragnar, and Phyllis Harper. Comparative studies on the peripheral and central retina. II. Synaptic reactions in the eye. *Am. J. Physiol.*, 1930, 95:211-228.

# X

# CONTOUR

**The inadequacy of present concepts of interaction to account for contour.** In the preceding chapter matters of summation and inhibition were discussed. Interaction as to outcome was classified into four groups, summation, inhibition, synchronizing activity, and contour formation. Inhibition was considered to be the result when neural activity, which on account of its peculiar timing or on account of its spatial relation to that in other pathways, interferes with or completely obliterates activity there.

Some of the experimental examples which were used to illustrate interaction forced us to the conclusion that when adjacent areas of the retina were illuminated at markedly different levels, excitation tended to be exaggerated in the intensely illuminated area and depressed in the dimmer of the two, action for which summation and inhibition are unable to account. This is what in the terms of perception has been called brightness contrast and has at times erroneously been used as a causal principle. As a phenomenon it has long been known and is perfectly easy to demonstrate.

To say the least, no notion of interaction that has been put forth thus far has accounted for brightness contrast. What is more, the kinds of interaction that have been mentioned are the whole stock in trade of current physiology. This is to say then, that up to now, physiology has not been able to deal with brightness contrast even in a conceptual way.

**Blackowski's experiment.** That the formation of threshold borders is in part governed by the already existent borders in the visual field is shown by the following examples in which one border seems to have an influence upon others somewhat remote. If a small disc test-object is surrounded by a larger annular area, the differential brightness threshold between the two decreases as the area of the annulus is increased. It was supposed by Blackowski that the increase in area is responsible through a summation process. Contrary to this idea, it is the outer border of the annulus which affects the threshold, through its influence on the formation of the border between the test-object and the annulus which must emerge before there is a perceived brightness difference between the two surfaces under comparison.

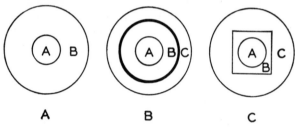

**A**        **B**        **C**

Fig. 46.—Patterns to study the effect of one border upon the threshold of another. Pattern (A) Blackowski's figure; (B) Fry and Bartley's figure to test Blackowski's explanation; (C) Dittmer's figure. (*Fry and Bartley—Am. J. Physiol.*)

By surrounding the small disc test-object (A) by a field (B) bounded by a narrow dark ring outside of which was another field (C), a check on the supposed influence of total area was made by Fry and Bartley. The total area of B plus C was kept constant, and the diameter of the ring was manipulated to change the distance of the ring from the test-object. In this way, the inner border of the ring was made to vary in distance from the test-object while the total illuminated area remained fixed. The actual experimental result was that as the ring was removed further away from the test-object A, the threshold progressively decreased. B plus C remained the same and could not be a factor in the systematic drop in the threshold. The only factor which varied was the distance of the ring, and its inner border must have had the necessary influence.

This pattern demonstrates the second fundamental property of a border, that of preventing activity from spreading. Since the same results are obtained with the outer annulus C, present or absent, it may be concluded that the inner border of the ring blocks the outer border of the ring (the inner edge of C) from affecting the threshold of A. This general phenomenon is closely related to the fact that the threshold for a disc on a slightly darker ground decreases as the area of the disc is increased. Some investigators have attributed this to the inclusion of more receptors within the area. Evidence shows, however, that this is to be assigned to the action of border processes. When a disc-shaped area is employed for measuring the threshold, the borders opposite each other tend to interfere. When the disc is small the interference is great and the threshold high; when the disc is larger the separation of the borders is greater, the interference is less and the threshold lower. When the results of such an experiment are compared with those of the first situation it is seen that the influence on the threshold vanishes at the same separation of borders in both cases; namely, at about four degrees of visual angle.

**Dittmers' figure.** The same type of border phenomenon comes into play in another situation demonstrated in the pattern in Figure 46, used by Dittmers. In this pattern the effect of varying the brightness of C on the differential threshold for A is demonstrated. Two different situations are possible, one in which A is brighter than B and the other in which it is darker. The results are shown in Figure 47. In both cases the smallest threshold value occurs when B and C are equal in brightness; it rises when C is either higher or lower than B. It has been suggested that the *contrast* which maintains the border between B and C is the factor responsible for the behavior of the threshold, and accordingly the facts may be summarized as follows. (1) When the surrounding field C is either brighter or darker than area B, the resulting contrast border interferes with the formation of a border at the edge of A and therefore raises the threshold for A. (2) As the brightness of B and C approach equality contrast between them is diminished and the border of A due to release from interference can more easily emerge and thus the threshold falls. (3) It is inconsequential which of the two sides of the activating border is dark or bright; qualitatively the effect upon the border is the same, one of interference. (4) It also does not matter whether A is darker or brighter than B; the result upon the border between them is still one of interference. (5) Since the border between A and B is a circle the activating border acts sidewise against it.

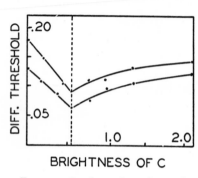

BRIGHTNESS OF C

FIG. 47.—Graphs to show the results obtained with the test-object in Fig. 46 (C) in which the effect of varying the brightness of C upon the differential threshold for A was tested. In the upper curve, A was darker than B. In the lower, A was constant and B was varied. The vertical line indicates the level of the constant field. Both the ordinate and abscissa are given in c/ft.² (*Fry and Bartley—Am. J. Physiol.*)

**Additional figures of Fry and Bartley.** The effect of an influencing border upon the end rather than the side of a test-border is demonstrated with a pattern such as Figure 48, in which the two areas which differ to produce the test-border are adjacent rectangles. They appear on a darker ground and the border is influenced by a bright annulus some distance from them. The inside border of the white annulus or ring acts on the ends of the boundary between the two rectangles, but is prevented from acting upon the sides of it by the outer borders of the rectangles which separate them from the surrounding dark field. It is impossible to directly demonstrate this by any manipulation of the situation, but it is possible under more suitable circumstances to show that one border can block activity spreading from another, and there seems to be no reason why such principles should not operate in the present case. An example of the blocking of the influence of one border by another is found in the previous situation pictured in

Figure 46 where the outer border of B blocks the inner border of C from affecting A.

Figure 48, analogous to Figure 46 but involving a reversal of relationships is the most difficult to analyze of any yet considered. The effects obtained from varying the brightness of area

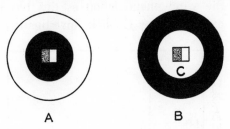

Fig. 48.—Figures for the demonstrating the effect of an activating border upon the ends of a test border. (*Fry and Bartley—Am. J. Physiol.*)

C are confusing since so doing manipulates the borders both at the outer edge of C and at the junctures between C and the test-object. Since it is highly desirable to show the effects of these borders separately, the patterns in Figure 49 have been designed. The first experiment is simply a modification of the one just

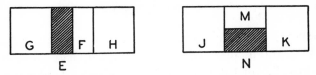

Fig. 49.—Patterns for analyzing the effect of varying the brightness of C in 48 (B). (*Fry and Bartley—Am. J. Physiol.*)

described. The effect of the border between G and E upon the bisecting border is similar to that of the border between B and C, upon the borders at the edge of A when it is brighter than B. Similarly the effect of the border between H and F upon the bisecting border is comparable to the effect of the border between B and C upon the border at the edge of A when it is darker than B. On the basis of the results in the earlier experiment it should be expected that the borders between E and G and be-

tween F and H would interfere with the institution of the bisecting border, when G and H are above or below E and F in brightness, and that this interference would diminish as G and H
approximate the brightness of E and F. This is precisely what
occurs.

Essentially the same phenomenon as this has been demonstrated in an experiment by Cobb in investigating the effect of

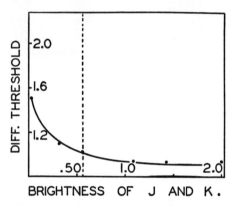

FIG. 50.—The effect of the bright side of a border upon the ends of a test
border resulting from manipulating the brightness of J and K, in Fig. 49.
Units in c/ft.² (*Fry and Bartley—Am. J. Physiol.*)

manipulating the brightness of a field surrounding a bisected
test-object, but in place of using a limited field with definite
boundaries, he used the whole field of vision. Under these circumstances the only borders which can act on the bisecting one
are those which separate the test-object from the surrounding
field. These borders raise the threshold of the bisecting one,
and therefore it should be higher when the surrounding field is
either above or below the level of the test-object than when equal.
Cobb substantiated these results.

The graph in Figure 50 indicates that when the level of J
and K in Figure 49 is raised the threshold for the bisecting border continues to fall without a subsequent rise when the brightness of J and K exceeds the level of M and N. It would seem

that the explanation of this is that the extreme borders of J and K set up processes which spread across the squares and act on the ends of the bisecting border reducing its threshold. It is not certain, however, that the effect is not produced by changes at the inner borders of the squares, although it seems that if this were true it would have occurred as the brightness of the squares transcended that of the test-object.

**Wilcox's visual acuity experiments.** The behavior of light bars on a dark ground is one of the situations obviously not explained by anatomy and the associated concept of threshold response. This situation has been criticized as being not proper to study for visual acuity measurements. It has been called a *glare* situation by its critics, owing to the fact that the eye in general is not illuminated. Naming it that is little argument against using it. All that can be said which might be of some significance is that the variable is not the general retinal illumination as in standard experiments. That is, the conditions are not comparable to those in many other experiments; but when taken for what they are, they throw light on the behavior of the eye in resolving spatial patterns. The idea of glare does not apply here, for the values obtained in the experiments in some respects are comparable to those in the more conventional set-ups. (See Fig. 11.) If glare were to function it would increase gradually as the intensity of the bars was raised and would offset the increases of visual acuity due to the finer anatomo-functional resolution of the eye. Instead, the curve shows that the increase in visual acuity proceeds as in other experiments up to a certain point, and only after this does its course change. The curve describing it reverses quite abruptly. A hint as to the underlying basis for the reversal in the curve is given below.

In the visual acuity experiment the two parallel bars, though constant in width, subjectively undergo pronounced variations in width as intensity is manipulated, which is in keeping with the well-known simpler observation that a very bright object on a dark ground appears larger than under other conditions, classically known in simpler situations as irradiation. The unexpected thing is that with rising intensity the bars expand, contract, and finally expand again under some conditions. Wilcox took this subjective alteration in the width of the bars in his visual acuity experiment to lie at the bottom of the variation of visual acuity itself.

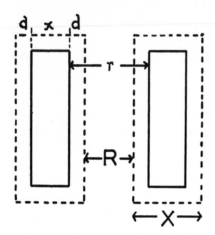

FIG. 51.—Diagram to illustrate Wilcox's irradiation measurements. The solid lines represent the bars as they would be without irradiation, while the dotted lines show them expanded by irradiation. X = width of bars under irradiation; x = their width originally; d = the amount of expansion of each border of the bars. (*Modified from Wilcox—Proc. Nat. Acad. Sci.*)

His test for the assumption that these variations in subjective width are the basis for changes in acuity with intensity is the following. With a fixed intensity, the two bars used to measure visual acuity are gradually separated until the observer judges the width of the space between them to be equal to the sum of the widths of the two bars. The discrepancy between the physical and apparent widths then furnished a measure of the shift in apparent contours. Figure 51 shows the principle of the experiment. The bars are illustrated with a physical separation of $r$ and a width of $x$. These same bars are subjectively widened on each side by an amount $d$ so that the total subjective width of each is $x$ plus 2d or X. If R is the subjective separation of the inner contours, then according to the experiment, R equals 2X or r — 2d. By combining these we find that 2d equals $r/3 - 2x/3$. After the observer has made his judgment, the interspace between the two physical stimuli is measured and divided by 3. Two-thirds of the physical width of each bar is subtracted and thereby a numerical measure of the displacement of the two apparent contours is obtained.

In the case of bright bars on a dark ground, $d$ is large and positive at low intensities decreasing to zero as intensity is raised and then finally increases again.

With dark bars on a bright ground, $d$ is positive, meaning that the bars are widened, verifying the existence of Volkmann's negative irradiation. This subjective widening of the black bars persists throughout a wide range of intensities, though gradually decreasing to zero. At intensities beyond this point $d$ becomes increasingly negative.

Let it be supposed that if irradiation were absent the bars would have to be separated by a certain distance $S_0$ before they would be seen as separate. This represents a hypothetical threshold. But if the bars so separated are themselves subjectively widened (so-called irradiation) they will not actually appear separate; no gap will be seen between them. Since it is the apparent displacement of each contour, the distance between the bars will have to be increased by an amount 2d before the gap will be seen. $d$ can be quantitatively specified under any set of intensity conditions but the value of $S_0$ needs to be known before the quantitative validity of the hypothesis can be tested. $S_0$ is the resolution threshold in which there is no irradiation, the quantity $d$ being zero. As it happens the experimental data provide a way of ascertaining the value of $S_0$. In the case of the dark bars on bright ground, $d$ passed through a zero value at an intermediate intensity value of the ground ($I_0$). By determining the value of the threshold for the resolution of the dark bars at this intensity ($I_0$), we find the quantitative value of $S_0$. Since in every one of Wilcox's experiments, $d$ assumed a zero value at some intensity in the range, it was possible to construct curves representing *theoretical* values of the resolution threshold. The curves shown in Figure 11 in Chapter II were checked by this method.

So far we have been dealing with what is classically known as irradiation, but it has been pointed out that this phenomenon is a matter of a shift in contours. In this, it has become evident that the mechanism of contour formation is involved in still another type of situation in addition to those previously mentioned.

**Kravkov's experiment.** Not alone has Wilcox studied the matter of *irradiation* or the shift in contours. Kravkov performed some tests of visual acuity in which the bars instead of being 2′22″ (as were Wilcox's), were 6′33″. Kravkov interpreted his findings as a combination of irradiation and brightness discrimination (contrast-sensibility), stating that irradiation increased throughout the whole intensity range instead of dropping to a

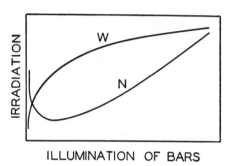

ILLUMINATION OF BARS

Fig. 52.—Irradiation as dependent upon illumination where bright bars are used on a dark field. The results are those of Kravkov. The curves do not represent absolute values but only the general relationship. The upper curve is for a wide bar (a visual angle of 6′53″), the lower for a narrow bar (3′27″).

minimum and rising again as intensity was increased. Galochkina in the same laboratory, later tried two sets of bars, the smaller pair having a visual angle of 3′27″ and the larger a value of 6′53″. Using an illumination range of 0.5 to 71 lux, and considering the difference between the width of the interspace and the total width of the two bars as the irradiation value, he obtained with the smaller bars curve N, as in Figure 52. It will be noted that the curve first falls sharply and then ascends as intensity is increased. A minimum is exhibited in corroboration of Wilcox. With the larger bars, the results are not at all identical. Curve W rises throughout the whole range of intensities.

Musylev in the same laboratory determined the visual acuity for still larger bars (7′), throughout a range of from 1.5 to 700 lux, the bars having a reflection coefficient of about .80 per cent. In this experiment, the visual acuity reached a maximum though

Galochkina showed that the curve for the development of irradiation does not reach a minimum for bars of this size. This, the investigators felt, indicated that other factors besides irradiation were at work.

Summing up so far, it may be said that with narrow bars, *irradiation* reaches a minimum, and with broader ones it does not. *Brightness* discrimination improves throughout the whole range. Action of the two factors should produce a maximum in the visual acuity curve at medium intensities. This is what results by experimental test.

**The factors in irradiation.** To explain the difference between the factor of irradiation with narrow and broad bars, Kravkov has resorted to the findings of Fry and Bartley, and Fry and Cobb, on the influence of contours upon one another. The specific application to this situation is as follows. The presence of one border in the visual field depresses the perceptibility of another when it acts at right angles upon it. The borders which are the edges of the bars are parallel and fulfil this condition.

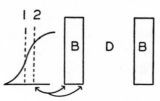

FIG. 53.—Diagram to show the bright bars (BB) on a dark background (D). The inset at the left represents the shift in contour of the bright bars due to the depressive influence of contours on each other. The contour comes at 2 instead of 1, and will compensate for the depressive influence, according to Kravkov.

Edges bb and aa as shown in Figure 53 will depress each other. Since the actual distribution of the light for the images of each of the bars is tapered rather than abrupt, the mutual depressant effects of their opposite edges bb and aa will cause the boundaries to be formed at a higher point on the blur gradient of each edge of the bar.

This Kravkov labels "contrast of perceptibility." The nearer the borders aa and bb are to each other the greater is the effect. Likewise conditions such as increasing intensity which would produce more perceptible borders aa and bb would heighten their depressant effects on each other and tend to decrease their irradiation. Irradiation due to this factor must constantly *decrease* as illumination increases.

In addition, it must be recognized that as illumination is raised, the steepness of the *blur gradient* between the bright bar and the dark field increases and consequently tends to *increase* irradiation. The net irradiation due to the two factors may be plotted as Kravkov has done, using illumination as the abscissa and irradiation as the ordinate; and choosing proper ordinate values for the two factors, it can be shown how net irradiation will first wane and then finally increase as illumination is increased. Actual irradiation is the result issuing from the two opposing factors, "contrast of perceptibility" and the level of illumination.

With wide bars, "contrast of perceptibility" is absent and thus the minimum in the middle range of the curve due to it is also absent. The curve rises from the very first.

**Contour of the finest resolvable line.** One of the beginnings of the inquiry into the basis for seeing contour is the study of the minimum resolvable line in terms of visual angle and the retinal sense-cell mosaic.

Following their experiments in which they obtained a value of 0.5 sec. for the finest visual acuity, Hecht and Mintz also calculated the distribution of the light upon the retina for each of several widths of lines, and showed what they believed to be the basis for the perception of contour in the limiting case. Since they found that the pupil diameter is never less than 3 mm. they used this value for their calculations with Rayleigh's equations which the latter worked out for the blurredness of the retinal image. The light distribution of the line corresponding to the smallest resolvable angle is so flat that it can scarcely be shown in a drawing which includes the distributions for the threshold resolutions at low illuminations. From the diagram of a geometrical image of 3 mm. it would seem that the total width of the blur is about 8 $\mu$ instead and falls on a band of at least five cones. The blur of a geometrical image to a line 2.6 $\mu$ wide would be about 15 $\mu$ and cover about seven cones. The absolute values found by Hecht and Mintz are different from those con-

ceived by Hartridge, who made computations of the same sort
for a line subtending 8 sec. of arc.  He used a 2-mm. pupil and
a 3.2 $\mu$ cone width, and as a result found a difference of 10 per
cent between the illumination of a single row of cones and the
ones adjacent to it.  By actual experiment, however, the value he
found as a resolution threshold was between 3 and 4 sec. for a
black line on an illuminated background.  This would indicate
that the difference between the central row of cones and its immediate neighbors would be 5 per cent instead of 10 per cent.  Hecht
and Mintz point out that this is a coarse intensity difference to
be the limiting factor in visual acuity.

Furthermore this coarse difference cannot be accounted for by
employing the fact that intensity discrimination becomes poor
with extremely small areas, i.e., when few elements are involved.
Small areas are not used in these measurements, for in order to
obtain the fine resolutions they did, the test line must be an
extended one.  The number of retinal elements involved would
correspond to the total in areas yielding the best values for
intensity discrimination.

Hecht and Mintz used a smaller value than Hartridge for cone
width.  They found by using the same type of calculations that
the central row of cones differs from its adjacent neighbor lying
to either side by less than 1 per cent, a value approximating those
found for intensity-discrimination thresholds at quite high light
intensities.

They believe then that a fine line is perceived at the small
angles they found because even its blurred shadow reduces the
light on one extended row of cones to a level which is just functionally less than the light on the row of cones to either side of it.
They think the line appears sharp because it produces a recognizable shadow on one row of cones only.  Considering the general retinal illumination as 100 per cent, the second row of cones
on either side of the central row has its illumination reduced by
only .22 per cent from the illumination adjacent to it.  If one
considers this difference by itself it would mean that it was only
one four-hundredth less brightly illuminated than the cone row

next to it. The other rows nearer the edge of the blur band have their illumination diminished even less. From this they conclude that no neural mechanism is necessary for compensating for the blur. A sharp line is seen simply because the illumination of only the center row of cones is sufficiently different from the rest.

This explanation does not seem to cover the situation with low illuminations where the minimal resolvable angle is 10 min. of arc, a spatial value 1200 times as great as the one we have just dealt with, and again we may have to resort to some neural process to account for contour.

**Visual discrimination of two bright lines on a dark field.** Fry and Cobb studied the behavior of two bright bars on a dark field to discover the relation between their width, brightness, and the minimum separation for their resolution. Their investigation has similarities to that of Wilcox, Kravkov, and Hecht and Mintz. It is similar to the first-mentioned study inasmuch as visual acuity for bright bars on a dark field is tested in both. It is similar to the second on account of the fact that they both show that the width of the bars is a governing factor in their resolution, and that they offer, in part, the same answer. It is like the third investigation since the blur of the image is recognized in both and treated in essentially the same way.

Hecht and Mintz have accounted for the resolution of a single fine line and have seemed to dismiss successfully the need for a neural mechanism for producing sharp contour. The present study of Fry and Cobb has taken lines somewhat coarser than the minimal resolvable one and has examined the minimum separation at which they can be seen as two. They find that they cannot fully account for the behavior of the lines without the use of a contour process in addition to the type of mechanism described by Hecht and Mintz. It can be concluded from this then that one does not need to get very far away from the simple terminal conditions such as Hecht and Mintz used until the explanations used to account for such conditions will not handle the new conditions in question. It is anything but axiomatic that explanations from terminal cases of maximum simplicity can be carried over to others higher in the scale, though this caution has been ignored over and over again.

**Fry and Cobb's experiments.** Fry and Cobb used two bright bars each 22″ in width. In keeping with their previous study which determined the distribution of the blur in the retinal image, they first called attention to the fact that as bars are brought close together, their blurs overlap. This forms an illumination distribution of two maxima with a minimum between. As the bars are brought still closer together the overlapping blurs sum to a greater intensity than the original maxima and thus the original distribution gives way to one in which there is but a single maximum. Before this occurs the bars have become too close together to be seen as separate. According to the Hartridge principle used by Hecht and Mintz, the bars have reached the resolution threshold by the time that the minimum described above is just enough lower than the maxima on either side of it to be discriminated under the laws of brightness discrimination. With a very narrow line Hecht and Mintz were able to show that a single row of cones was stimulated at a discriminably higher level than those on either side of it. Such cannot be the case here for the bars instead of being but 0.5″ wide are 22″ or 44 times as wide, and the interspace never drops below about 25″. This necessitates the action of a neural process for the initial phase in the discrimination.

Another important finding is that broad and narrow bars do not act alike. The same workers investigated the difference by using two sets, one whose width was 1000″ and the other 168″. Their length in both cases was 2000″. The results are plotted in Figure 54 where it is shown that as the brightness of the bars is increased from a very low level up to 3 c/ft.$^2$, visual acuity first rapidly rises, but for the narrow bars falls again very slowly. For the wide bars, it continues to ascend slowly after the first rapid rise.

To explain this, they utilized the principle that Fry and Bartley first set forth and which Kravkov was later able to employ in his study of visual acuity; namely, that borders interfere with each other's formation. A threshold border is demonstrably interfered with by the existence of another border in the vicinity. In the case in hand, this applies to the contours of the bars themselves, and makes bar width a critical factor in determining the minimum perceptible interspace between them. When the bars are wide, the opposite edges of the bars themselves are far enough removed from each other to interfere very little. Such was the

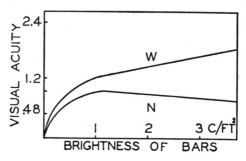

Fig. 54.—The effect of varying the brightness of two parallel bars in a dark field upon visual acuity. W represents the result with bars having a visual angle of 1000 sec., while N gives the result with bars only 168 sec. wide. The results are from Fry and Cobb.

case with bars 1000″ wide, whereas when they were only 168″ wide, the influence was much greater.

**Demonstration of the Fry-Bartley principle.** When the results of Fry and Cobb are plotted in terms of the distribution of the light in the retinal images of the bars and the interspace, an essential difference can be shown between the behavior of the narrow and broad sets of bars. For the ordinate, the threshold difference in intensity between the images of the interspace and the bars was used, for the abscissa, the intensity at the center of the images of the bars. The curve for the narrow bars rises rather rapidly, while that for the broad bars only slowly and at a decelerating rate. Since the shapes of the two curves are not alike, it cannot be said that the one is a simple multiple of the other. The curve for the narrow bars shows that a greater threshold difference is required for each increment in general intensity level than for the broad bars, and instead of tapering off as one might expect, the effect even tends to accelerate. The difference between the results with narrow and broad bars is presumably due to the difference in the separation of the borders of each bar from one another. This is an example of the principle announced by Fry and Bartley, already discussed.

**Binocular effects.** That border contrast alters the brilliance of an object seen binocularly is demonstrated in the case of Fechner's paradox, as the two following situations will show. If the light coming from one of two closely placed squares is held constant for the right eye but manipulated from zero to 1 c/ft.$^2$ for the other, and the physical brightness of the other square whose light falls equally on both eyes is adjusted so that the two squares appear to be equal in brightness, the values shown in Figure 55 are necessary.

Beginning at zero, as the level is increased for the left eye up to a certain point, the brightness of A decreases, but beyond that point it begins to increase and finally reaches a brilliance much greater than the original. This paradoxical decrease in the net result when stimulation of the one eye is added to that of the other is due to the fact that summation is not the only process involved.

The following is another situation showing the same thing. In this the brightness of the ground is held at .225 c/ft.$^2$ instead of zero. The brightness of A seen by the right eye is kept constant at 1 c/ft.$^2$ and the brightness as seen by the other alone is set at various levels from .225 to 1 c/ft.$^2$ If the brightness of A for the left eye is lowered below the brightness of the ground the binocular effect is that of rivalry. A unitary and constant brightness level is not observed, but rather an alternation between a level below the background and that of one above. This is why a brightness for the left eye which is equal to the brightness of the ground is taken as the low point. As the brightness of the left eye is gradually raised above that of the ground, the brilliance of A decreases at first but begins to increase, ultimately reaching a value much greater than the original.

Inspection of these experiments reveals that the paradoxical decrease in brightness when the stimulation of one eye is added to that of the other depends not upon the brightness of the dimmer one taken absolutely, but upon the difference between its

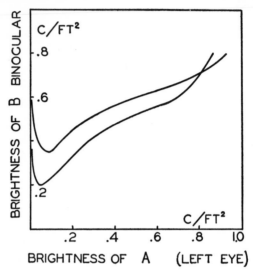

FIG. 55.—The effect of varying the brightness of the ground upon Fechner's paradox. The brightness of A seen by right eye = 1 c/ft.² Brightness of ground = 0. When the brightness of the ground is set at .225 c/ft.² the curves begin at that brightness for A seen by the left eye (abscissa) at a level of .7 on the ordinate. As the brightness of A seen by the left eye is increased the curves dip slightly at first, then rise slowly. (*Fry and Bartley—Am. J. Ophthal.*)

level and that of the ground. That is, upon the existence of a border between the dimmer stimulation reaching the left eye, and its ground. *Fechner's paradox then is not a question of the presence or absence of summation but rather a demonstration of one of the roles played by contour processes.*

The foregoing facts make it seem in order to postulate that the processes subserving border contrast between the brightness seen by the left eye and its ground in some way depress the processes initiated by the right eye and it might also be supposed that the

latter processes depress those initiated by the left eye. If we
examine the curve of the results from Figure 55, the following
theoretical analysis will apply. In the diagram, Figure 56, curve
C, represents the activity initiated by the right eye from its stimulation by rectangle A. It remains constant. Curve D represents

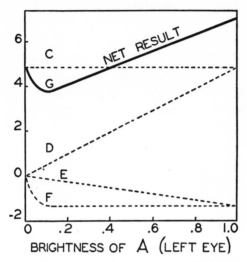

FIG. 56.—An analysis of the factors involved in Fechner's paradox. The
values of the axes are only hypothetical, + values of the ordinate representing
activity; − values, depression of activity. C = Dextrocular activity, D = Sinistrocular activity, E = Depression of sinis. activity, F = Depression of dex. act.,
and G = Net result after summation. (*Fry and Bartley—Am. J. Ophthal.*)

the activity initiated in the left eye by A. It is supposed that it
increases gradually as the brightness of this component increases.
Curve E represents the amount by which the dextrocular process
depresses the sinistrocular activity when the two monocular processes converge in the brain. Curve F represents the amount by
which the sinistrocular process depresses the dextrocular one.
The algebraic summation of these four curves gives the resulting
curve G. It represents the net amount of activity from the summation of the two monocular activities, taking into account their
depressive effects on each other. This curve is quite similar to
the experimental ones which represent the net brightnesses re-

sulting from the various combinations of stimulating the right
and left eyes. This concept accounts for Fechner's paradox.
When the stimulation of the left eye is .05 c/ft.$^2$ Fechner's paradox reaches its maximum. In this situation the dextrocular activity is definitely depressed by the sinistrocular, an amount not
offset by the slight summation of the sinistrocular and the dextrocular processes.

When the brightness of A as seen by both eyes is equal
(1 c/ft.$^2$), the two monocular processes in interacting produce
depressive effects upon each other but these are more than offset
by summation, the outcome being that A as seen by both eyes is
much brighter than when seen by the right eye alone.

The following arrangement shows what happens when a dark
object on a white ground confronts one eye and a uniform white
ground the corresponding parts of the other. The brightness of
A as seen by the right eye and the brightness of the ground are
kept at 1.23 c/ft.$^2$ and the level of A as seen by the left eye is
set at various places from zero to 1.23 c/ft.$^2$ The observer determines the brightness of B, which is viewed by both eyes alike,
at which it appears to be equal to A.

When A as seen by the left eye is black, it seen binocularly is
almost black and seems not to be influenced by the fact that the
right eye sees it as considerably brighter. The light presented to
the right eye raises the net brightness very little. The dextrocular
activity set up by the light from A reaching the right eye must
be depressed by the corresponding process in the left eye. Since
A as seen by the left eye is black and since we know it is not
stimulated, no process is set up and the inactivity of the left half
of the visual apparatus cannot be said to depress activity arising
in the right. Consequently the depression must be assigned to
the process responsible for the contour between A as seen by
the left eye, and its ground.

What happens when a light gray object on a white ground is
presented to one eye and a dark gray object on a white ground
is presented to the corresponding area of the other is shown by
the following situation. In it the brightness of A seen by the

right eye is set at .695 c/ft.² and the brightness of the ground at 1.23 c/ft.² The brightness of A as seen by the left eye is set at various levels from zero to 1.3 c/ft.² For each combination of A as seen by right and left eyes is matched against the brightness of B as seen by both eyes to be equally brilliant, the following results occur. The brightness of A increases as the intensity of A as seen by the left eye is increased from zero up to the point where the brightness of A as seen by the left and right eyes is equal, but beyond this point the subjective brightness of A is not increased by adding to the stimulation of the left eye by A. Lowering the stimulation from A to the left eye below that of the stimulation reaching the right eye from it decreases the subjective brightness of A, but raising it above the brightness of A fails to increase the subjective brightness.

Binocular rivalry between the processes in the two eyes set up by stimulation from A, occurs only when the one is above and the other below the brightness of the ground. The intermittent disappearance of A as seen by the right eye cannot be attributed to the blackness of A, as seen by the left eye, but rather must be assigned to the process subserving the contour between A as seen by the left, and its ground.

**Helson and Fehrer's study.** The further role of contour formation in the determination of subjective brightness of areas can be shown by introducing the factor of time. That is to say, not only the spatial relationships of stimulation but also the temporal are involved. Contours require a certain amount of time for their formation. The absence or presence of certain areas as "things" and their diminution or enhancement in brightness depend in part on this factor. This is ably shown by the following group of experiments in which both the temporal sequence and the spatial patterns are manipulated. Helson and Fehrer showed that objects presented tachistoscopically were first seen as dim patches of light before any definite form was recognized, but as the interval of exposure was lengthened definite form emerged.

**Werner's experiments.** Werner presented pairs of figures of many shapes, varying from circles and discs to irregular and incomplete forms. For example, if a solid black disc is briefly presented on a light background and in about 150 ms. a black ring whose inner border coincides with the outer edge of the disc is also briefly presented, the disc will not be observed. That is to say, the area within the ring or annulus will not be black. If the temporal presentation of these figures is reversed, the black disc is seen. The temporal features of the succession in order that the disc will vanish are more or less critical. If the rate of succession is slow, the disc will be seen first and then the ring; if more rapid, the ring is seen with a darkened inner field; if still more rapid the inner field brightens and may become even brighter in some cases than the field outside the ring. It is possible to interchange the brightness relation between the figures and the ground on which they are presented so that the figures are white and the ground is black and still have the original phenomena occur. Werner's many additional figures, from the simplest to the most irregular, consisted in areas whose outer edges coincided with the inner edges of other areas (figures) non-simultaneously presented. The second figure had both an inner and an outer border or boundary, whereas the first had only an outer boundary. Since the results differed in keeping with which of the two was presented first, they indicate that the outer boundary of the second figure played a part in the outcome. It may be also added that Werner later determined that his results are not dependent upon monocular vision; they may be obtained when the first object is presented to one eye, and the second to the other eye.

The following is an account of what may occur. When the disc is presented first but is followed very soon by the ring, the *border* of the disc has not had time to form. Since the border has not formed at the only time it could, the ring simply develops as a ring without the disc ever having been seen. At a critical stage in the decay of what little was formed of the border of the disc, the presentation of the ring may be able to utilize it to accentuate its own inner border, for the directions of the two developing gradients would be the same. Extra border contrast may also develop and the inner field look brighter than otherwise. This account is, of course, based on the principle originally recognized in threshold studies, namely, that borders must emerge before difference in the brightness of two areas can be distin-

## WERNER'S FIGURES

FIG. 57.—A set of figures to show what happens under certain conditions of stroboscopic succession. If the disc is given first and then the ring whose inner border is in the same position as the outer border of the disc, the disc will disappear. That is to say, the area within the ring remains white. If, however, the disc is followed by only a semi-ring only part of the disc will disappear. The part being absorbed is that which is bounded by the semi-ring; the remainder exists as a half-disc whose surface becomes darker and darker as one proceeds from the area enclosed by the semi-disc. This is shown in the third figure from left. (*Werner—Am. J. Psych.* 47:40, 46. 1935.)

guished. *Whatever depresses or destroys border formation, obliterates the appreciation of the brightness a surface would otherwise have.* We may continue with the account by describing the events when the order of presentation is reversed. In this case, the temporal interval between the presentation of the two is not critical. The ring is presented and regardless of how soon the disc appears it is seen as a black surface. That is to say, if the disc is presented before the contour process of the inner border of the ring is developed, it is simply forestalled and the whole figure is seen as a disc whose outer border is the outer border of the ring. However, if the inner contour of the ring has had time to develop before the presentation of the disc, this event by changing the illumination within the ring obliterates the condition for its continuance, especially under the depressive influence of the outer border of the ring.

An experiment performed by Fry may have some connection with explaining the phenomena just described, though it deserves mention in its own right. He showed that the brightness of

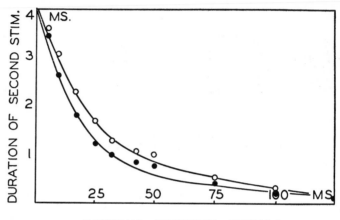

INTERVAL  BETWEEN  STIMULI

Fɪɢ. 58.—The duration of the second stimulus which elicits a sensation as bright as that produced by the first whose duration is fixed, when various intervals between the two are used. Duration of first stimulus = 4 ms. Intensity of both stimuli = 28,000 photons. Upper curve represents results from using stimulus b, then a. Lower curve shows results when their order was reversed. (*Fry—Am. J. Physiol.*)

the first of two successively presented adjacent test areas was diminished by the presentation of the second. Figure 58 shows how this diminution is related to the temporal interval separating the two. He also showed that if the two areas are not actually adjacent but are slightly separated the effect is less and less, depending upon the distance. Figure 59 shows the relationship. The net outcome is dependent upon the way borders act upon one another, or to put it more accurately, upon the way the processes responsible for borders interact.

**After-images and contour.** Certain quantitative facts concerning the development of after-images help to show how contour processes behave.  The experiments that are to be related were performed by Creed and Granit, though the implications drawn from them belong to the viewpoint expressed in this chapter.

For example, if a small disc is used as a fixation point and a second similar disc is placed a little distance to one side, the after-image of the latter emerges at least 2 seconds before that of the former, and their periodicities are independent.  If the two

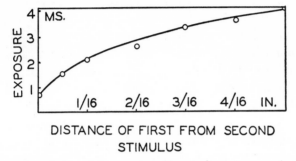

DISTANCE OF FIRST FROM SECOND
STIMULUS

FIG. 59.—The relation of the exposure (duration) of the second stimulus to the retinal separation between it and the first when the temporal interval is kept constant at 50 ms. and the duration of the first is fixed at 4 ms.  (*Fry—Am. J. Physiol.*)

discs are made the ends of a single figure by tying them together with a white strip whose breadth is the same as the diameters of the discs, the appearance of the negative after-image is controlled in a different way and varies somewhat with different observers.  Only the dark image of the peripheral end may appear first with the blackness sweeping across like a shutter until the whole image is complete, both ends disappearing together at the end of the first stage.  On the other hand, the outline of the whole figure may appear simultaneously, with the image at first graded in darkness, the peripheral end being the darker.  In this case also, the whole figure fades simultaneously at the end of the first phase.  Then again, the whole image may be seen simultaneously and with uniform darkness and sharp outline. The fading may begin from the distal end and proceed inward from the fixation point at the end of the first phase.

It is obvious from this that the existence of a contour uniting the two discs markedly modifies the appearance and time relations of the after-images set up by foveal and peripheral stimulation, and to a great degree synchronizes them, despite any functional difference between the fovea and the peripheral retina.

The effect of contour in the development of after-images is also shown by the way their latency behaves as area is varied. Latency ordinarily shortens as the size of the disc-like test-object increases. More extended experimentation shows that this is approximately true when the center of the disc is the fixation point; but when it is outside of the macula, the area of the test-object is devoid of influence. That is to say, the number of sense-cells activated is of no significance, at least with test-objects subtending more than 22′, if the edge of the image falls predominantly on sense-cells outside the area of transition from rods to cones; and, we might say, if the borders are far enough apart so as not to influence each other. *Changes in latency with test-objects in the central field of vision are dependent not upon the effect of spatial summation but upon the fact that the edges or contours fall successively on sense-cells of changing character as area is increased, and that the edges become further and further separated.* This means that the latency of the after-image depends upon the contour-building processes as a critical factor. The principle that is to be isolated here is that if the contour is to be built by one set of elements it will be different than if built by another group of somewhat different character. This has, in part, the same basis as other phenomena which reveal a spatial gradient from center to periphery, and would be expected to be more especially dependent upon a difference in the richness and type of synaptic connections in this axis than upon any property of the sense-cells themselves.

If the area of the test-object whose center is fixated is varied in size from a value covering only the fovea or thereabouts to one whose diameter subtends about 4.5° of visual angle, it is found that the latency at first is quite long. As the area is increased, latency shortens rapidly to a point 2° from fixation, and then increases again between this and about $3°$ after which it again shortens. This produces a hump in the curve with its peak at about $3°$, which is the place on the retina marking the transition from a predominance of cones to a predominance of rods. We see then that if the image of the test-object falls in this transition region the contour processes set up which control the latency of the after-image require more time than if they involved regions just central or peripheral to this point.

It is not known just how contour processes account for the latency of the after-image and under many conditions the simultaneous appearance of all portions of the after-image, but some investigators have envisaged a situation as if the central region were a blind spot. If we refer to the description of the curve relating latency to radius it will be remembered that the central region is much slower than the peripheral. The latency of the after-image is controlled then by the most peripheral region and requires only a start from the periphery to be set into activity and the whole after-image is completed almost simultaneously.

It is interesting to anticipate beforehand what would happen if the edge of the after-image were made to be dependent on the slow transitional regions whose latency is greater than regions just central or peripheral. It might be expected that the after-image would appear first as a ring corresponding to the region of the faster part of the retina—just central to the hump of the transition region—and spread inward and outward from this. But this does not happen. No trace of the after-image appears at the short interval characteristic of the faster parts of the retina, but appears only later with all parts simultaneous. Here again the edge seems to be the determining factor.

**Contour in relation to visual movement.** It is characteristic for sharp contours to emerge in stationary visual fields. It has already been stated that contour formation takes time, so that it is to be expected that, if ever, contours should be found in stationary fields. In fact we are so familiar with the existence of contours, borders or edges, that we feel that objects are scarcely objects without them. Actually blurred transitions or borders give rise to the conviction that the two levels of brightness seen in the visual field are but part of a gradient within a single physical object, and not two objects.

Despite all of this, the existence of sharp visual boundary lines is not the indispensable attributes of independent physical objects or independently variable patches of light. This was seen at the very beginning in our first description in Chapter I of the role of intensity in the appearance of visual form.

It is true that if we find an object or area in the visual field bounded by a sharp contour while stationary we at once assume that it is an intrinsic property of the object and that motion of the object will not modify this property. It was found, however, in Chapter VII, that certain rates of movement destroyed the sharp boundaries of objects and some finally reduced the objects to nothing more than a gray streak. These gray streaks, even though they have lost the attribute of contour, still carry the conviction of movement, with the observer.

This being true it should become obvious that cases of apparent movement should form examples in which the conviction of movement is amply strong though the passage of a well contoured object from one definite place to another cannot be seen. Optimal movement results from setting the stage in terms of distance, time between onset and termination, and brightness to give the conviction of movement of a single object.

It is only when the fact that actual moving objects may fail to exhibit contour is not recognized that the existence of apparent movement becomes its greatest puzzle. At certain critical rates of real movement, sharp contour is lacking and it is only within such ranges that optimal apparent movement of the beta variety can be established. If it were to be produced to simulate most any rate of real movement, its existence then would truly be a puzzle.

### CONTOUR AS GEOMETRICAL SHAPE

**Shape as a function of the vector-field.** It will be recalled that Brown and Voth made a study in which they demonstrated the practicality of using the concept of a vector field to predict the cause of seen movement. This field was made up of two kinds of forces, cohesive and restraining forces acting in opposite directions. Their strength at any point is a function of time, space, and intensity distribution. Three limiting conditions for the field are possible, (1) when the combined restraining forces ($\Sigma R$) are *greater than* the combined cohesive forces ($\Sigma C$), (2) when the combined forces of the two kinds are *equal,* and (3) when the combined restraining forces are *less than* the combined cohesive field forces. Brown and Voth stated that the first condition described chaos, and such phenomena as autokinetic movement occur; that the second describes stability; and in the third predictable movement occurs.

While the above workers applied themselves to studying condition (3), Orbison has taken up the study of condition (2). He points out that if stable patterns are to be accounted for by field forces such as postulated, it should be possible to demonstrate their behavior experimentally. For this, he suggests the introduction of objects into the field, as is done in electromagnetic fields in order that the field and object may interact. Thus if by this method it is possible to predict alterations in shape of geometrical patterns introduced into stable configurations from theory previously laid down, the latter may be regarded as substantiated.

To carry out his experiments, Orbison used three separate fields, into each of which were introduced four or five figures. Considerable space would be required adequately to describe the results and discuss their significance. The first field was a circle containing many closely and uniformly spaced radii; the second, a pattern of concentric circles; and the third, a pattern of acute angles evenly spaced, and so arranged that their corners lay in a straight line through the center of the field. The objects which were introduced were, a circle, two or three parallel lines, a triangle, a square, and two lines forming an angle.

In each case the introduced figure was distorted in the direction of the *positions of cohesive equilibrium.* It happens that the position of cohesive equilibrium for the first field, a circle with radii, are circles concentric with the circumference of the field; for the second field they are radii; and for the third field, they are imaginary lines at right-angles to the lines in the field.

The results from the shifting of the figures about in the fields used, confirm the vector-field hypothesis ($\Sigma\ R = \Sigma\ C$) for stable perceptions by demonstrating the distortion which is implied

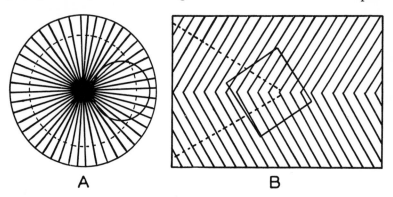

**A**                                                  **B**

Fig. 60.—Two sample patterns used in a vector-field analysis of stationary visual fields. The dotted lines represent single positions of cohesive equilibrium. (See text.) (*Orbison—Am. J. Psychol.* 52:37, 44. 1939.)

when $\Sigma\ C$ is changed. The results show not only that shape is determined by the total field, but that by viewing it as a vector-field it is possible to predict the shape an object will have in a given situation.

If as Brown and Voth, and Orbison contend, the activity of the retina and the optic cortex can be ordered to a vector-field, specific problems may emerge which in turn may throw new light on our understanding of vision. In order for the concept to apply, it is likely that activity in terms other than synaptic functions may need to be recognized. Much has been said about such by a few psychological theorists but nothing has been done in attempt to hasten the verification of such assumptions. Much less than full credit will be due such prognosticators if the day arrives when they can say "I told you so."

**In summary.** Contour has meant two things: Edge, boundary or gradient, and also shape. Both imply coordinate activity in the neural mechanism of a nature that is not predicted by a random conduction of nerve impulses through a system of synaptic connections viewed as an aggregate of independently characterized junctures. The only coordinating influence we now recognize as containing adequate potentialities is a field.

## REFERENCES

Creed, R. S., and Ragnar Granit. On the latency of negative after-images following stimulation of different areas of the retina. *J. Physiol.*, 1928, 66:281-298.

Fry, Glenn A. The relation of border-contrast to the distinctness of vision. *Psych. Rev.*, 1931, 38:542-549.

Fry, Glenn A. Depression of the activity aroused by a flash of light by applying a second flash immediately afterwards to adjacent areas of the retina. *Am. J. Physiol.*, 1934, 108:701-707.

Fry, Glenn A., and S. Howard Bartley. The effect of one border in visual field upon the threshold of another. *Am. J. Physiol.*, 1935, 112:414-421.

Fry, Glenn A., and Percy W. Cobb. A new method for determining the blurredness of the retinal image. *Trans. Acad. Ophthal. & Otolaryngology*, 1935.

Fry, Glenn A., and V. M. Robertson. Alleged effects of figure-ground upon hue and brilliance. *Am. J. Psych.*, 1935, 67:424-435.

Orbison, William Dillard. Shape as a function of the vector-field. *Am. J. Psych.*, 1939, 52:31-45.

Orbison, William Dillard. The correction of an omission in shape as a function of the vector-field. *Am. J. Psych.*, 1939, 52:309.

Werner, Heinz. Studies on contour. I. Qualitative analyses. *Am. J. Psych.*, 1935, 47:40-64.

Werner, H. Studies in contour: strobostereoscopic phenomena. *Am. J. Psych.*, 1940, 53:418-422.

# XI

# THE ELECTRORETINOGRAM

**The discovery of electroretinogram.** As early as 1849 Du Bois-Reymond noted a potential difference between the cornea and the fundus. This came to be known as the *resting potential*. It often reached several millivolts and was found to be independent of illumination. In the external circuit the fundus was negative, the current passing from the distal end of the sensory cells towards their base. Dewar and McKendrick found an opposite polarity in the external circuit in examining invertebrate animals. But Piper (1904) showed that there was no difference in principle; only an anatomical difference between the two types of eye. In the invertebrates, the sensory epithelium lies with its free end towards cornea and the light, whereas in the vertebrates the elements are inverted. The directions of current therefore differ only in relation to the eye as a whole but are the same within the sensory cells. The free end is negative relative to the base with its afferent fiber. Waller regarded inescapable mechanical injury as the cause of the resting potential, while Kühne and Steiner (1881) considered it the manifestation of the physiological activity of the rods and cones.

It was in 1865 that Holmgren discovered the retinal *action potential,* called the retinogram, or ERG. The literature of the discovery and early investigation of it is exhaustively treated elsewhere by Kohlrausch, Graham, and later by Granit. As in the case of the resting potential, the direction of the action potential was first thought to vary in certain species but the view was finally corrected by v. Brücke and Garten (1907) and also by Piper who made it clear that the ERG is essentially similar in all of the vertebrates.

After the discovery of the *action potential* of the retina, various relations between the size of it and the resting potential were found. So far these have thrown little or no light upon the physiology of vision and do not merit further consideration here.

It was only in 1903 that the distortion in recording the potential was to a great extent overcome. Gotch did this by use of the capillary electrometer and produced a picture which is essentially like the ones recorded today. Even before this, various phases of the recorded activity were recognized by such investigators as Dewar and McKendrick and Holmgren. Kühne and Steiner made the first attempt to attribute the phases to certain postulated components of the underlying activity. Hartline showed that the ERG in the intact animal and in the excised eye are alike. Those included later in the history of the analysis are Einthoven and Jolly, Piper, Frölich, and Kohlrausch.

The most extensive recent analysis is that of Granit and colleagues, 1933, and succeeding years, which has been achieved first by the use of agents applied to the eye or to the animal which would alter the shape of the recorded ERG, and next by the manipulation of the "off effect." It was found that certain drugs would alter the shape of the response in such ways as to suggest that certain fixed components had thereby been eliminated.

**The normal retinogram and its components. ERG.** The typical ERG is recorded by placing one electrode upon the cornea and the other at the back of the eye close to the exit of the optic nerve. Either wick or metal electrodes may be used, but if the latter they must be of such material or so placed that the illumination of the eye does not strike them and set up photoelectric currents.

The typical succession of electrical variations which are recorded from such a preparation as light is suddenly flashed into the eye is as follows. The first is a slight negative deflection of short duration ($a$-wave), followed by a rapid but much larger positive excursion ($b$-wave), which after reaching a peak, declines; but finally swings more positive again into a prolonged sweep (*c*-wave) if the illumination is continued for a second or two in the light-adapted eye.

Upon cessation of illumination, there is first a momentary positive hump (*d*-wave) ending in a slow return to the base-line. The length of the flash, and its intensity, have a great deal to do with the shape of the ERG as-a-whole. If the flash is short only the *a*- and *b*-waves are clearly observed. If the flash is weak, the *a*-wave may be absent. The latter is also small or absent in cer-

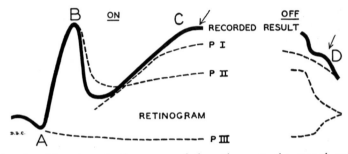

Fig. 61.—The on- and off-responses of the retinogram, the massed activity of the retina. Granit's analysis is indicated by the dashed lines PI, PII and PIII. The main waves of response are indicated by A, B, C, and D. (*Bartley—Psych. Rev.*)

tain species such as the rabbit, while present, and large, for example, in the cat. Its absence is not to be interpreted as total absence of the activity which accounts for it, but to a difference in the latencies of the components of the retinogram.

Granit has analyzed the sequence of deflections, just described, into three components, PI, PII, and PIII, as indicated in the accompanying diagram. PI is the prolonged positive deflection, responsible for most of the elevation of the *c*-wave; PII is the positive deflection largely responsible for the *b*-wave. PIII is a definitely negative component which, as the illumination ceases, swings positive to the base-line, just prior to the time PII swings downward to it. Its first uncompensated part produces the *a*-wave at the onset of stimulation. Granit and his followers have manipulated these three components by use of drugs and other agents. PI is most sensitive to ether, PII being affected only if etherization is continued. PIII is last to be obliterated, which is in line with the fact that it is thought by some to be ontogenetically the oldest.

**Ganglion-cell axon records.** One of the occasional findings in recording the ERG is a series of ripples superimposed upon the usual pattern of slower potential changes. These might well be expected since a rhythmic discharge in the optic nerve is very frequently observed. But the ERG ripples are often absent when the rhythm is distinctly evident in the nerve. The optic-nerve rhythm is due to the ganglion-cell discharge and it is to be expected that the ERG ripples arise from the axons of these same cells. Even so, the activity of the ganglion-cell axons is seldom recorded in the ERG.

A method consisting in varying the location of the lead-off electrodes was devised by Fry and Bartley to determine the origin of the ripples that are observed in the ERG. If one electrode is placed on the cornea and the other on tissue adjacent to the eye, ripples are not recorded at all, although the $b$-wave is. When the grid electrode is removed from the cornea to the sclera on the side of the eye, that is, placed close to the ganglion-cell axons which line the inside of the eyeball and converge in the optic disc, fast monophasic waves are recorded. The fact that the ripples are recorded only when one of the electrodes is located on the sclera demonstrates that they must be produced by activity in the immediate vicinity of the electrodes. The duration of these ripples is from 7 to 10 ms. and must represent the response in a number of fibers, it being immaterial whether each responds once or several times during each ripple. The waves represent changes in the total frequency irrespective of the repetition of the fiber response. If the fiber discharges several times during each ripple it would mean that the frequency of discharge is modulated. Synchrony in the modulation rhythms of the different fiber might accrue from the concurrent onset of stimulation for all parts of the retina, or it might entail a synchronizing process at the synapses. If each fiber discharges only once during each ripple, the ripples represent partially synchronized discharges in a number of fibers.

The results of a group of records in which the grid electrode was placed on a series of corneal and scleral points, the ground

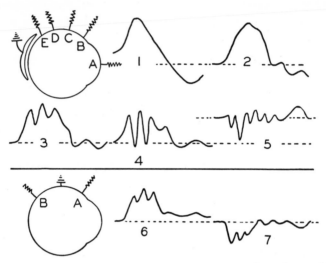

FIG. 62.—The retinogram as obtained by placing the electrodes at different points. These are indicated by the letters in the diagrams of the eye. The upper five records were obtained with the ground on the tissue back of the eye, while the lower ones were obtained with the ground on the eyeball. Records 1 to 5 were obtained with the grid electrode in positions A to E, respectively. Records 6 and 7 were obtained with the grid electrode in positions A and B, respectively. Note that the ripples are not obtained when the grid is on the cornea (position A), while in every other case they appear. This holds true even though the large wave (*b*-wave) on which they are superimposed is absent when an insufficient section of the total front-back gradient is recorded from. (*Fry and Bartley—J. Cell. and Comp. Physiol.*)

electrode resting on tissue back of the eye, are shown in Figure 62 (upper). The timing of the ripples and the onset of stimulation are quite similar in all cases, tending to indicate that the ganglion cells over the entire retina are more or less synchronized in their activity.

The ripples can also be recorded when both electrodes are on the eye itself. Points progressively farther and farther back on the eye contain more ganglion-cell axons as they pass to the optic disc. When both electrodes are placed on the eye, the one nearer the front than the other, they are in turn made negative as the impulses pass to the optic disc. Since more axons pass the back electrode, the negative potential of this electrode will be stronger than that set up in the region of the other.

The peaks of the impulses arising at the two electrodes would be slightly out of time due to the fact that the impulse would arrive at the front electrode first. If the electrodes are in line with the fibers so that the impulses in some of the fibers would, in effect, be recorded twice, a separation of the two sets of fibers could be made; those passing both electrodes and those passing only the back electrode. The electrodes are very close together, and the impulses passing both leads will produce only a very slight diphasic wave, whereas those passing only the rear electrode will set up a large monophasic excursion. Figure 62 (lower) represents the outcome of putting the grid before and behind the ground electrode. The reversal of sign is in keeping with the analysis just proposed.

Although it was shown that the activity responsible for the ripples is located in the immediate locality of the recording electrode, the *b*-wave is not thus localized for it can be recorded when the electrodes are both on inactive tissue, namely, the cornea and the tissue adjacent to the eye, respectively.

**Analysis by application of drugs.** One analysis of the ERG consisted in the administration of various drugs to excised cold-blooded eyes whose corneas have been removed so as to enable direct application. Therman has done this with glucose potassium, calcium, eserine, acetylcholine, atropine, strychnine, veratrine, nicotine and adrenalin. The following represent some of the chief results.

Isotonic *glucose* solution (3.15%) produces an initial increase of the *b*-wave and a lesser increase of the *d*-wave. The condition of the eye improves with glucose and after the initial augmentation of response, its excitability remains constant longer than normal. Glucose enhances the increase of the *b*- and *d*-waves during regeneration of visual purple, that is, while partially light-adapted. While in a dark-adapted eye it causes no momentary increase of the retinal response. In Therman's study it was used as a bath for the retina and a solvent for the other drugs.

*Potassium* accentuates the negative *a*-wave and finally obliterates PII, giving a purely negative potential similar to the component PIII. The impulse discharge in the optic nerve soon disappears, and with it any small waves which had been superimposed on the *b*- and *d*-waves. In a light-adapted eye the negative deflection is greatest at about 560 m$\mu$, in a dark-adapted at about 500 m$\mu$.

PII and PIII both increase with a solution under 0.1%. This stimulating effect of potassium on PIII is precluded in an eye previously treated with calcium or after the addition of calcium. Previous treatment with eserine does not change the potassium response. The latency of the *a*-wave is shorter after treatment with K. The latency of the *b*-wave seems practically unchanged at first but later becomes lengthened as the K effect continues. This is a good example of how the onset of the *a*- and *b*-waves is determined by the balance between PII and PIII, the *a*-wave being reduced in latency when PII imbalances PIII earlier. Soon during the K effect the off-response becomes completely inhibitable by a superimposed flash.

*Calcium* eliminates PII without an appreciable effect on PIII, and, as was said, also prevents the excitatory effect of potassium on PIII.

*Eserine* most usually causes depression, though in exceptional cases an increase is manifested in the response. It is not synergic with acetylcholine on the retina so that the uncommon excitatory effect is to be attributed to unspecific stimulating influence of eserine on the nervous processes. In keeping with this, it alters the discharge in optic nerve in concomitance with retinal activity.

*Acetylcholine* is a general depressor even during its early stages.

*Atropine* produces no definite effects on the *a*-wave. It has, at the outstart, an excitatory effect on the *b*-wave which is followed by a general paralysis. The excitatory effect is most definite in rod region of the stimulus spectrum (*circa* 450 m$\mu$), and the comparative size of the rod and cone responses is shifted as if due to dark-adaptation. Frequently cone potentials are depressed, while rod potentials are excited. It most usually diminishes the *d*-wave. This may be due to a quicker or sooner return of PII to base-line.

*Strychnine* first excites the *b*- and *d*-waves and then depresses them, but produces no certain change on the *a*-wave. Thus it does not seem to affect PIII.

*Veratrine* excites first the *a*-, *b*-, and *d*-waves, and then depresses them. This is first seen in *b*- and *d*-waves. The optic-nerve discharge disappears while the retina is yet active. Veratrine is not as effective in removing PII as is potassium. During the excitatory phase, the off-effect becomes completely inhibitable by a superimposed flash.

*Nicotine,* even in a concentration of 0.1%, is surprisingly ineffective in changing the retinal action potential.

*Adrenalin* is a depressant to the *b*-wave, but exerts a heightening effect on the *d*-wave, which may be due to the differential prolonged effect upon PII and PIII. Adrenalin prolongs the discharge in the nerve both at *on* and *off*. Adrenalin increases the latency of all components, especially of the *b*- and *d*-waves. More than 2 minutes' latency has been observed for the *d*-wave in which case the response can occur after the second of two widely spaced flashes. Adrenalin does not alter adaptation but expands the range within which the retina responds to an increased illumination by a concomitant increase in the *b*-wave.

It will have been noted that PIII is affected by fewer drugs than is PII. Most often the result of drug administration is depression and elimination of PII, before PIII. Even some drugs, such as eserine, which produce initial excitation of PII have no definite effect on PIII.

PII and PIII have been taken to be more or less independent variables ever since their first analysis. The results under the influence of this group of drugs are in line with this idea. The likelihood that the two are due to the activity of separate structures seems to follow.

**ERG represents gross spatial activity.** The electroretinogram technique does not provide for the differentiation between the activity of one part of the retina and another. This is due to the fact that under most conditions enough stray light falls on the retina in general to produce a considerable action-potential, despite the common belief that the retinal action-potential is determined for the most part by the elements in the focal area, the area of the retina receiving the image. Though it has not been generally recognized, it is not surprising that *if stray light is at all adequate to stimulate the many thousands of photoreceptors in the nonfocal area, this area by virtue of its large number of elements might produce a potential of great size, while that initiated by the focal area could not be detectable.*

The following experiment is a test of whether the focal *b*-wave is measurable under ordinary conditions. The experiment consists in alternately presenting to the eye two bright discs on a dark field, the one disappearing as the other appears. Since both produce an equal quantity of stray light and since the distribution of it in both cases is quite similar, that is, nearly uniform, over the retina the alternate exposure of the two areas does not produce any change in the stray light. The alternation then is only of the two retinal images. When one disc is presented alone every two seconds, a definite *b*-wave is recorded. The rate of repetition is slow enough that if a second disc should be included and the consequent retinogram should consist in the response of both of the focal areas they would not overlap and should appear as a definite sequence of ripples in the record. This, however, does not happen. There is, instead, a waveless base-line. This means that since stray light is kept constant there is no intermittent stimulation of the larger population of the retina and thus no stimulus conditions for a series of on-responses or *b*-waves. The intermittent responses of the focal areas that are elicited are not large enough to appear in the record. This finding is confirmed by the fact that changes in the stimulus *area* and the stimulus *intensity* control the latency of the *b*-wave in exactly the same manner. The fact that stimulus area can manipulate the latency of the *b*-wave can conceivably be due to one or the other of two things: either the *b*-wave is the response of the focal area and is a post-synaptic response, the variation in latency depending upon spatial assumation at the synapses; or else the *b*-wave is produced by the nonfocal part of the retina. Since changes in stimulus area and changes in its intensity both alter the intensity of the stray light on the nonfocal part of the retina in the very same way, the latency of the *b*-wave should be changed alike by both of the factors. This is just what happens, and this, along with other findings, makes it certain that unless special conditions were set up to eliminate stray light, its role in stimulation of the retina would outweigh that of a small but very intense image.

The existence of stray light as has just been shown to occur under ordinary conditions thwarts the attempt to determine what, if any, difference the distribution of stimulation on the retina makes. That this has been attempted, however, is illustrated by the following experiments.

The focal stimulation is divided into parts. That is, a given stimulus area was divided into several smaller areas whose total was the same as the original single area. The distribution of these several areas was varied. When this procedure was tried, the large area whether in the form of one disc or several gave the same latency, which was shorter than the latency for one of the smaller areas alone. The separation of the four small areas as corners of various-sized squares did not change the latency whatsoever.

Granit, for example, used a disc 6 mm. in diameter, and then four such discs arranged as the corners of a square. The latencies he obtained were 67 and 59 ms., respectively. That is, increasing the area fourfold with this distribution, decreased the latency about 11.9%. When the area was increased fourfold by using a 12 mm. disc, the latencies were 64 and 54 ms., respectively. The reduction in this case was 15.4%. The difference in reduction was taken to mean that the distribution of the stimulus on the retina is a factor determining latency. The fact that the recorded latencies of the 6 mm. disc were different in the two cases by almost 5% means that the eye was in a different condition in the second experiment. This precludes precise statements as to the role played by the distribution of the stimulus in the two cases. The evidence in itself is anything but decisive and is made more doubtful by the demonstrated participation of stray light.

**Assumptions concerning the electroretinogram.** Some sort of tentative assumptions as to what the electroretinogram does and does not represent, must be made before its analysis progresses a great distance in order to decide the value of further investigation and to direct its course. Despite the extended work upon the retinogram by Granit and colleagues, the components PI, PII, and PIII have not been individually attributed to the activity of specific retinal structure, i.e., receptors, bipolars, and ganglion cells. It has seemed that some good reason has arisen to preclude such an assignment each time it was attempted. Nevertheless the idea has always seemed attractive and has never really been totally abandoned.

If the correlation between retinogram components and the activity of specific retinal elements were to be established, the behavior of the components would mean a great deal more to us, and further analysis could proceed step by step on a firm and clear basis.

**The assignment of the components to specific structures.** Much evidence favors the assignment of PIII to the sense-cell. It is the first component to appear in the ERG, though it must be remembered that it is impossible at present to determine the precise beginning of PII and PIII. Their origin in the record merely shows the instant at which the balance between the two is lost, and the one emerges. Experimental evidence from several sources seems to show, however, that PIII always begins before the discharge in the nerve, and that PIII is the last component blocked by any of the effective agencies. PIII may exist when there is no optic-nerve activity, a fact which puts it among the first activities in the chain, if not the first. But when PII is obliterated the optic-nerve discharge vanishes.

PII in order to be a precursor for optic-nerve activity and possibly represent the bipolars, should begin earlier than the discharge in the nerve. At present for the reason just mentioned above, it is impossible to tell just when PII starts. Though it has been thought that the optic nerve discharge begins before PII, the onset of PII may yet be found to precede it.

The burst of the off-response in the nerve is preceded by a small positive rise in the retina visible with high amplification, but the steep major rise follows the beginning of the nerve discharge by about two milliseconds. This permits of the possibility that PII may begin before the onset of nerve activity, as it should in order to be its precursor. On the other hand, the deflection that is observed in such a case may be that of PIII, the $a$-wave.

Even though it is possible to assign PIII to the activity of the sense-cells, and PII to the bipolars on account of the way they behave in the on-response, the data obtained from examining the off-response do not fall in line with any such simple relationship. The details of the optic-nerve discharge are reserved for the following chapter, but there is one fact about the discharge that must be known now. An off-response can be elicited in the optic nerve with flashes of less than 10 milliseconds. The typical complete off-response cannot be identified in the retinogram until flash duration becomes a matter of hundreds of milliseconds.

This might in the first place be attributed to the fact that the retinogram and the optic-nerve discharge are much different in contour, the former being much less detailed and more prolonged in its major deflections. With very short flashes, possibly the large deflection representing the retinogram on-response is not completed before the off-response is set up. Nevertheless there should be some indication of the existence of the off-response before the flash duration is much prolonged, for in the optic-nerve discharge the off-response is about the size and shape of the on-response when the flash reaches 70 milliseconds. The conclusion that the retinogram and optic nerve off-effects do not represent the same thing seems to be inescapable. Hence it must be realized that the off-effect of the retinogram is not to be directly identified with neural activity, except in the broad sense that it is the algebraic summation of the components PII and PIII and sometimes PI in the record. *This precludes the use of wide sweeping deductions concerning the meaning of specific items of retinogram contours.* It should be kept in mind that flash durations employed in virtually all experiments, except those on intermittent stimulation, are very long. The retinogram off-effects that have commonly been studied are typically those following flashes one-half to five or more seconds in length.

**The excitation-inhibition theory.** In contrast to the attempt to go as far as possible in the identification of the components of the retinogram with the activity of specific retinal elements, the data from the early electroretinogram experiments have led some workers to envisage the components in terms of excitation and inhibition.

The basic assumption is that the two components PII and PIII represent excitation and inhibition, respectively. One of the first examples used to show this was the case in which PII was eliminated by the use of ether or other agency, leaving PIII alone. As a result the discharge in the optic nerve was also eliminated. This was taken to mean that the activity of PIII was inhibitive. This conclusion is not by any means inescapable for if it is assumed that the activity of PII follows that of PIII then the elimination of the PII would necessarily eliminate the optic-nerve discharge.

The conclusion that we suggest then is that the optic-nerve discharge fails to materialize on account of the depression of its forerunner, PII, by the anesthetic, that PIII inhibits neither PII nor the optic-nerve discharge. Quiescence of the optic nerve due to processes of nervous inhibition is another matter and under some conditions possibly occurs, though perhaps not in such a wholesale fashion as is implied in the E-I theory. Furthermore, it would seem that such processes could scarcely be deduced from experiments employing strong doses of anesthetics or other drugs which in themselves block activity.

**Dark adaptation and the retinogram.** The most noticeable changes during the light adaptation of an initially dark-adapted eye include the obliteration of the *c*-wave, diminution of the *b*-wave, and a definite increase in the size and rate of rise of the off-effect (*d*-wave) along with the reduction of its latent period.

In preparations of the eye in which PII was eliminated it has been found that negative PIII increases in size and rapidity during light adaptation. Eyes retaining PII may fail to show concomitant changes in PII and thus in the *b*-wave. The initial *a*-wave may or may not be bigger than in dark adaptation depending upon how it and the *b*-wave balance.

The chief difference then between light- and dark-adapted eyes resides in the negative component PIII. Slow adaptation which is involved in producing the changes in the retinogram that have just been described is presumably a photochemical matter. Naturally it would take place in the sense-cells. The findings then are in line with identifying PIII and the activity of sense-cells rather than making PIII simply the potential sign of inhibition according to the E-I theory.

**Analysis of the off-effect.** The fact that discharge activity once begun continues after the external stimulus has ceased, makes it possible to use the off-effect in a unique way in the analysis of retinal phenomena. The abrupt onset of illumination following a period of darkness sets up various processes each of which may have its own period of latency, each of which sums with the others to give the recorded electroretinogram, and in addition each may continue a different length of time. In fact we now know that the very cessation of illumination gives rise to certain discharges of its own, the total of which in the optic nerve looks much like the on-response.

It is profitable to study the off-effect in connection with the on-, and this is done by introducing flashes of various lengths at different intervals after a period of steady illumination has been withdrawn.

For our purposes the essential characteristic of the off-effect when it appears is an initial positive deflection which takes an appreciable amount of time to develop and to decay. When flashes are introduced during the development of the off-effect, a negative notch is produced in the rising deflection indicating a burst of PIII. The size of the notch is in accordance with the place in which it appears. If introduced at the peak of the deflection, it is maximum, and of course if earlier or later than this, it is smaller. If the flash (or resumption of steady illumination) is introduced very soon after the cessation of previous illumination little or no off-effect will develop, nor will there be a negative notch. If the flash occurs quite late, the effect begins to take on the appearances of the response to an isolated flash. The negative notch is followed by a new positive deflection. In all cases the negative notch is to be considered due primarily to PIII, that is to say, it is an *a*-wave, and the positive deflection primarily due to new PII is a *b*-wave.

The negative dips caused by flashes occurring soon after the cessation of steady stimulation have a relatively long latent period, whereas the dips due to later and later flashes have shorter and shorter latencies. Due to this the dips tend to occur in much the same region while the intervals between stimuli are lengthened. Granit and Riddell cite a series of trials in which the interval between stimuli varied between 25 and 125 milliseconds with the result that the interval between the onset of the off-effect and the onset of the negative dip varied only from 40 to 90 ms.

In the light-adapted frog's eye, a gap of darkness of about 5 ms. produces a just noticeable reaction. A gap of darkness need not be much greater than this before *status quo ante* ceases to be the only effect of the reappearing illumination. With gaps twice the one mentioned there are beginning signs of new excitation.

With long gaps the retina has time largely to recover from previous stimulation and under such conditions the reappearing illumination becomes a new and independent stimulus. Manipulation of the gap of darkness makes it possible to trace the origin and development of the *a*- and *b*-waves and with the courses of the components PII and PIII throughout their length, and to correlate them with events in the nerve and in experience or consciousness. Since PIII, which seems to represent in some way the activity of the sense-cells, not only precedes PII but requires less of a dark gap to cause it to appear in the retinogram, it is faster than PII. This is in line with the idea of the dependence of the c.f.f. on the nervous part of the retina.

There is an optimal duration of the dark gap for both retina and nerve. It was found to be about 30 ms. With it, the renewed excitation appeared with a minimum delay. Naturally as the gap is prolonged its own duration postpones the instant of the reactivation of PII. According to the E-I theory the latent period of the excitatory effect consists of two phases, (1) the duration of a period which some wish to call the inhibitory effect coinciding with the $a$-wave, and (2) the latent period of excitatory effect itself. If we look upon the first event as that of sense-cell activity signaled by the appearance of PIII, we need not call this first phase a purely inhibitory one. It is rather one in which the sense-cell begins its discharge into the bipolars, and the second phase one in which, after some delay, the complicated organization of neural units and synapses begins to discharge, giving the $b$-wave and the activity in the optic nerve. The second phase decreases with a lengthening of the dark gap. In some experiments a decrease from 100 ms. to 40 ms. has been demonstrated.

**Intermittent stimulation and the ERG.** Our interest in the analysis of the retinogram takes us beyond the events evoked by a single flash following continuous illumination, to those involved in response to intermittent stimulation (flicker). We wish to know to what extent a positive deflection, which is not an off-effect, can play a part in producing ripples in the retinogram under flicker conditions. Granit and Riddell, the first to analyze the off-effect, have plotted as ordinates the amount of rise above the off-effect produced by short flashes against time as abscissae. Curves so constructed show that with flashes at rates producing small ripples in the retinal action potential (just below fusion frequency), a positive swing which is not an off-effect is not involved. The real positive effect is involved only when inter-mittent stimulus rates are low enough to allow the off-effect to reach its plateau height. The shortest time thus involved is about 120 ms. while generally the time elapsing from the cessation of stimulation to the peak of the off-effect is much greater, let us say 200 ms. Within this interval, definite ripples may appear before any positivity other than the rising off-effect has had time to develop. That is to say, that fluctuations in PII are not in a material sense involved in flash rates faster than 4 or 5 per second, if the completion of PII is to be identified with the completion of the off-effect.

According to Granit and Riddell, each dark interval produces an off-effect (the return of negative PIII upward toward the base-line) which the next flash of light opposes with a negative wave (new negative PIII). As flash rate is made slower the waves become much larger due to the increased size of the negative dips and by their being followed by positive deflections (*b*-waves) above the level of the off-effects. That is to say, fresh PII is finally activated every cycle.

This is the same as saying that the ripples in the retinogram when flash rate is high, are a series of off-effects alternating with negative deflections of PIII. Such off-effects are simply the up-ward deflections of PIII as it returns toward the base-line during each dark interval and not new bursts of activity as are known as off-effects in direct studies of sense-cells or the optic-nerve dis-charge. This is to say, fluctuations in PIII alone are concerned when the flash rate is very fast.

The fact that PIII can follow light intensity fluctuations at higher rates than PII is in line with expectations from other evi-dence which makes the nervous part of the retina slower than the receptor. PII activity we know is not absent under conditions of fast flicker. It has simply become uniform.

If fusion of the retinogram ripples and sensory fusion were but two aspects of the same thing, the latter would be a PIII affair. Assuming that PIII is the expression of the activity of the sense-cells, sensory fusion would be determined by the intrinsic properties of the sense-cells.  This does not take into account what may be happening with regard to PII.  Since its contribution to the retinogram ripples disappears before that of PIII, the activity PII represents is, as a sum total, quite uniform, but it must not be forgotten that it still exists.  If it is uniform, the activity that follows it must likewise have become uniform, at least insofar as its pattern is determined by PII.  That is to say then, that in spite of superficial appearances, sensory fusion is determined by PII rather than PIII.

It should be stated here that the fact that PIII reacts to a single dark interval of about 5 ms. should not be taken as indicating that each phase of intermittent stimulation so short as that could set up an observable response with the result that ripples would appear in the record.  A 5 ms. interval compares to a repetitive rate of 100 complete light-dark cycles per second, and no c.f.f. reaches that level.  The rate, however, compares to that of a sense-cell discharge.  The highest flash rates which will produce ripples in the ERG of the same animal are much below that.

In the dark-adapted eye, the ripples are small and fuse at very slow flash rates (less than 6-8 flashes per second) whereas, in the light-adapted eye, fusion frequency may reach 20-30 flashes per second.

There is a still further consideration which must not be overlooked in this connection, namely, that of the spontaneous or intrinsic rhythms which occur in the retinograms under certain conditions.  One of these conditions is the use of several well-timed flashes.  After the flashes have disappeared ripples may still be exhibited in the retinogram.  There are times when rhythmic ripples appear in the retinogram during repeated stimulation which bear no direct relation to the flash frequencies being used, though they must be a result of the total set of stimulus conditions.

It would be supposed that the "spontaneous ripples" would produce fluctuations in sensation just as would those induced directly by stimulation.  The occurrence of spontaneous ripples is in line with sensory evidence concerning the conditions for fusion.

Sensory experiments have proved that the rate of subjective fluctuations is not always the same as the rate of objective flashes; the latter may be either much higher or much lower. Therefore both the sensory phenomena and those of the electroretinogram show definitely that the pattern of some of the essential phenomena of the eye is under many conditions largely determined intrinsically, a situation which must be taken account of in any analysis of the eye.

**Intermittent stimulation—direct tests.** With high frequencies of stimulation, the retina sometimes responds with a wave to every second stimulus. This is more often noticed with high intensities and when the eye is enucleated. In fact it is then almost the rule. If the amplification is very high, a very small retinal wavelet may be noted in some cases between each two definite responses. If the flash frequency is reduced either a wavelet of easily discernible size will be produced where none was before or else the very tiny one which was there initially will be increased. This increase in the size of the wavelet continues as flash frequency drops still further, until the response to each flash is of equal size.

This was first reported by Granit and Therman and later by Bartley. Granit and Therman give a series of pictures showing the retinal response at several different flash rates, the significance of which they do not discuss. The highest frequency is 27.8 ps. and the lower ones are, respectively, 21.8, 17, 10.3 and 6.7 flashes per second. With the highest rate, responses are discernible only to every second flash; with the next lower rate, the flashes elicit alternately small wavelets, and the expected-sized responses; with the third flash rate (17 ps.), these wavelets are becoming larger; with the fourth flash rate, all responses are the same height, all flashes eliciting responses. With the lowest rate (6.7 ps.), the responses are of much longer duration than those to higher rates.

A probable explanation for this failure for all flashes to elicit responses, and in some cases the failure to elicit equal-sized response, was given by Bartley. His statement was to the effect that these phenomena were additional evidence that elements representing a retinal area could not be re-activated at a very high rate. In fact none could be re-activated at rates as high as is represented by flash rates approaching fusion frequency. As flash frequencies become lower, the successive flashes pick out elements which are just able to respond at the rates they represent. This means that, whereas, at frequencies just higher, only every second flash was eliciting a response, now the alternate flash is just becoming able to activate a few elements, hence a wavelet for a response. As the period between the onsets of the flashes is lengthened more and more elements are picked out by the alternate flash. Finally each succeeding flash is evoking equal-sized responses, but the elements responding to one flash are not those responding to the previous one. If flash frequencies become very low, this selective activation fails, for the time elapsing between flashes is more than great enough for all elements representing any given retinal area to become rested and ready for reactivation again. *All* elements whose threshold is now at or below the level for the illumination of the flash can be reactivated by each flash, hence one reason why in sensation slow flashes are brighter than rapid ones. Threshold rather than latency is now the critical factor in the number of elements activated.

It is certain that the sense-cells themselves are not the elements whose latency is involved in the alternation, but rather some elements further along in the pathway, possibly the bipolars. Under such an hypothesis the point-to-point representation of the retina upon cerebral cortex, as rigidly conceived, is likely to be thought in jeopardy by assuming that alternate pathways can represent a single retinal point. This assumption, however, does no more to point-to-point representation than does the necessity of admitting that there is interaction between retinal points to account for the influence of one part of the visual field upon another, or in particular to account for the seeing of contours.

## REFERENCES

Adrian, E. D., and R. Matthews. Action of light on the eye: I. The discharge of impulses in the optic nerve and its relation to electric changes in the retina. *J. Physiol.*, 1927, 63:378-404. II. The processes involved in retinal excitation. *J. Physiol.*, 1928, 64:279-301. III. The interaction of retinal neurones. *J. Physiol.*, 1928, 65:273-298.

Bartley, S. Howard. A comparison of the electrogram of the optic cortex with that of the retina. *Am. J. Physiol.*, 1936, 117:338-348.

Bartley, S. Howard. Some observations on the organization of retinal response. *Am. J. Physiol.*, 1937, 120:184-189.

Bartley, S. Howard. Some factors in brightness discrimination. *Psych. Rev.*, 1939, 46:337-358.

Fry, Glenn A., and S. Howard Bartley. Electrical responses of the retinal ganglion cell axons. *J. Cell. & Comp. Physiol.*, 1934, 5:291-299.

Fry, Glenn A., and S. Howard Bartley. The relation of stray light in the eye to the retinal action potential. *Am. J. Physiol.*, 1935, 111:335-340.

Granit, R. Components of the retinal action potential in mammals and their relation to the discharge in the optic nerve. *J. Physiol.*, 1933, 77:207-238.

Granit, R., and L. A. Riddell. The electrical responses of light in dark adapted frogs' eyes to rhythmic and continuous stimuli. *J. Physiol.*, 1934, 81:1-28.

Granit, R., and P. O. Therman. Excitation and inhibition in the retina and in the optic nerve. *J. Physiol.*, 1935, 83:359-381.

Therman, P. O. The neurophysiology of the retina. *Acta Societatis Scientiarum Fennicae*, 1938, 11:1-74.

# XII

# THE OPTIC-NERVE DISCHARGE

**The experimental use of the optic-nerve discharge.** For our purposes, the optic-nerve discharge has two functions, (1) to give some idea as to how the retina works and (2) to demonstrate the nature of the input into the higher centers. As the last chapter has shown, persistent attempts have been made to investigate retinal function through the medium of the electroretinogram and, as the following chapter will show, the nature of the activity in higher centers has been studied by the electrical records obtained directly from them when the responses were initiated by excitation carried in by the optic nerve. This input has characteristics dependent upon whether it was initiated by direct electrical stimulation of the optic nerve or photic stimulation of the retina.

It is evident then that the information gained by recording the optic-nerve discharge can be used for comparative purposes. Since it gives much of the detail that would be expected from Hartline's study of the specific kinds of discharges that go to make it up, it can be used as a basis upon which to judge the retinogram which lacks such detail. The retinogram, moreover, is obtained under geometrical conditions which make its interpretation less certain than those gained from a bundle of fibers in air, or otherwise directly recorded from. The optic-nerve discharge initiated by the retina can be used for comparison with that obtained by the direct electric stimulation of the nerve. The cortical or basal gangliar results of optic-nerve discharge initiated by the retina can be compared with the results set up by electric shock to the nerve. The nerve discharge in the one case is both prolonged and complex; in the other, it consists in merely one impulse simultaneously originated in either part or in all of the fibers.

It is interesting that the cortical end-result, as far as can be seen, is so similar in the two cases when we reflect that in the one case some of the fibers involved in the on- and off-responses are activated at different times, whereas in the other, all fibers are activated indiscriminately (except for their threshold) and concurrently.

**Earlier findings.** In recent years, the electrical discharge of the optic nerve has been studied by Adrian and Matthews in the eel. Excised eyes were stimulated under well controlled conditions, and from their results they pointed out the rhythms in the discharge. Owing to the fact that they were using the whole nerve and slow speeds of photographic recording, analysis telling what specific fiber groups were doing could not be made. They were able, however, to generalize that discharge *frequency* was a function of stimulus intensity and area. By using four patches of light, arranged as the corners of a square, they found the area effect to be noticeable over a range later calculated by Bartley to be 20 degrees of visual angle.

They found what they believed to be a constant interval between the onset of the retinal response and that of the nerve, referred to as the constant retina-nerve interval. This seems to have been a function of their experimental conditions, and need not be taken as a critical finding.

Following these experiments, Granit (1933) recorded the optic-nerve discharge in the frog along with the retinograms he was analyzing. The main findings were the conditions under which a nerve discharge was absent when retinal activity could be recorded. We have already mentioned some of these results in the preceding chapters.

It is significant to note that the records of the above investigators were made on such a slow time line that little intimate analysis was possible; this, with the fact that the whole nerve was used, prevented all but gross generalizations about the discharge.

**Detailed analysis.** More recently, Bartley and Bishop have recorded the optic-nerve discharge of the rabbit *in situ.*

**Choice of animal.** First of all Bartley and Bishop chose the rabbit, an animal, various other parts of whose optic pathway had already received considerable attention. Inasmuch as it is a warm-blooded animal, its eye is particularly subject to injury through loss of blood supply. The removal of the eye and the optic nerve to a holder where they would be much more accessible was therefore out of the question. Consequently, the technique which Adrian and Matthews employed with the eel eye was not possible.

**The preparation.** After once being resigned to the impossibility of working with an excised eye, it was found that there was little or no opportunity to utilize the nerve between the bulb and its exit through the fossa of the orbit. Failing here, the optic nerve further along its course had to be made available.

The way in which a sufficient length of optic nerve is obtained in the rabbit is to remove most of the skull with the animal under ether anesthesia, beginning at a point just above the eyes and continuing until a large part of the skull is removed. Once the *dura* is removed from the brain, one or two skilful cuts of a spatula will remove the anterior of the brain. Bleeding is seldom excessive even though no attempt is made temporarily to occlude the carotid or vertebral arteries. Careful backward pressure on brain tissue just posterior to the eyes will soon reveal the *optic chiasm.* If very fine needle electrodes, insulated except at the very tip, are to be used they may be inserted into the optic nerve without noticeable injury to it and recording accomplished in spite of the gradual accumulation of fluids in the basin of the skull around and over the nerves. If larger needle electrodes are to be used, further precautions are necessary. The nerve not wanted for recording should be sectioned where it emerges from the fossa. A fine thread is tied to the free end next to chiasm, and is used as a delicate means of handling the nerve preparation for clearing away of further tissue, a task which immediately follows. After practice, a scoop with a scalpel or a cutting with scissors will free the chiasm from the brain to which it is attached, without damaging the circle of Willis which lies just underneath on the bone floor.

One needle electrode, for example, may be inserted alongside the intact nerve where it emerges through the fossa into the brain case, and the other may be hooked into the remnant of the chiasm. This electrode is balanced over the edge of the skull (the rim of the basin) and holds the nerve in the air throughout the whole free length. The basin must be kept dry of blood and cerebro-spinal fluid, otherwise the activity will be shunted. Whenever a clot or fluid gathers so that contact between the nerve and the bone or other tissue is made, the existing large waves of the optic-nerve impulse immediately disappear. Clearing the basin of this shunting material instantly restores the waves to their former height. If very small insulated needles inserted into the nerve are used, the precautions against shunting may be obviated.

**Recording apparatus.** The instrument which Bartley and Bishop used to record the features of the optic-nerve discharge was the cathode-ray oscillograph. The discharge was first fed into a vacuum-tube amplifier to step it up to the size necessary to activate an RCA 2000-volt 6-inch screen tube. A special camera was used to photograph the face of the tube, at about half size. The tube-sweep circuit was activated by the mechanism that controlled the timing of the flashes for the eye. The recording paper, 60 mm. wide, was carried a fixed distance along its track between each trip of the sweep by a manual ratchet so that the records were a series of transverse pictures on a long strip of paper. Each picture is accurately placed in line with its predecessor so that the examiner need only rule lines lengthwise on the recording paper from which to measure latency and other temporal features of the response.

**Stimulus conditions for studying the optic-nerve discharge.** The difference between success and failure in studying the optic-nerve discharge, as in many other types of investigation, depends upon the ability of the investigator to supply the proper stimulation. The apparatus provided for this purpose must be very labile, since responses must be obtained under stimulation ranging from very short flashes to prolonged illumination, from very weak flashes to those of almost blinding intensity, from isolated flashes to those repeated at high frequency, from very short dark intervals injected into continued illumination to those long enough to separate the off-effect from the on-effect which follows it. This is not all; the responses to various *rates* of *onset* of illumination must be tested, and if need be, diverse wave lengths of monochromatic light must be used.

**Apparatus for stimulating the retina.** The almost indispensable feature of stimulating equipment is its provision for changing conditions by known amounts during the course of recording. A number of pictures can be taken under one set, following which a factor such as flash duration is changed during the usual interval between trials, the recording continuing as if no adjustment had been made. This feature was found necessary for the satisfactory recording of the optic-nerve response. Flashes were timed by the use of a revolving sectored disc (episcotister) which interrupted a beam of light whose intensity could be regulated either by filter or rheostat by known amounts. The rate of revolution of the episcotister was adjustable and read directly from the scale of a Weston electric tachometer. Flash frequency then could be changed without pause in recording.

To regulate flash duration in the midst of recording, the principle of Abney, by which the angle of the opening on the episcotister is changeable during rotation, was employed. By this method it was possible to change duration step by step during a single set of trials and have the results photographed on a single strip of recording paper.

To photograph the flash itself, the light which passed the episcotister was divided and a small amount directed onto a Weston Photronic cell, the output from which was fed into the same amplifier as the nerve discharge. To record flash duration, a switch substituting the photronic cell for the nerve was turned, and a rectangular wave whose onset and termination marked the duration of the flash was obtained. This took its place in the column of transverse records such as is seen in Figure 63.

To provide for sufficient intervals between flashes even when the episcotister was rapidly revolved, a second sector disc was geared to it so that only one flash in eight was allowed to reach the eye. The flash onset was reduced to less than a ms. under

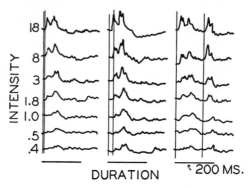

DURATION          ⌐ 200 MS.

Fig. 63.—A group of records of optic-nerve discharge. Both duration and intensity of flash were varied. Each column shows a series of responses in which intensity is decreased in each succeeding response. The numbers in the ordinate represent intensity in thousands of candles per sq. ft. Beginning at the left, flash duration is increased in each column. In the first, it is 8 ms.; in the second, 30 ms.; in the third, it is 135 ms. Note the clear separation between the major waves of the on-response and off-response in the third column. (*Bartley and Bishop.*)

these conditions. On the other hand, very slow onsets were provided by wedge-like openings in the peripheries of discs which could be substituted for the regular sectors of the episcotister.

**The general characteristics of the response.** The monophasically recorded optic-nerve pattern produced by a flash of light on the retina, is a complex series of oscillations, one group instituted by the onset of the flash and the other by its cessation.

The on-response is, in the main, duplex. The two large waves, in the response to strong light, are fused into a large potential with two sharp peaks, the latencies of which vary only slightly with flash intensity till near extinction.

At threshold intensities, the second of the two deflections emerges first, and remains the larger of the two until the light is fairly bright. By the time that stimulation has reached a moderate level, the contour of the descending limb of the first wave is sometimes broken into several evenly spaced and uniformly sized wavelets. These vary from being mere ripples to piercing the wave half-way to the base-line. The second portion of the first response is generally smoother. Its peak appears about 30 ms. after the first and its amplitude falls off as intensity is further increased.

The off-response first appears when the light flash is very short. In fact, it need not be more than 7 ms. under the conditions used, before it is discernible as a single peak midst the irregularities of the later part of the on-response. Its identity is ascertained by recording a series of responses to a range of flash durations beginning, for example, with flashes too short to elicit response and increasing till the off-response has fully matured and completely separated from the on-response.

The full-fledged off-response as observed when separated from the on, is also a group of oscillations, the tallest of which is the first. The response as a whole approximates the on-response in its appearance.

**Latency of the on-response.** Of the two major waves of the on-response, the onset of the first is much more easily identified. Despite the masking of the origin of the second by the first wave, its latency can be estimated throughout part of the intensity range.

The latency of the first wave was measured for six different flash durations ranging from 8 to 195 ms. and through an intensity range from log 2.25 to over log 4. Figure 64 (lower) is a family of curves obtained by plotting latency against log intensity, each curve representing a different flash duration. Although the intensity range is not as great as for certain functions such as flicker recognition, it is bounded on the one end by what is probably the physiological limit and on the other by a response that has disappeared below the recording limits of the amplification used. Added amplification would scarcely have improved matters much, for at low levels the response contour loses its differentiation regardless of the size of the record. In line with this it will be noted that the curves reach a place where intensity no longer reduces latency, and at their other end, a place where

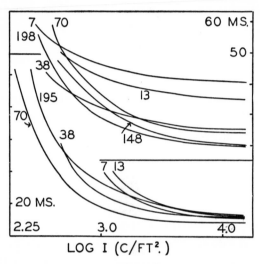

Fig. 64.—Curves indicating the relation between the logarithm of stimulus intensity and the latency of the optic-nerve discharge. The bottom group of curves represents the on-response while the upper group shows the off-response. The ordinates in both cases are calibrated in units of 10 ms., and represent latency. The numbers labeling the curves indicate the duration of the flashes used as stimuli, in terms of milliseconds. (*Bartley and Bishop.*)

latency is about to become infinitely long. Within this range latency varies from 15 to 65 ms. in absolute amount.

The onset of the second wave is difficult to discern at the lower end of the intensity and duration scales. On this account, latencies for only the three longest flashes were plotted. These do not show as much of a range in absolute value as did the first wave. Each of the curves begins at a value of 75 ms. at the low-intensity end of the scale and ends at about 52 ms. for the highest brightness.

**Latency of the off-response.** The off-responses were plotted over the same intensity range as the on-response. The same six flash durations were also used. Figure 64 (upper) shows the family of curves plotted in the same manner as were those of the on-response. One difference in the results will be immediately apparent. The curves for the different length flashes are much more widely separated on the ordinate axis. The latency for the shortest flash varies from 40 to 50 ms., whereas the latency of one of the longer flashes varies from 20 to 45 ms. over an intensity range not quite so great. That is to say, the latency ranges of the two flashes overlap little while those of the on-response all fall into a single cluster. However, the curves for the on- and off-responses of the longest flash are virtually congruent throughout. This signifies that even though the off-response is more affected by flash duration, after the flash passes a critical length, the off- and on-responses act very much alike.

**Gradual onset.** In contrast to the responses elicited by flashes whose onset occupied only a

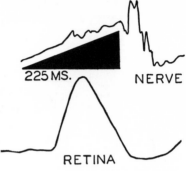

Fig. 65.—A comparison of the optic-nerve discharge and the retinogram elicited by a flash of light having the very gradual onset indicated by the black wedge. The wedge represents the flash which was 225 ms. long; during its whole existence it was becoming brighter. The optic-nerve discharge did not respond with the usual large on-waves, but rose more or less gradually. The retinogram was virtually like the response to an abrupt flash, except that it appeared later. (*Bartley and Bishop.*)

fraction of a millisecond, responses to flashes whose onset required 225 ms. were themselves not abrupt and did not manifest the two large waves of the usual on-response. Instead, they consisted in either a slowly rising base-line carrying tiny saw-toothed ripples or a rising base-line exhibiting a moderate upward deflection halfway along its course.

Since the cessation of these gradually developing flashes was abrupt, the off-response to each of them was well marked and did not differ essentially from one following the usual flash of about the same length.

**Comparison of the optic-nerve record and the retinogram.** As was suggested at the beginning of the chapter, the optic-nerve record can be used to indicate certain features of retinal activity. Since the discharge in the nerve can be obtained under the same type of recording conditions as are used in peripheral-nerve work, it is directly usable for analysis in the light of the vast amount of precise knowledge which has accumulated under that technique. This simplicity does not hold for electrical potentials obtained from larger masses.

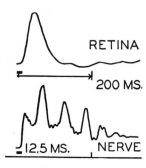

Fig. 66.—A comparison of the optic-nerve discharge and the retinogram elicited by the same short flash. Note that retinogram does not exhibit the details of the activity nor does it indicate the complete duration of it. (*Bartley and Bishop.*)

The precise origin of the potentials which constitute the electroretinogram still remain in doubt. The recording conditions under which they are obtained are such that the neural elements which we know must be active during their manifestation cannot be segregated one from the other. Despite the success in recent years in parceling out the three components, this remains largely true. On this account, then, the retinogram cannot be used as a fixed point from which to start in analyzing retinal activity. The retinogram requires evidence from other methods to make it meaningful. Though it is possible that a great deal more may be learned about it by further manipulation of stimulus conditions, it is likely that it will always remain a less definitive method for the study of retinal function.

Since we have begun to study the optic nerve in detail it is possible that more light may be thrown on the meaning of the retinogram. Already certain comparisons between the two have been made. A single flash will produce a retinogram as pictured in Figure 66. The same flash will produce the optic-nerve discharge that is pictured beside it. The two arise at somewhere near the same interval after the onset of the flash, and for short flashes, the total duration of the main deflections is about the same.

There is considerable difference in the contour of the two responses, however. While the retinogram is ascending to form the more or less smooth positive deflection (*b*-wave) the optic-nerve discharge is rising abruptly to the first of two major deflections with superimposed wavelets all of which constitute the on-response. There may follow then a series of minor oscillations, but in the retinogram there is usually nothing but the descending phase of the *b*-wave. This may swing below the baseline and slowly return. The most nearly intimate way that the retinogram and the optic-nerve discharge compare is when under very limited conditions, the retinogram *b*-wave exhibits a series of tooth-like notches on its descending limb. These come at times which coincide with notches in the optic-nerve record.

If flash duration is lengthened, the optic-nerve discharge reflects this change by an increase in the size of the two major waves constituting the on-response. The ripples which succeed them may drop out. When the flash passes 70 to 75 ms. in length the off-response begins to separate from the *on* and becomes larger and more prolonged and complicated as the flash is made longer. Nothing of this sort happens to the electroretinogram. It is easy to see then why the use of the retinogram will reveal much less to the investigator, for besides lacking the detail it does not reveal the off-response occurring in the eye. Figure 67 shows the retinogram and the optic-nerve discharge for three different flash durations, the shortest being 13 ms., the middle one, 68 ms., and the bottom one, 157 ms. Little difference can be seen in the retinograms. Figure 65 represents the two responses when the onset of the flash is very gradual. The wedge indicates the rising intensity and duration of the flash. It will be noted that the retinogram *b*-wave emerges when the quantity of stimulation reaches a sufficient amount. That is to say, in the retinogram, a definite on-response occurs which differs in no way from that produced by an abrupt flash. The contour of the optic-nerve discharge mirrors the gradualness of the onset of the flash by exhibiting no marked burst of activity. The off-response, on the other hand, is large and is like the off-response to the more usual flash. The retinogram exhibits no off-response whatsoever, despite the fact that the duration of the flash was about 225 ms.

This shows again the fact that the retinogram does not exhibit an off-response under conditions in which a very large one appears in the optic-nerve discharge. In this case, the off-response of the optic nerve is much more abrupt than the on-effect and

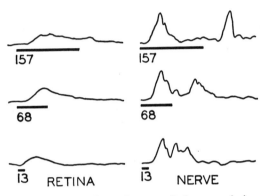

Fig. 67.—A comparison of the optic-nerve discharge and the retinogram as flash duration is increased from 13 ms. to 157 ms. Note the absence of an off-response in the retinogram. (*Bartley and Bishop.*)

its reflection in the retinogram might have been supposed for this very reason. The only difference in the retinogram produced by the gradual onset is that the latency of the *b*-wave is lengthened. In this case it is about 130 ms., and the wave peak, 175 ms. The *b*-wave following an abrupt flash of the same final intensity had a latency of 35 ms. and a peak of 55 ms. Under limited conditions the retinogram does exhibit an off-response. The two major conditions which seem to be essential are strong illumination and its prolongation for seconds.

If the off-response of the retinogram does not emerge until flashes of an entirely different temporal order are used, the off-responses in the two records (nerve and retinogram) do not represent the same phenomena. There are several alternative deductions to be made from this fact. It may mean the assignment of any of the features of the retinogram on-response to neural components of the retina may be precluded; or it may mean that the off-response is mediated by a different set of neural elements in the retina and are so oriented that their potentials are not registered from the surface of the eye or even by electrodes inserted into its interior.

It will be recalled that Granit and his colleagues have described the retinogram off-effect as an algebraic construction in which the negative PIII returns upward toward the base-line faster than PII returns downward. Granting that it is that sort of a phenomenon, its significance is left in doubt until more can be said about the meaning of the components, and we must rely upon the more directly obtained potentials from nervous tissue.

**Application of synchrony analysis to the optic-nerve discharge.** We may suggest conditions under which the elements in the optic-nerve discharge become synchronous and thus give rise to definite ripples in the record. Examination of the records, picturing the discharge as stimulus intensity and duration are varied, usually shows that when the flash is quite short and not too strong the most marked ripples appear. If intensity is increased, the duration necessary for their maintenance must be shortened to compensate, a relation suggesting the requirement of a certain critical quantity of stimulation.

It will be noted that the required quantity is just greater than the amount producing the first rapid increase in response size above threshold. This suggests the applicability of Adrian's treatment of the water-beetle data here. He called attention to the fact that one of the essentials for producing synchrony is a single discharge frequency among the elements and that the diversity of thresholds among a population of elements works against this except at the upper end of the intensity scale, where they reach the same maximum. According to this, it is clear why more than a threshold quantity of excitation is required in the present case. The ripples appear when the response is moderately well up in the size range toward maximum. At this point a sufficiently large fraction of the elements constituting it is discharging at a common frequency. The reason that a fully maximal response is not required before synchrony appears may be explained by supposing that quantity of stimulation first increases discharge frequency of the receptors and only later prolongs dischárge duration. This is borne out by the discharge from the single ommatidium of the Limulus under various combinations of intensity and duration.

At some intermediate point in the quantity scale of stimulation, the rates of discharge of a large proportion of the elements will have reached maximum and, when so, will have become equal.

Brevity of flash is also necessary in order that the initial and the later discharge frequencies of the receptor have most nearly the same value. This is also supported by the Limulus sense-cell behavior.

**Sensory significance of some of the response waves.** In addition to the specific waves of the on-response which we have just described, a number of ripples follow, especially when the flash is short. They are entirely absent when the off-response is separated at some distance from the *on*. As shorter and shorter flashes are used and the off-response draws in closer to the *on* they begin to appear. Finally when the flash is so short that the off-response is about to disappear, a large wave emerges in the line beyond the original specific on-response.

At first it might be thought due to synchrony and algebraic summation of the ripples following the on- and off-responses. This is hardly likely, for if so, there should be a train of large waves instead of a single one. Furthermore, the initial wave of the off-response has just about disappeared and it is not likely that the ripples anywhere in the record are now instituted by the cessation of light.

An additional feature which accentuates the large wave in question, is the fact that when it appears the ripples surrounding it diminish in size. The appearance of this wave as a result of critical stimulus conditions is one of the most interesting features of the whole optic-nerve discharge for those wishing to correlate sensation and nerve-physiology. In order to make this clear we must go back to sensation for some facts. Long ago, Young (1872) observed that the flash of light emitted by an electric spark gave the impression of being double. Later others confirmed this and established conditions for the clearer observation of this and allied phenomena.

One of the ways of observing this was to use an illuminated radial slit on a revolving black disc with a fixated eye. This spreads the stimulation over the retina, and sensation pattern is spread out in space, putting the sequence of events in a row before the observer. In such a situation a short flash of light produces a series of alternate dark and bright bands. Such bands also arise when a black and white sectored disc is revolved at a critical speed.

During the investigations by several men on this general subject, it came to be noticed that a second prominent flash impression followed the primary one under a limited range of conditions. This was called Bidwell's ghost, after the first man to report it. It is also known as the Purkinje after-image or the fifth in a series of light and dark phases noted by Dittler and Eisenmeier.

There are two important points to be gained from these old experiments, namely, that a single flash will give rise to an oscillatory impression rather than a steady unitory one if flash duration and intensity lie within the proper range; and that one of the observed impulses following the primary impression may become very pronounced while the others recede. This gives rise to the impression of there being two flashes instead of a single very short one.

The picture of the optic-nerve discharge follows very closely what would be expected were the oscillations in it to lie at the basis for the individual sensory impression we have just described. We have pointed out that there is a large (though bi-modal) primary oscillation called the on-response, and that when the flash is too short to give rise to a marked off-response a second moderate-sized wave appears at a considerable distance from the on-response. Here then we have the duplex nerve response which must give rise to the duplex sensory impression. When the record includes, instead, a series of ripples, we must have the condition for the sensory fluctuations. To substantiate this, Bartley made a special study of the stimulus conditions for the phenomena both in the sensory sphere and in the nerve record. The conclusions made above are the outcome.

## REFERENCES

Adrian, E. C., and R. Matthews.  Action of light on the eye: I. The discharge of impulses in the optic nerve and its relation to electric changes in the retina.  *J. Physiol.*, 1927, 63:378-404.  II. The processes involved in retinal excitation.  *J. Physiol.*, 1928, 64:279-301.  III. The interaction of retinal neurones.  *J. Physiol.*, 1928, 65:273-298.

Bartley, S. Howard, and George H. Bishop.  Optic nerve response to retinal stimulation in the rabbitt.  *Proc. Soc. Exptl. Biol. and Med.*, 1940, 44:39-41.

Bartley, S. Howard.  Some factors in recurrent vision.  (*Unpublished.*)

# XIII

# THE CORTICAL RESPONSE

## THE CHARACTERISTICS OF RESPONSE

We are now ready to examine the visual response as it occurs in the optic cortex of the brain. Although Caton and Danielewsky, over a half century ago, noticed that flashing light in the eye of a dog produced electrical changes in the brain, the first intimate analysis of the visual response did not begin until 1933 when Bartley and Bishop reported a number of findings from recording the activity of the rabbit cortex under controlled stimulus conditions.

Their work came at the beginning of the time when encephalographic techniques were being developed. Electrodes were being placed on the scalps of human individuals and the resulting electrical potentials were being recorded under a few general external situations. In some of them, an opportunity existed for direct recording from the brain itself. Little work on animals had begun. The advent of the type of electro-cortical work described in this chapter, employing a precisely controlled stimulus input, such as the direct electrical stimulation of the optic nerve, was a definite advance in the direction of finding out the basic principle of brain activity in terms of known nerve physiology.

**Types of stimulation.** There are at least two possible choices as to types of stimulation to be used. One is the direct electrical stimulation of the optic nerve after the eye itself has been removed. In a situation of this sort, the stimulation can be well controlled. Stimulation can be made very short in order that repetitive discharge does not take place in the optic nerve as we know it does in responding to the shortest flashes of light. The intensity of the electric shock controls the number of fibers of the nerve that will be stimulated. Naturally it selects them according to threshold, which in this case is largely according to diameter. There are some disadvantages, nevertheless, which are entailed by this type of stimulation. To begin with, one cannot select fibers which represent a discrete area of the retina, for the selection proceeds on the basis of threshold, and not according to retinal location. Since all parts of the retina apparently contain fibers of all sizes, electrical stimulation acts on the optic nerve as light would when falling on the whole retina.

The second choice in stimulating conditions is to employ light flashes activating the retina. These may be made of various lengths, and a great range of repetition rates may be used. By taking into account the facts set forth in the chapter on stray light, separate parts of the retina may be independently activated. It will be recalled that intense light sources always result in activating the whole eye to some extent, this being brought about mainly through internal reflection from the intense image. To obviate this, and at the same time provide a large enough total of stimulation, large but dim light sources can be used. It should be noted, however, that the sum total of light provided in the image must be less than what will reflect a supraliminal amount onto other parts of the retina. This being the case, the cortical response from such conditions will be quite small as compared to the ones to which we are ordinarily accustomed. Though this is a decided disadvantage it still allows for experimentation.

**Spontaneous cortical activity.** The cortex is always occupied by a continuous parade of spontaneous activity, i.e., activity which is not the result of experimental stimulation. It is not certain whether the truly spontaneous cells are located in the cortex itself or in some of the lower nuclei. It is this activity that has received most of the study, in what has so far been called *encephalography*.

It is obvious that since the cortex unstimulated by experimental intent displays activity in the form of a continuous train of complicated waves, the onset of specific responses is often masked. This is, of course, especially true when the difference between the size of the responses themselves and the spontaneous activity is not great.  But it happens that under a great many conditions, the specific response is both much larger and more abrupt than the spontaneous waves.

The slowest waves usually observed in the rabbit under light ether anesthesia are about 3 to 5 per second.  In the cat they vary between 6 to 8 per second, and in the human free from anesthesia they range between 8 and 12 per second, as a usual thing.  This rhythm has become known as the Berger rhythm or more commonly as the *alpha* rhythm.  The waves of higher frequency are much lower in amplitude and do not seem to occupy the same cells, or at least in the same way.  Sometimes some small multiple of the alpha frequency is present, but usually the frequency of these smaller waves varies from 30 to 50 per second.  In the human, the frequencies other than the alpha rhythm have been analyzed into several groups.  Detailed discussion of them is impertinent here for they have so far neither yielded any information relative to vision nor (with few exceptions) with regard to their origin and the way specific stimulation affects them.

On account of the frequent masking of the response onset, the *peak* of the response wave was used by Bartley in his early studies as the measuring point in determining the lag of response behind stimulation.  The interval between the beginning of stimulation and this peak was called *implicit time* in distinction to commonly measured *latency*.

One of the most obvious characteristics of the cortical response to electrical stimulation of the optic nerve or to photic stimulation of the retina is its great variation in size from trial to trial when stimulation is kept uniform.  The spontaneous waves that we have just described play their part in producing this variation, for the specific responses arise one time in one kind of spontaneous activity, and at other times in greatly different kinds.  The responses are superimposed on various phases of spontaneous waves, so that their apparent size varies for this reason.

If stimulation is repeated only at long intervals, the chances of series of responses being nearly the same height are fair, but if trials are made every 2 or 3 seconds, or thereabouts, the variation generally shows up markedly. Early during the study of the cortex, it appeared that there was a factor in addition to the spontaneous variations in the cortical picture that was determining response size. There seemed to be an intrinsic periodicity in the brain itself, the investigation of which will be described later.

**The specific response.** The cortical response to a brief electric shock is in the simplest terms a triphasic series of deflections, the

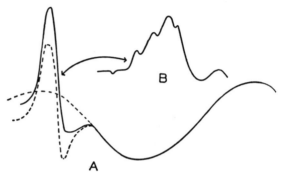

Fig. 68.—The essentials of the response of the optic cortex to stimulation through the optic nerve. Diagram A shows in dotted lines the first diphasic sequence and the beginning of the longer triphasic sequence. The solid lines show the net result of the two. Diagram B shows the initial series of rapid waves described for the response of the cat by Bishop and O'Leary.

later components of which are more prolonged than the first two. What the response actually consists in depends upon the degree of analysis employed. To say the least, it has been found quite complicated. Above threshold, the first wave which at threshold was a simple monophasic deflection, is covered by a diphasic or sometimes triphasic abruptly emerging potential tapering off from its last phase into a slowly rising monophasic positive excursion.

Upon further analysis, both by the use of convulsant drugs (Bartley; Bartley, O'Leary and Bishop; and Bishop and O'Leary), and by appropriate placement of the leading-off electrodes as well as by the manipulation in timing of paired or repetitive stimulation (Bartley), a clearer view of the components of the response is obtained.

In the rabbit, two series of potential are detectable in the immediate response of ⅕ second. One sequence consists of a slow triphasic pattern, first phase surface-positive. This is depressed only by deep anesthesia and its amplitude and duration are not enhanced by strychnine. On the contrary, this drug extinguishes it while enhancing certain other parts of the response. This sequence is related in many ways to the alpha rhythm. Indeed it has been inferred that abrupt peripheral stimulation, such as a momentary electric shock, produces in the cortex an alpha cycle, or perhaps a progressively diminishing train of them.

The second series of events consists in a diphasic succession, the first phase of which is also surface-positive. The waves of this series are each about one-tenth as long as those of the former series and are typically superimposed on the first wave of that series. There is no indication that they either repeat or set up other observable consequences after a single stimulus.

In the cat, as studied by Bishop and O'Leary, the response can be differentiated into *three* concurrent series of events. The *first* is a series of waves, each brief enough to be an axon spike, and generally surface-positive, distributed at intervals of 1.5 ms. Occasionally more than three spikes are recorded, and when so they form a diminishing series. It is not yet clear whether the additional waves are a repetition of one or more of the one just mentioned or represent additional activity.

The first of the spikes in the series indicates the activity of the axons of the afferent radiation; the second, activity within the cortex comparable to the spread of intercalary neurons of the cord; the third, appearing to be a cortifugal discharge perhaps in the pyramidal cell to such regions as the superior colliculus and can be recorded below the cortex.

It must be pointed out that these spikes were not mentioned as a part of the response in the rabbit, though they have since been found to exist there. It happened that they were much less prominent and were entirely overlooked until recording technique was improved to its present status.

The *second* is a series of waves (seen also in the rabbit) in the diphasic or triphasic component, each phase of which is 5 to 10 ms. long. The initial wave of this succession usually emerges exactly with the second spike of the first series, and has the succeeding waves of the first series written on it.

The *third* series is the succession of slow waves, the first-mentioned series in the response of the rabbit, and possesses the same temporal dimensions as the animal's alpha waves.

Thus it may be said that the components of the cortical response in the two animals, rabbit and cat, are essentially alike.

Examination of the temporal relations of the responses obtained from various levels of the optic tract through the placement of needle electrodes there, shows that of two discrete waves in the optic tract exhibiting different thresholds and conduction rates, only the more rapid has to do with a cortical response, the slower continuing past the lateral geniculate to the superior colliculus without a synapse. The synaptic delay of the afferent impulse in the geniculate is about 0.5 ms. while the time spent between the afferent radiation and the cortical neuron of the second spike is nearly 1.5 ms. Between the second and third spike neurons, the time is the same. The first wave of the slower cortical series originates during the second spike.

The fast wave of the tract conducts at about 60 m.p.s. while the second travels at a rate of 25 m.p.s., there being no third potential or c-wave. The cortical response becomes maximum when stimulation produces a maximal first wave in the tract, and no noticeable change in the cortical record follows elicitation of the second wave.

Bishop and O'Leary conclude from their physiological observations in connection with anatomy, that the division of the optic tract fibers into two size groups as represented by two separate response waves, represents a definite functional division, and that the optic cortex is activated by the lower threshold large fiber group, in which there are perhaps only one-fifth as many fibers as in the slower conducting group.

**Response at various cortical depths.** Bishop and O'Leary analyze the cortical response in the rabbit by placing needles at various depths of the cortex. The exact locations were determined afterwards by microscopic examination.

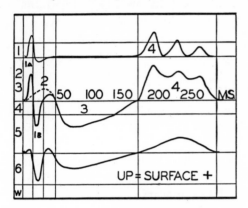

Fig. 69.—Diagram of waves recorded from different layers of the optic cortex. The numbers in the left-hand column indicate cortical layers. The numbers 1-a, 1-b, 2, 3, and 4 label the components of the response. (*Bartley, O'Leary and Bishop—Am. J. Physiol.*)

It will be remembered that Hartline found that one-fifth of the optic-nerve fibers (ganglion-cell axons) responded with a continuous train of impulses during extended retinal stimulation, whereas the remainder behaved otherwise. The question now arises as to whether there is any connection between this particular one-fifth of the total nerve fiber population and the low threshold one-fifth that Bishop and O'Leary find activating the cortex. Whether or not there is, it still means that all of the fibers in the optic nerve are not directly represented in the so-called *cortical retina*. This then, as was earlier indicated as one of the implications of Hartline's findings, means that the representation of the retinal mosaic of sense-cells is not as simple as might be expected, and that theories of visual acuity must recognize this.

For clarity, four depths of needle will be reported on. These subtend three different cross sections, the upper, middle, and lower strata. In these, several components which are to be understood in terms of preceding descriptions can be recognized, the difference here being that various components are augmented, decreased, reproportioned or absent.

The components are as follows: (1) a rapid diphasic deflection, often masked; (2) a slower monophasic wave; (3) a surface-negative still slower wave; and (4) a final surface-positive component. In the upper stratum, (1) emerges as a small monophasic spike, (2) is absent or nearly so, (3) is also absent, and (4) may appear as several monophasic spikes.

In the middle layer, (1) is symmetrically diphasic, (2) and (3) are maximum, and (4) is large and either smooth or else topped by several small slow ripples. In the bottom level, (1) is primarily surface negative, (2) has not been identified, (3) is small and shorter in duration so that the base-line is reached before a smooth form of (4) appears.

The second, third, and fourth components may be looked upon as a single sequence, the last series of the previous descriptions.

**The course of impulses through the cortex.** There is not sufficient information on hand to assign specific potential waves to the activity of given types of cells. Bartley, O'Leary and Bishop have suggested the distribution and the features which such cell groups might possess in order to produce the potentials already observed.

In doing this, they first suggest how an active element may influence a nearby electrode. Since the electrodes are placed one above the other in the cortical layers, the records are of vertical components of the potential fields originated about active neural elements. A distinction is to be made between such vertical components and the field surrounding a vertically directed active neural element. For example, a vertically directed axon in passing two electrodes will be diphasically recorded and in the components of the integrated response from a group of such elements, if out of phase, will tend to cancel each other in the

record. If such an axon arising or terminating between electrodes passes another electrode it will make them maximally
opposite in sign. That is to say, any directed element will affect
a record possessing a vertical component if it ends within an
inter-electrode space, or changes from a horizontal to a vertical
direction there, whichever the direction of conduction along the
element, making negative the closer electrode.

Even a horizontally directed element may possess a vertical
component of potential with a value in keeping with its location
in relation to the electrodes and other similar elements. That
is to say, the electrode closest to the active element will be more
negative.

Since these assumptions hold just as well for cell bodies providing they possess gradients of potential, it is not of consequence
what suppositions are made with regard to the role played by
the cell bodies. They suggest that the distribution of the strength
of the mass impulse with time during response may be the way
to regard the activity. The records are only representations of
the vertical components of the potentials which arise, and do not
reflect the individual polarities of the elements, nor the conduction directions of the impulses. The electrodes truly measure
the field forces at a given moment with reference to two points.

The reader may be reminded that if it turns out in the future
that these forces operate to affect individual elements within the
field, in ways not specified by our present notions of localized
synapses, then the records will take on new significance by being
able to measure these field potentials.

Bartley, O'Leary and Bishop continue by showing that three
propositions should be applicable in specifying the course of activity in the cortex. *The first is that when an electrode is more
negative than another, more elements are active in its neighborhood. The second is that when no potential difference is exhibited between two electrodes, their activity is similar in amount.
This may range from zero to maximum, its degree being determined by reference with other electrodes. The third is that a
uniform difference of potential per distance between electrodes*

*indicates a progressively increasing activity in the direction of the more negative electrode.*

The first surface-positive potential of the slow sequence of three, indicates negativity in the middle layers of the cortex, the region of the terminations of the optic radiation. Here it would seem to be most intense and its comparative restriction to this region suggests elements with short processes as responsible. The surface-negative potential which succeeds the first, evidences a shift of the negative portion toward the surface. The last wave becoming surface-positive at all depths shows the existence of an increasing negativity from cortical surface clear down through the strata. This may be dependent upon the increasing number of pyramidal cell or other fibers passing the lower of the electrodes as they exit from the cortex.

The initial phase of the rapid diphasic potential in the early part of the cortical response indicates also a negativity in the middle strata near the terminals of the afferent fibers of the optic radiation though seeming to extend higher toward the cortical surface than the component previously considered. The second phase indicates an approximate isopotentiality in the upper third of the cortex, negative to the middle third, along with a further and progressive negativity in the lowest layers. This would be in keeping with the existence of cells in the lower two-thirds of the cortex with fibers reaching through the upper third, leaving there via the plexiform layer. It might account for the propagation of spontaneous activity from strychninized regions to their surrounds, apparently involving the cortical surface.

**Effect of strychnine on the cortical response.** Strychnine may be administered to the animal in one of two ways; applied topically to a few square millimeters of the cortex or injected intraperitoneally or into the blood stream. The former method, first used extensively by Dusser de Barenne in his sensori-motor studies on the cat and monkey, was used in the present study. Bartley used strychnine on the rabbit cortex a few years ago, and more recently Bartley, O'Leary and Bishop continued the work, the findings of which are now presented.

The initial effect of the application of strychnine by a moist wisp of cotton to a few square millimeters of cortical surface is an increase in the height of the first diphasic component. All of the results from strychninization are considerably more easily obtainable on the rabbit than on the cat. This may be due to a difference in tissue in the two species or it may be due to a difference in neural organization itself. Even different rabbits are affected to different degrees by what seems to be the same dosage. Depth of anesthesia also influences the ease of involvement.

This initial effect occurs about as soon as one can begin to record after placement of the electrodes. To begin with there is no apparent effect on the remainder of the response nor on the spontaneous activity. The leads in the upper layers of the cortex are affected first but the others are influenced promptly in turn.

More strychnine further enhances the height of the first response, the second or surface-negative component being frequently enlarged more than the first. Even by the time that the first part of the cortical response is greatly enhanced, still no change may be wrought in the later slower components. By this time, however, a rise in threshold is becoming definite. The first effect on the third and fourth components is not an enhancement but a diminution. This occurs at first without marked change in contour, but later changes involve lengthening of the waves. These changes occur hand in hand with similar ones in the alpha rhythm.

With a still greater degree of strychninization, the third and fourth components disappear and with them the alpha rhythm and the remainder of spontaneous activity. The first diphasic component is now possibly 10 times its original size; response which had been graded is now all-or-none. Spontaneous spikes quite similar to the diphasic response which had begun to appear some time back, are now much more frequent and are as large as the present responses. At first they began to appear singly. But by this time they have begun to appear in pairs, threes, fours or, at times, even in longer trains. In neural terms, these may be thought of as spasms, though customarily spasms are seen as muscle symptoms.

Before such spasms appear spontaneously they may be evoked as responses to stimulation. Following the appearance of one of these trains, the cortex is for a time completely inexcitable by

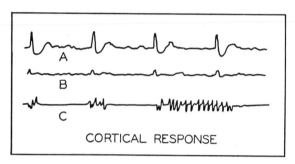

CORTICAL RESPONSE

FIG. 70.—Cortical response to shocks spaced at 1 sec. intervals. Line A indicates response under ether anesthesia prior to administering strychnine. Line B shows the effect of strychnine before producing large spontaneous waves, or increased response potentials. Line C shows the behavior of the severely strychninized cortex. The amplification here is about ⅕ of that in the upper two lines. By this time, the response tends to become repetitive. A stimulus at first evokes a few waves and its recurrence elicits a long train. (*Bartley, O'Leary and Bishop—Am. J. Physiol.*)

way of the optic nerve. This is often true for a short period following a single spike.

The single spontaneous diphasic spikes simulate responses to stimulation in every detail; in amplitude, in form, and in its variation at different cortical depths. *This with the other features already mentioned forces the suggestion that the spontaneous diphasic wave and the response to stimulation occupy the same elements and do so in the same manner.*

Extreme local strychninization brings about complete depression of the area involved, but though no activity can be induced there, adjacent areas vary from normalcy to showing spontaneous activity quite similar to the center of the originally involved region. This modified activity is presumably effected by conduction from the margins of the now inactive region. Application of strychnine to adjacent areas outside the conduction range may repeat all over again the sequence of events just described. The effect of strychnine on the response can be manipulated reversibly by controlling the depth of anesthesia, as if ether and strychnine were reciprocal in action. Nevertheless there is a limit to this, for in compensating the effects of severe strychninization, the depressant effects of the anesthesia supervene, obliterating the response itself.

**Response to retinal stimulation.** The general shape of the cortical response to photic stimulation of the retina is very much like that just mentioned for optic-nerve stimulation, with the possible difference that the constituents within may be prolonged by repetition. The stimulus in this case is applied to sense-cells and must pass through several layers of synapses before emerging into the optic nerve. The optic-nerve activity consists of a repetitive volley of impulses instead of the well synchronized single group instituted by the electric shock. This repetitive factor makes the response capable of less analysis than when the electric shock is used. We know furthermore that the retina does not cease discharging immediately after the flash is past. This prolonged discharge which even the shortest flash induces is bound to make some difference in the temporal spacing of the activity in the cortical response.

Marked alterations occur in the nature of the spontaneous waves which follow the immediate specific response. Many of these changes are so elusive as to be scarcely capable of description while others are quite definite. Sometimes the response is followed by a diminution of the antecedent spontaneous pattern, at others by an enhancement of the waves in the picture. Many times the large last wave in the third series of the immediate response itself is repeated, anywhere from one to five times. As many as seven repetitions have been seen. They are spaced so as to be identical to the animal's alpha rhythm. In the rabbit this is every fifth of a second, in the cat about once every seventh of a second. These waves, in the rabbit, were taken as part of the response to stimulation. *We can now say that stimulation elicits*

*them, but they may now be considered as part of the alpha activ-
ity just as well.*

**Effect of intensity and duration.**  Bartley measured implicit
time of the cortical response to retinal stimulation by light under
variations of flash duration and intensity, in which case he found
it to vary concomitantly.  He used a stimulus subtending an
angle of 7° and with a maximum intensity of 2400 c/ft.² and

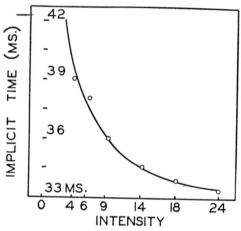

Fig. 71.—The relation of the *implicit time* of the cortical response to intensity
of stimulation.  (*Bartley—Am. J. Physiol.*)

an occasional minimum of 20 c/ft.²  These intensities covered
the larger fraction of the usable range for the response as measured.

The results are pictured in Figure 71.  Duration was also varied
from 1-20 ms. for each of several intensities.  The results of this
experiment are shown in a family of curves in Figure 72.

The results in the main resemble those describing various other
processes occurring in the sequence from photoreception to sensation.  The optic-nerve discharge of the eel, and the overt response of a simple organism such as the *Mya* to light as well as
a number of other functions are dependent upon what has already been described in an earlier chapter as critical duration.
Below it, duration is a factor controlling such properties of re-

sponse as threshold and latency. Above it, intensity alone is a variable for any given stimulus. The implicit time of the cortical response acts in this same way. Critical duration for various reactions increases as intensity is reduced. McDougall, for example, found this to be the case for action time for light flashes.

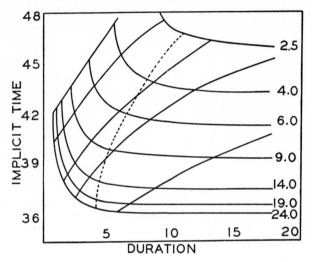

Fig. 72.—Curves showing the relation of flash duration, intensity, and quantity to the *implicit time* of the cortical response. The ordinate represents milliseconds, as does the abscissa. The numbers labeling the curves, when multiplied by 100, indicate flash intensity in c/ft.² The solid unlabeled curves represent equal quantities of light throughout their individual courses. The dotted curve denotes *critical duration*. (*Bartley—Am. J. Physiol.*)

This same thing is evidenced in the present family of duration curves.

**The area effect.** From what has already been said about stray light it will be apparent that changes in stimulus area will do two things. *It will increase the size of the image on the retina* and thereby increase the total light in the image. This in turn will increase the amount of light reflected to other parts of the retina. *Increasing the area of the image thus also increases the intensity of the light falling on the vast portion of the retina outside of the image.*

Bartley measured the implicit time of cortical response as the area of the stimulus-object was varied from about 1.5° to 90°. The nature of the curves obtained by plotting visual angle against implicit time is shown in Figure 73. The first thing to be seen

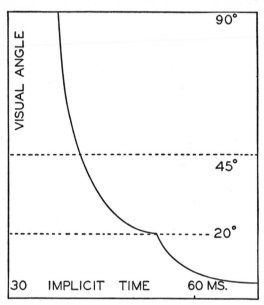

Fig. 73.—A curve representing the way the *implicit time* of the cortical response varies with stimulus area. The original graph contained many different curves representing various flash intensities. Note the abruption at a visual angle of 20°. For explanation of this, see text. (*After Bartley—Am. J. Physiol.*)

is that area changes implicit time throughout the whole range used. The second is that the curve is not smooth but suffers a break in the 20° region.

If the long upper sections of the curves were to be projected past the break their lower sections would end much farther out along the abscissa for any given visual angle represented in the ordinate than they now actually do on account of the break. Thus the break is, in each case, in the form of an added drop in latency.

This result signifies that as area is reduced to the point of the break in the curves, an additional factor begins to operate in determining latency. There is some clue to what this added influence is since it begins to take effect at a visual angle of about 20°. It cannot be added intensity of any material amount. If we assume, as we well can, from the experiments on the effect of stray light to produce a retinogram and an optic-nerve discharge, that *the shape of the upper portion of the curve is due to progressively increasing intensity of illumination* over the whole retina as the area of the retinal image is increased, *the lower portion may be taken as the actual area effect,* since Bartley had previously calculated Adrian's area-effect to cover a visual angle of that order.

The results of this experiment taken as a whole corroborate Adrian, and also fall in line with the already demonstrated phenomenon of stray-light effectiveness.

## RECURRENT STIMULATION

The changes brought about by stimulation as are evidenced in the response to the second of a pair, or in the response to each successive stimulus in a train, give us many clues as to the nature of the underlying mechanisms involved. Manipulation of stimulation in the form of the pairing of shocks or light flashes, or by various spacing of a series of them has become one of the most fruitful means of learning about the nervous system, and there is no exception in the case of the visual pathway. It is also a method used in sensory studies as will be remembered from Chapter VI.

**Paired stimuli.** The response to the second of two shocks of equal strength is not always as large as to the first. The size of the second depends upon the time elapsing between the two shocks. Under light ether anesthesia, two shocks close together will produce a single response, much larger than the wave produced by either one of them alone, unless the final shock is itself so intense that no increase will enlarge the response. This occurs somewhere within the range of about 20 ms. Beyond this the second shock fails to produce a noticeable response. If the separation is extended to about 80 ms. a threshold second response begins to appear, and with a stimulus interval of 200 ms. the response to the second shock reaches its full height. With further separation between the two shocks the height of the second response begins to decline, but regardless of extension it never

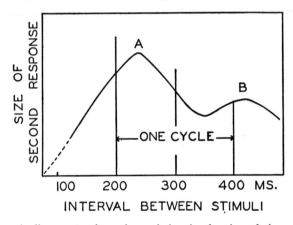

Fig. 74.—A diagram to show the variation in the size of the response to the second of two stimuli as the interval between them is varied. Note that the cycle recurs; when the interval between stimuli is lengthened further a new but lesser maximum (B) appears. Still lesser maxima are sometimes observed with long precisely timed intervals. (*Modified from Bartley—J. Cell. and Comp. Physiol.*)

vanishes. At about 300 ms. it reaches a minimum from which it rises again if the second shock is made still later. Putting the description into other words, the second shock produces an augmentation of the size of the single response originated by the first shock, when the two are close together. As they are separated a refractory period sets in. Following this there is a quickly vanishing train of maxima and minima of diminishing amplitude, which, it should be noted, appear at intervals comparable to the alpha rhythm of the animal. The second response begins to become effective at the onset of the third potential of the slow component of the first response and the first maximum of the second response occurs at the peak of the third potential. That is to say, if the second shock is delivered during the third main component of the first response, it is ineffective, but as it falls nearer and nearer to the peak of the fourth potential it increases and wanes again as it passes it. Under favorable conditions, for example, in animals without anesthesia, the second of two shocks will never be completely ineffective in producing a response.

Stimuli need not be delivered close together to take advantage of this situation in the optic mechanism. The apparatus delivering the shocks may be so tuned as to provide a shock again and again at some multiple of this rhythm. Shocks may be sent into the cortex about every two or three seconds when properly timed and produce a maximum response, or the series may be shifted a little so that each shock falls somewhere in the refractory period, producing equal but diminished responses. We see then that proper timing obviates to a very great extent the extreme variation in size of the cortical responses resulting when stimuli are sent in at chance instants. The experiments also connect one of the consequences following stimulation to the cortical periodicity represented in the spontaneous activity by the alpha rhythm.

**Serial stimulation.** Serial stimulation consists in a train of shocks or flashes delivered closely enough together to make some difference upon the response, to diminish its size, change its latency, etc. It is characteristic for only the first flash in a very rapid series to elicit a recordable response. We know that at least after a very short time the pathway continues to respond even though the activity is not so organized as to appear in the cortical record. Vision functions in response to all flash frequencies up to and beyond those which just begin to act like continuous illumination. The cortex responds also to very rapidly recurring shocks. In fact, shocks may be applied at a much higher rate than flashes and still produce discrete responses, which indicates that fusion is ordinarily brought about by the overlapping of various activities in the pathway rather than by the unavailability of elements for response to quickly recurring stimuli.

If the rate of the sequence of shocks or flashes is reduced below the point where the first response is the only discernible one, the following occurs. The first stimulus, of course, elicits a large response, the second, and perhaps the third or fourth, none. At least the first response appearing after the lapse is likely to be a very small one. It is followed by others, with few or no further lapses, but the first few are irregular in size. Soon, however, this irregularity is replaced by uniform responses, their size depending upon the rate of stimulation. It is as if the imposed stimulus series were far too rapid for any one particular cell se-

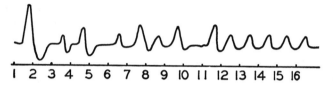

FIG. 75.—A typical series of cortical responses to a series of electrical shocks applied to the optic nerve. The frequency is about 20 per sec. Note that it is only after the delivery of a number of the shocks that the cortex can follow each one. It is deduced from this and other facts that a period of reorganization in the timing of the individual elements involved takes place. (*Bartley—J. Cell. and Comp. Physiol.*)

quence in the pathway to follow, and that after the first response, a time had to elapse before any of the elements (cell sequences) were sufficiently recovered to be re-activated. The third or fourth stimulus is able to find a few of them ready, and sets them off, producing but a very small response. Succeeding stimuli find varying numbers of elements ready and so produce for a time a series of unequal-sized responses. It is conceivable that this irregularity would shift into uniformity, and every stimulus would activate its own fraction of the total number of elements and produce its own small response. It is implied then that any single cell sequence in the pathway responds only at a rate measured by the results with paired stimuli or at intervals of about .20 seconds under very light anesthesia. This interval is not absolute, for it has been shown that depth and kind of anesthesia produce definite changes in it.

It appears that not all of the elements of the unstimulated cortex are in the same phase of the excitability cycle at the same time. A flash of light or an electric shock to the optic nerve cannot activate all of the elements of one threshold due to this dispersal in the cycle. But in the elements that are activated, the cycle is started anew. It so happens that although a short flash of light may produce more extreme synchronization in the elements than usually exists in the unstimulated cortex, prolonged illumination succeeds in most cases in doing just the opposite. As evidence of this, the alpha rhythm vanishes. Sometimes it is stated that the alpha rhythm is blocked, but such an inference from its disappearance is not necessary, and from all the collateral evidence, we would say that it disappears simply because synchrony has been done away with.

**The relation of the alpha rhythm and the response to stimulation.** We may examine the relation of the response to stimulation and the alpha rhythm more closely. The information from a recent study of Bartley provides a suitable means, for although it is only one of a number of studies on the alpha rhythm, it is one of a lesser number on the visual area of the cortex and the most applicable.

His method consisted in confronting the animal's (rabbit) eye with a succession of flashes at rates varying from about 1 p.s. to double or treble the alpha rhythm. These produced two principal results; a specific response to retinal stimulation, and a modification of the alpha rhythm, the kind depending on a number of factors to be outlined subsequently.

From the results of manipulating the flicker rate up and down through the alpha rhythm rate the following may be concluded. First of all, the alpha rhythm and the activity involved in the specific cortical response to incoming peripheral excitation markedly influence each other. The effect of photic stimulation varies between two extremes, the abolition of an existing alpha rhythm in the record and the initiation of one if absent. The specific outcome is dependent upon the temporal distribution of the stimulus, its intensity and relation to the existing activity.

Instead of a series of flashes typically abolishing the alpha waves in the record, it more usually tends to enhance them. There is a critical interval by which two flashes may be separated and elicit a train of pronounced alpha waves. This, as might have been expected, is the time represented between the peaks of two successive alpha waves. It happens that a multiple or submultiple of this interval produces effects in line with anticipations.

The initial flash of a train may chance to be delivered at such a time that the consequent excitation is out of phase with the

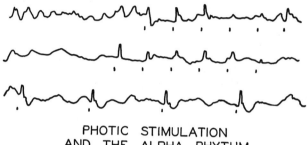

PHOTIC  STIMULATION
AND  THE  ALPHA  RHYTHM

Fig. 76.—Records of cortical activity showing the interrelation between the specific response to peripheral stimulation and the alpha rhythm. (*Bartley—J. Exptl. Psych.*)

spontaneous cycle. If the flash is feeble it utilizes the available elements according to their threshold and the phase it finds them in. If it is strong, by the same token it is able to induce a large response. High threshold is not so great an obstacle, neither is the fact that a great many elements are only partially recovered from their last activity. Such a flash may consequently be able to gather a great number of elements into a single phase of activity.

But if it so happens that the cortex is already exhibiting a pronounced alpha rhythm, the result will not be so successful for many elements are already synchronized into phase. It is as if the fewer the elements of the alpha cycle that could be expected to be ready to respond, the less the effect of peripheral stimulation. This is virtually to say that the cortical excitation from peripheral stimulation involves the same elements employed in the alpha rhythm. This was implied in a sense in the original description of the cortical response.

What has been said has further implications. Even if a flash is so timed that its excitation arrives in the "active" phase of the alpha cycle, the huge waves which result need not be thought of as being huge specific responses, but are to be viewed as largely

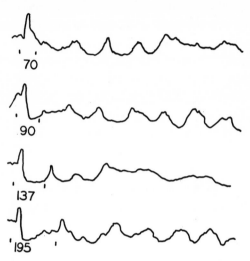

Fig. 77.—Records of cortical activity showing the relation of the interval between two stimuli, the specific responses evoked, and the succeeding alpha activity. (*Bartley—J. Exptl. Psych.*)

the alpha rhythm. This will be evident in their conformation.

Irrespective of the timing of the first flash of a train, the successive flashes will tend to alter *status quo*. The shifts in wave form are seldom, if ever, the simple algebraic results of two sets of waves of dissimilar frequencies as they slip past each other in the record. They represent instead the progressive reorganization toward a new outcome. It will be a succession of regular waves at the rate of the flash train, a succession whose waves are elicited by every second or fourth flash, a diminished alpha rhythm and a series of discrete responses to stimulation, or else an enhanced alpha rhythm into which the response series is intermingled.

Since a uniform illumination is the limiting case of a high-frequency succession of flashes, the result of the former in doing away with alpha waves in the record must be identical to the result with flashes repeated at an adequately high rate. Inasmuch as it has been shown that photic stimuli can set up the alpha rhythm in the record as well as abolish it, it can be concluded that uniform illumination, which results in unsynchronized retinal activity, will institute unsynchronized alpha activity in the cortex. Evidence of it will fail to appear in the record.

Bartley makes a distinction between alpha activity and the alpha rhythm. The latter is the occurrence of a discernible rhythm of certain specified characteristics in the cortical record. Alpha activity is the particular activity of a certain group of cells which when it happens to be properly synchronized, gives rise to the alpha rhythm. Thus it is possible to have alpha activity without the alpha rhythm, but never the alpha rhythm without alpha activity. When the elements of this activity assume a uniform distribution, no waves appear in the record, but when a sizeable number of them are brought into the same phase relations then the synchrony appears in the form of the alpha rhythm the waves of which assume various degrees of regularity and various sizes.

The idea of blocking of the alpha rhythm has been expressed in several places, as also have the terms adaptation and facilitation. If the rhythm is a product of timing rather than the activity or quiescence of certain elements, the disappearance of the alpha waves in the record can scarcely be a matter of blocking but a matter of dispersing the activity producing them. Adaptation scarcely applies as a concept for some change in the recorded picture as flashes are repeated has been taken care of also by the matter of timing, and no intracellular concept need be invoked. It is true, however, if the term adaptation is simply reserved for labeling change in outcome as activity progresses it can be applied here. It would seem preferable to use some other term.

The alpha rhythm may be accelerated as a result of a series of properly timed flashes, and this may be in the accepted sense a case of facilitation.

In dealing with the electrical activity of the cortex in response to peripheral stimulation, we are dealing with two groups of elements, one expressed in the immediate specific response, and the other expressed in the alpha rhythm. Though the second group is spontaneously active, the first is not. Strychnine affects the two oppositely, the activity of the spontaneous elements vanishing and certain components of the specific response becoming enhanced.

The two groups interact. A specific response tends to institute an alpha train, while the amplitude response to an isolated stimulus is partially a function of the place it falls in the alpha cycle. Under strychnine the specific response, though larger than before, no longer sets off an alpha train. This probably is not due simply to the failure of connections between the response and spontaneous groups, for alpha waves have ceased to appear spontaneously. Any repetitiousness that local strychnine induces is manifest in the activity of the non-spontaneous, non-rhythmic units producing the specific response.

The outcome of repeated stimulation depends not alone upon the place in the alpha rhythm each stimulus falls, but also upon the distribution of stimulation and the extent of repetition. This seems not to be due to refractoriness in any individual element, such as a synapse, but to factors involving much more time.

## REFERENCES

Bartley, S. Howard. Action potentials of the optic cortex under the influence of strychnine. *Am. J. Physiol.*, 1933, 103:203-212.

Bartley, S. Howard. Relation of intensity and duration of brief retinal stimulation by light to the electrical response of the optic cortex of the rabbit. *Am. J. Physiol.*, 1934, 108:397-408.

Bartley, S. Howard. The time occurrence of the cortical response as determined by the area of the stimulus object. *Am. J. Physiol.*, 1935, 110: 666-674.

Bartley, S. Howard. Temporal and spatial summation of extrinsic impulses with the intrinsic activity of the cortex. *J. Cell. & Comp. Physiol.*, 8:41-62.

Bartley, S. Howard. A comparison of the electrogram of the optic cortex with that of the retina. *Am. J. Physiol.*, 1936, 117:338-348.

Bartley, S. Howard, and Geo. H. Bishop. The cortical response to stimulation of the optic nerve in the rabbit. *Am. J. Physiol.*, 1932, 103: 159-172.

Bartley, S. Howard, and Geo. H. Bishop. Factors determining the form of the electrical response from the optic cortex of the rabbit. *Am. J. Physiol.*, 1933, 103:173-184.

Bartley, S. H., J. O'Leary and G. H. Bishop. Modification by strychnine of response of the optic cortex. *Proc. Soc. Exptl. Biol. and Med.*, 1937, 36:248-250.

Bartley, S. H., J. O'Leary, and G. H. Bishop. Differentiation by strychnine of the visual from the integrating mechanisms of optic cortex in the rabbit. *Am. J. Physiol.*, 1937, 120:604-618.

Bishop, Geo. H. Cyclic changes in excitability of the optic pathway of the rabbit. *Am. J. Physiol.*, 1933, 103:213-224.

Bishop, Geo. H. Electrical responses accompanying activity of the optic pathway. *Arch. Ophthal.*, 1935, 14:992-1019.

Bishop, Geo. H. The interpretation of cortical potentials. *C. S. Harbor Symp. Quant. Biol.*, 1935, 4:305-319.

Bishop, Geo. H., and S. Howard Bartley. A functional study of the nerve elements of the optic pathway by means of the recorded action currents. *Am. J. Ophthal.*, 1934, 17:995-1007.

Bishop, Geo. H., and James O'Leary. Components of the electrical response of the optic cortex of the rabbit. *Am. J. Physiol.*, 1936, 117: 292-308.

Bishop, Geo. H., and James O'Leary. Potential records from the optic cortex of the cat. *J. Neurophysiol.*, 1938, 1:391-404.

Cruikshank, R. M. Occipital potentials as affected by intensity duration variables of visual stimulation. *J. Exptl. Psych.*, 1937, 21:625-641.

Davis, Hallowell. Some aspects of the electrical activity of the cerebral cortex. *C. S. Harbor Symp. Quant. Biol.*, 1936, 4:285-291.

Goldman, G., J. Segal, M. Segalis, and H. Piéron. L'action d'une excitation intermittente sur le rhythme de Berger. *Comptes Rendus*, 1938, 127: p. 1217.

Hoagland, Hudson. Some pacemaker aspects of rhythmic activity in the nervous system. *C. S. Harbor Symp. Quant. Biol.*, 1936, 4:267-284.

Jasper, H. H. Cortical excitatory state and synchronism in the control of bioelectric autonomous rhythms. *C. S. Harbor Symp. Quant. Biol.*, 1936, 4:320-338.

Jasper, H. H.   Electrical signs of cortical activity. *Psych. Bul.*, 1937, 34: 411-481.

Jasper, H. H., and R. M. Cruikshank.   Electro-encephalography: II. Visual stimulation and the after-image as affecting the occipital alpha rhythm. *J. Gen. Psych.*, 1937, 17:29-48.

Knott, John R.   Reduced latent time of blocking of the Berger Rhythm to light stimuli. *Proc. Soc. Exptl. Biol. & Med.*, 1938, 38: 216-217.

Kornmueller, A. E.   Ueber einige bei Willkürbewegungen und auf Sinnes-reize auftretende bioelectrische Erscheinungen der Hirnrinde des Menschen. *Zeitschr. für Sinnesphysiol.*, 1940, 68:119-150.

Loomis, A. L., E. N. Harvey, and Garret Hobart.   Electrical potentials of the human brain. *J. Exptl. Psych.*, 1936, 19:249-279.

O'Leary, J. L., and Geo. H. Bishop.   The optically excitable cortex of the rabbit. *J. Comp. Neur.*, 1938, 68:423-478.

Perkins, F. T.   A genetic study of brain differentiation by the action current method. *J. Comp. Psych.*, 1936, 21:297-317.

Prosser, C. Ladd.   Rhythmic activity in isolated nerve centers. *C. S. Harbor Symp. Quant. Biol.*, 1936, 4:339-346.

Roracher, Hubert.   Die gehirnelektrischen Erscheinungen bei Sinnesreizen. *Zeitsch. für Psych.*, 1937, 140:274-308.

Rubin, Morton A.   The distribution of the alpha rhythm over the cerebral cortex of normal man. *J. Neurophysiol.*, 1938, 1:313-323.

Travis, L. E., and M. E. Hall.   Effect of visual after-sensations upon brain potential patterning under different degrees of attention. *J. Exptl. Psych.*, 1938, 22:472-479.

Travis, L. E., and J. R. Knott.   Brain potential studies of perseveration: II. Perseveration time to visually presented words. *J. Exptl. Psych.*, 1937, 21:353-358.

Travis, L. E., J. R. Knott, and P. E. Griffith.   Effect of response on the latency and frequency of the Berger Rhythm. *J. Gen. Psych.*, 1917, 16:391-401.

Wang, G. H.   Action potentials of the visual cortex and the superior colliculus induced by stimulation of the retina with light. *Chin. J. Physiol.*, 1934, 8:121-144.

Wang, G. H., and T. W. Lu.   Action potentials in visual cortex and superior colliculus induced by shadow movement across the visual field. *Chin. J. Physiol.*, 1936, 10:149-170.

Wang, G. H., and T. W. Lu.   Action potentials in the lateral geniculate body of the rabbit. *Chin. J. Physiol.*, 1936, 10: 391-402.

Wang, G. H., and T. W. Lu.   Action potentials induced by change in intensity of illumination in the visual cortex, lateral geniculate body, superior colliculus and retina of the rabbit. *Chin. J. Physiol.*, 1937, 11:335-342.

# XIV

# CONCLUSION

## ACCOMPLISHMENTS

Inspection of the foregoing description will indicate the aspects of neurophysiology which present methods can take care of. It will be noted that first of all, the way in which the structural units behave has either been rather well worked out or is in the process of being clarified. The way that one element can affect the succeeding one in the chain is also becoming better and better known. Not so much has yet been established concerning collateral influences, although certain skeletal ideas about summation, occlusion and facilitation, and even inhibition have been put forth in many places in the literature. The study of sensory phenomena has given us a large number of quantitative items to work out. For example, the relations between flash frequencies, intensity, area, and the point at which separate flashes are no longer observed have been studied in a host of ways. The results have led to more and more precise knowledge of how the elements of the pathway must act. Studies of the single sense-cell discharge have told us the nature of the elemental activity, which starts off the process of vision.

We know then, in terms of the nerve impulse, pretty well what the activity in the pathway is like. We know some of the conditions for one unit to influence another. We know many of the conditions for propagating the impulse from one element to its successor. Though we are not sure what the influence of the field around the units is able to do, our knowledge goes a long way in taking care of temporal sequences in nervous pathways themselves. We are now ready to think about spatial relations, the interdependence of the units lying side by side, and we are about to inquire how and why complicated and widespread collateral or convergent phenomena occur.

**Sense-cell behavior.** A great many kinds of detailed studies have been made upon the visual pathway, wherein the information that has been gained from neurophysiological study elsewhere has been brought to bear both on the formulation of the experiments and the interpretation of the results. A running account of the way the visual pathway works in a simple situation will give some idea of the kind of knowledge that can be handled by the methods now in use.

In describing the activity of the optic pathway, we shall use its response to one or more short flashes of light. There are several important things to remember about sense-cell activity in order to relate it to the activity which follows it in the succeeding segments of the pathway. First of all, the activity of the sense-cell consists in a serial discharge of brief impulses, varying from only one impulse per flash at threshold to many. Since the light quantity per flash we have chosen is well above threshold, we shall consider that the sense-cell produces an output of several impulses per flash. The rate of these is of course dependent upon the intensity of the light and would be expected to be fairly high.

As far as we know, the sense-cells are independent one from another, so that their differences such as in thresholds do not directly influence one another. Light may be increased over a material range from the absolute threshold upward before all of the sense-cells that will ultimately respond will be activated. When a cell first begins to respond its rate is low and increases as intensity is increased. As the thresholds of other cells are successively being reached as intensity is increased new slow frequencies are being added to the faster ones which have already risen from the minimum. Consequently, at any intensity much above threshold, the combined sense-cell discharge into the bipolars is a heterogeneous mixture of frequencies.

Since the sense-cells are independent, their activities are not dependent upon any such factors as resonance. The frequency of one, though different than its neighbor, will not for that reason affect it.

Sense-cells of different discharge rates supposedly converge on the same bipolar cells. If so, the bipolars are not dependent upon any single rate to activate them. This would suggest that sensory fusion is not dependent upon the uniform discharge in any single sense-cell. Each bipolar, whether the flashes are subfusional or not, is probably receiving impulses at several rates. Between the flashes of subfusional rate sense-cells cease fire, and perhaps do so even at flash rates somewhat above fusion on account of their inherent quickness of response.

Additional properties of sense-cells will be related when the succeeding elements in the chain are described. These are deduced or are directly made necessary from the facts that emerge from experiments with them.

**The bipolars.** The bipolars, unlike the sense-cells, are provided with lateral connections and thus are the recipients of collateral influences, though it is possible that a fraction of the impulses may arrive over these channels at such times as to be ineffective.

The discharge rate of the bipolars would be expected to be materially slower than that of the sense-cells by reason of this lateral coupling. It is to be presumed that they are slower in being set into action and carry on longer after stimulation (the input discharge) than do the sense-cells.

For these reasons, the bipolars may determine c.f.f. Intermittent groups of impulses from the sense-cells may keep the bipolars in a virtually uniform state of discharge long before there is anything that approximates a uniform discharge in the individual sense-cells.

**The ganglion cells.** The third element in the pathway is the ganglion cell which is the recipient of processes from several bipolars, except in the fovea. By direct experimentation, it has been found that there are three kinds of discharge from ganglion cells, each cell quite consistently maintaining one of the three following types: a discharge at the onset of illumination which continues during the persistence of the light and fails soon after its disappearance (type X); a discharge that bursts into a short volley at the onset and again at the cessation of illumination (Y); or a discharge which appears only at the cessation of illumination (Z).

It is not known just where or how this differentiation is made. If it were made in the sense-cells themselves, it would mean that there were three kinds of them irrespective of whether rods or cones. This would provide a thinner distribution of any one of them over the retina and would seem to require some modification of the common concept of visual acuity based upon the density of sense-cell population.

If the different types of ganglion-cell discharge are dependent upon action at a point past the sense-cell, only one type of sense-cell in this respect would need to be assumed. Since only about 20 per cent of the ganglion-cell fibers exhibit the maintained type of discharge (X), we may have to assume that in effect only $\frac{1}{5}$ of the sense-cells are involved in maintained response. This would have the same effect on the current concept of visual acuity as if the sense-cells themselves were dissimilar or thinned out to $\frac{1}{5}$ the density.

**The optic-nerve discharge.** The optic-nerve discharge carries the three kinds of response that have already been described, the combination manifesting itself as an on- and an off-response. In addition, the ripples of the intrinsic rhythm appear under the proper conditions. At other times, the discharge exhibits a moderately large late wave which has been correlated with the sensory experience of an auxiliary flash. In sensory psychology this second flash has traditionally been designated an after-image, but since it occurs as an integral part of the response the terms after-image or after-sensation do not well apply to it. This is especially true since under other conditions after-images are the phenomena that are seen up to many seconds after the cessation of external stimulation. It would seem that these, the true after-images, are largely central, both from the late time that they occur and from the peculiar binocular effects that are involved.

**The intrinsic rhythm.** It has become evident that the retina possesses an intrinsic rhythm. This was shown by the records of Adrian and Matthews and by the more detailed studies of Bartley and Bishop on the optic-nerve discharge. These rhythms emerge at certain critical ranges in intensity and flash duration.

That these rhythms manifested by ripples in the optic-nerve records have a sensory significance was demonstrated by Bartley by correlating them with specific sensory phenomena. He also demonstrated that subjective flash frequencies which persist just before fusion do not compare in frequency to the actual physical rates of the flashes themselves. Regardless of the physical flash rate required to produce fusion, the last vestige of flicker is about the same. It is neither extremely slow nor does it anywhere nearly compare with the actual flash rates required for maximum c.f.f. These facts suggest very strongly that the dominant action of the neuro-retina in such cases is its intrinsic rhythm. The intrinsic rhythm is a synchrony of its many constituent elements. Conditions which would tend to force c.f.f. up to a higher level act to throw these elements out of synchrony rather than merely to increase the frequency of the individual element's discharge. When flash intensities are low, synchrony is difficult to obtain, and the perception of flashes is dependent upon their being delivered at a very slow rate, a rate at which neural activity can appreciably diminish between flashes. As flash intensity becomes higher the thresholds of more and more of the sense-cells have been reached and exceeded so that the sense-cells will be discharging more nearly at a single frequency. Under such conditions synchrony of impulses can and does occur, and subjective flash rate can surpass physical flash rate.

**The alternation of response theory of retinal action.** It seems that not all the elements representing a given retinal area respond to each flash in a rapid series, but take turns in accordance with the degree of recovery at the time of the arrival of the next flash. Bartley has suggested this sort of action not only from the results of his own studies but from those of others.

The first of these is the fact that the retinogram sometimes manifests *b*-waves only to alternate flashes of light. As the flash rate is lowered and the interval between flashes made longer, all flashes are soon responded to; those which at first elicited no response now produce small ones. As flash rate is made still slower these small responses grow and the large ones decline. Hence it seems as though when flashes are delivered rapidly all

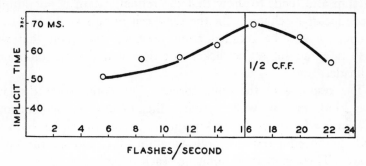

Fig. 78.—The relation of implicit time (latency) of the response of the optic cortex to flashes of light, and their rate. Note that as flash rate increases the response lags more and more, until a certain point, after which a reversal sets in. (For explanation see text.) (*Bartley—Psych. Rev.*)

of the responding elements (they may be chains) in the eye are not able to recover between times. Only those that do can respond. Those that cannot respond to a given flash respond to the following one. With longer intervals between flashes more and more of them are able to recover and are reactivated, so that elements that were formerly activated only by alternate flashes can now be activated by each succeeding flash.

The second experimental fact contributing to this theory is that the latency of the cortical response at first increases and then declines as flash frequency is raised. It is easy to see why this could happen. Increased frequency causes succeeding flashes to appear earlier and earlier in the recovery phase of the activated units, thereby increasing latency. If succeeding flashes become too frequent, they are no longer able to elicit response, and only alternate ones are effective. A much longer time is again allowed for the recovery of active units and their latency returns to somewhere near the original value.

Another fact which can be interpreted as being in line with the theory is that the latency of flashes is sometimes greater than the flash intervals themselves.

Furthermore the fact that the retina has an intrinsic rhythm of its own which sometimes eclipses the otherwise imposed rhythm also tends to show that the retinal system is not simply a conductor mechanism for the sense-cell impulses. In this connection it will be recalled from previous discussion that the flash rate and subjective flicker rate do not under all conditions coincide.

**The response of the optic cortex.** The optic cortex displays two kinds of observable activity: the intrinsic or spontaneous rhythmic activity, the better-known kind being the alpha rhythm; and the specific response following the discharge of the optic nerve. These noticeably influence each other.

The specific cortical response possesses many of the latency characteristics of the optic-nerve discharge or the retinogram. This parallelism extends in some cases to sensation itself though the absolute values in all of the comparisons just mentioned are dissimilar.

The individual functional elements of the cortex, like the retina, cannot respond to consecutive flashes if very rapidly repeated. The cortex succeeds in responding to rapidly delivered flashes by the same principle of alternation that was described for the retina. The pause needed before a second flash can elicit a response as great as the first is about equal to the time consumed between the peaks of two consecutive alpha waves.

**The outcome.** The preceding sections have given a running account of the neural activity that occurs in the optic pathway, with sufficient detail for the reader to see that there are many problems involved and to infer that much work has already been done.

The outcome leaves no doubt but what the neuro-retina revamps the simple discharge as recorded from a single sense-cell, in accordance with its own properties. Since this part of the retina does not seem to be so rapid in its response, it, rather than the sense-cell, determines critical flicker frequency, and is responsible for at least some features of Talbot's law. The Brücke and Bartley effects, other examples of neural revamping of the quantitative features of the sense-cell output, seem to be determined in the brain.

### THE MAJOR PROBLEMS OF VISION

In the current physiology of vision, the major puzzles cluster around the fact that interaction between parts of the retina and a supposed insulation between these parts to provide for visual acuity exist simultaneously. According to current concepts it does not even begin to be apparent how this can be. Consequently, it may be asked whether we simply have not yet progressed far enough in the present direction to reach a solution, or whether we must look for a new way of conceiving of the whole matter. If the first supposition, that our predicament is due to lack of factual information, be correct, the matter is simple. We need only to continue to work as we have, and to acquire more facts of the kind that have already been obtained.

Without risking devaluation of the work already done and the successes that have been achieved by current hypotheses, we may express doubts as to whether additional facts alone without a new viewpoint will ever solve the puzzle stated above. Data as they accumulate only add new puzzles unless there is an interpretation that will resolve them. Only a radically different hypothesis than any yet used by nerve physiology can evolve the solution for which we seek.

**Neural interaction.** Information from many sources has accumulated to demonstrate neural interaction in the retina. First of all the simple area effect, when entoptic stray light is ruled out, demonstrates interaction. Since this effect has been obtained with eye-nerve preparations, we now know that at least some of it occurs in the retina itself. The area effect occurs not only when simple brightness discrimination is put to test, but also in flicker experiments. In all such cases there is no hesitation on the part of most investigators in feeling that the concepts of summation which we now possess adequately cover the situation.

When the next step is taken the matter becomes more complicated. When two surfaces, a light and a dark one, are placed side by side a new phenomenon emerges. For a long time this has been called brightness contrast and consists in the fact that the region of the light surface lying next to the dark one looks lighter than portions progressively farther away. The same thing holds true of the various portions of the darker surface. The nearer they lie to the bright surface, the darker they are. This has been observed so many times by most of us it is as common as the major facts of gravitation. It simply seems as though it "ought" to occur, but why it does occur has never been explained. Notwithstanding, the phenomenon surely does not fall into the category of those facts of nature which are simply to be taken as axiomatic. The many efforts to explain it show that it hardly has been so taken. But, on the other hand, the phenomenon has been used in consecutive breaths both as a thing to be explained and the explanation.

The phenomenon, in principle, not only occurs when two markedly different levels of steady illumination are juxtaposed but also when two such levels are used as flicker fields. Critical flicker frequency for both becomes modified. The c.f.f. of the higher level becomes greater, and the c.f.f. of the lower becomes diminished. According to what was just said, it would be following a common tendency to declare that this is *due* to brightness contrast.

There is another way of attempting to explain it, that is, by invoking inhibition. It is known that increasing stimulus area raises c.f.f. when the two areas are nearly or actually the same brightness; a case of summation. Now since in the adding together of two areas markedly dissimilar in intensity, the c.f.f. of one of them becomes diminished, it is reasoned that inhibition must have occurred. It is as if the inhibition of summation had taken place, though it is not known or suggested why this occurs in one of the surfaces and not in the other. Thus, according to the common view, inhibition is totally arbitrary.

Our original question now takes on specific form. We may now ask whether added information will tell us why inhibition occurs at one time and not another, or in one area and not elsewhere, or whether we must always wait to observe what we now choose to call inhibition take place. Is there anything about the nature of the situation that leads us to believe that new facts around the corner will some time appear and give us the solution? Though it is always dangerous to predict futility or impossibility, there is something about the case that leads us not to expect to do more than to accumulate factual information or add to precision. It would seem that we should look to ideas rather than to facts themselves for success.

Ideas do not come out of the "blue." New information may evoke new ideas, and they may be much more novel than the facts themselves. Though emphasis may be laid on the facts, when presented to the wrong individual, they may only be catalogued in the traditional pigeonhole with nothing more to come of them. Indeed, "interpretation" is generally the point of argument.

**The fact of visual acuity.** We have already called attention to the fact of interaction both in simple cases where added area intensifies the end-result, and in more complex ones in which both enhancement and diminution occur.

These phenomena without the addition of any others introduce problems difficult of solution, but there is still another set of facts which seem to call for quite different action on the part of the nervous system at the same time and further complicate the situation. They are the facts which represent the ability of the visual system to respond to fine spatial gradations in the visual field. We call this the ability to make fine resolutions, or simply visual acuity. Presumably this requires a high degree of insulation between the parallel individual paths connecting point-to-point the retina and the visual cortex of the brain. Anatomy attests to this sort of connection while staging an obvious display of a vast lateral arborization. Anatomy has only one thing to say. It does not assure one of insulation as is commonly thought, in displaying frontal point-to-point connections, but it does lead one to believe in lateral intercommunication by the interconnections it manifests.

It can be concluded that the puzzle concerning interaction and visual acuity arises not out of their existence and the existence of both point-to-point retino-cerebral connections and the many cross connections, but out of the way we have been viewing these facts.

**Visual acuity and contour.** Visual acuity involves the formation of contours; it is scarcely a reality until this occurs. It will be recalled that many of the facts that came up in the chapter on visual acuity were remanded to the chapter on contour for further discussion. Now we see that the matter of contour formation is one of the central phenomena of sensory psychology and nerve physiology. Hence it is in line for further consideration.

Since sharply bounded areas are the common sensory outcome, and since we believe in the abrupt discontinuity of physical objects, the simplest notion of contour would be that the organism acts like a "copy system." That idea is spoiled at the very start, in that the sense-cell layer of the eye does not receive the light pattern from a sharply contoured object as a perfect copy of it. The retinal image is blurred and shall we expect that this "accident" be compensated for and that by some process the succeeding parts of the optic pathway reform the pattern so that it turns out to be a copy of the object viewed? Shall we not expect such an outcome in the physiological system? This question also has not been answered, although a great many of us assume that there must be a mechanism to resharpen what became blurred.

The particular mechanism, some of us have hoped would resolve the difficulty faced in the occurrence of the opposing phenomena of visual acuity and interaction, is conceived to be one of contour building and the beginning of it is attributed to the retina. Nevertheless, in the strictest sense, the attitude of regarding the organism as a copy system is not without its doubts.

**Two contrasting approaches in dealing with facts.** Most of the efforts in science are analytical. Detail is sought for; detail is found. Most of the preceding chapters was given over to experimental detail. The investigator expects that an understanding will inevitably follow the accumulation of facts.

An opposite tendency has grown up, namely, that of employing a concept to cover the observed part-action by using the system as a whole as the reference. Such concepts necessarily lack the very characteristics the opposite approach so obviously possesses. They are vague and seem to take too much for granted. They are as unwarranted axioms produced for the occasion. To summarize: we have then, the elemental and the field concepts in sharp contrast. And yet each holds out promises of helping us to our goal.

Both of these views have been employed with reference to neuro-physiology. Brain function, for example, has been discussed in terms of mass action, in terms of electrical fields, as if there were no neurons. In other quarters it has been discussed in terms of specific nerve tracts such as neurologists describe, or in terms of findings such as have been accumulated by Bishop, Bartley, and O'Leary, for example. At present we are willing to grant that both approaches have their place. Notwithstanding, it is well to comment here that those who speak in terms of fields of ionic concentrations and the like have done less to put their ideas to a test than has the opposite group.

It is a natural thing to wish for some sort of a resolution of the two approaches. That is to say, some of us are on the lookout for a way to envisage the nervous system as a complex mass of individual elements, and at the same time a fluid field of ions or the like. It is apparent that at present a definite shift is required when the two concepts are to be employed. They are as oil and water. But may the two not be reconciled? Is it not possible to find the role of the neuron in a field? Were this to be accomplished, surely the efforts to have learned about the neuron would not have been wasted, but would have been the perfect antecedents of a successful conclusion.

**Field theory applied to perception.** In two notable instances, the field theory has been applied to perception. In both the phenomena studied were ordered to a vector-field, and in both cases the results justified the attempt. The first case was that of Brown and Voth's treatment of movement within a field; the second was Orbison's study of stationary fields.

In both it was easily demonstrated that the hypothesis covered the facts in their experiments and that the hypothesis had predictive value. While it will be remembered that it was perceptual phenomena that were being dealt with, the implication was that the retina and the central nervous system behaved in the same way. That is to say, since perception had been ordered successfully to a vector-field, it was to be expected that the retina and the central nervous system could also be handled in the same manner, for they are the basis of perception.

**Field theory applied to the visual pathway.** Even though we were to approve of the assumptions that have just been mentioned and set out to order the retina and the cortical end of the visual pathway to a vector-field, we should find the task much more difficult than in the case of perception. Our information about the visual pathway consists in the knowledge of the cito-architecture of the various parts, the physiology of the individual elements, and a few facts relative to the more simple ways in which these elements work together. This type of knowledge does not yet yield itself well to a field hypothesis.

As yet we have no knowledge of the influence of a continuous ionic (or other) field upon the behavior of individual axons, of the kind that would fit into the vector-field hypothesis that was assumed for perception. At present, our physiology is almost totally atomistic, hence has to do primarily with what individual elements are able to do under standard conditions and not with the way that parallel elements may affect each other. Lateral influence is conceived of in the same way that action from element to element in the chain is regarded. All influences are considered to be synaptic.  On the other hand, the current treatment of nerve activity does not preclude influence in the field or matrix around elements.  In fact such concepts as the central excitatory state and its opposite, the central inhibitory state, are a beginning recognition of it.  The work instigated by the suspicion of influences between fibers in the same bundle may also be headed in the same direction.

**Space in nerve function.**  From what has been said, it has become apparent that the spatial characteristics of visual stimulation have been left almost untouched.  Only the simplest situations have been handled at all successfully.  These comprise only those in which homogeneous area is increased.  When differentiation begins to enter in, such as in the cases when various borders are introduced, the results can only be handled by hypotheses which are formulated in terms of perception.  An example in point is the study in which Fry and Bartley showed that borders influence one another in one of two ways and in accordance with their distance apart.  The vector-field analyses are other cases which are relevant.  The results in none of these studies have as yet been formulated in neural terms.

Even in one of the nearest approaches to dealing with space dynamically in neural terms, the treatment given by Bartley of gamma movement, the degree of success that was achieved was made possible by the ability to transfer space into time and intensity factors, rather than by the employment of a true field concept.

Our next hope then is to be able to do in neural terms what has been done in perception itself, be able to use our present physiological information logically in a field hypothesis.  In so doing we shall solve the major problems facing the physiology of vision, the present contradiction between visual acuity and neural interaction, for in a field concept strict insulation between units is not necessary in order for resolution to be possible.

# NAME INDEX

* Note: The name sometimes ends in *i* and sometimes in *y*.

# SUBJECT INDEX